FRIEDRICH SCHILLER

WILHELM TELL

Edited with Introduction, Fragen, Notes, and Vocabulary by
ROBERT WALLER DEERING

Revised Edition

D. C. HEATH AND COMPANY   BOSTON

PREFACE

As the plates had become worn by the many and large editions already issued, the publishers desired to make new plates, and they advised a revision which should include modernizing the orthography and any other changes suggested by the use of the book during the twenty-one years that had passed since it first appeared. After so long a time, the editor was able to look upon his earlier work quite objectively and to change it without hesitation, in order to put it in better accord with the needs of today.

The commentary is intended to serve not the critical scholar, but primarily the school and college student, as well as the occasional teacher who may not have access to adequate works of reference — hence its somewhat mixed character. Its chief purpose is to supply as briefly and simply as possible such help as may encourage the study of the play as a masterpiece of literature, as well as explain grammatical matters.

No effort has been spared to make the revision thorough. The whole book has been reset, almost all of it rewritten. The Introduction retains the sketch of Schiller, in slightly modified form, because the editor is convinced by experience that it is needed; many students have no access to a longer life of Schiller and often do not read it when they have. The rest of the Introduction has been entirely rewritten, the sections on the history and the legend made shorter, the treatment of the play itself somewhat fuller. The orthography of the Text has been made to accord with the 1911 edition of Duden's *Orthographisches Wörterbuch;* otherwise it agrees substantially with that of the original Cotta edition. As the play is now read more in schools and, therefore, often by younger students than formerly, the Notes are made fuller, in order to meet their needs, as well as those of older students who read it in college. Notes which sum up the progress and connection of plot and characters are given at the end of scenes and acts, because they mean more after the student has read the text. Such are intended as mere suggestions, which teachers can expand at will. This is also true of the *Fragen* which have been added. Meant for classes using the "direct method," they attempt, without great detail, to encourage

something like a continuous discussion in German of the more important things in the text, not a haphazard mention of this or that, or a
ja or *nein* answer to a question, equally useless. Moreover, suitable
subjects for short, simple written exercises have been added in proper
connection.

The Vocabulary has been reduced to as small a compass as possible,
consistent with practical usefulness. Proper names and common words
which students should already know have been left out; accents have
been put in to help in pronunciation.

The editor has made free use of all available material and wishes here
to express his sense of obligation to his predecessors. Particular
indebtedness is frankly acknowledged in its proper connection.

R. W. DEERING

PUBLISHER'S PREFACE

Practically all the printing now being done in Germany is in roman type, and American teachers of German naturally expect their editions of the German classics to conform to current usage in this respect. We have decided, therefore, to reissue Professor Deering's popular edition of *Wilhelm Tell* in this new format. The book has been completely reset, but the text, introduction, notes, and vocabulary remain unchanged except for an occasional modernization of spelling. No need was felt for a more thoroughgoing revision, since this fine edition is still eminently suited to the American classroom. Schiller scholarship has of course been active in recent years, but its findings have not materially affected the fundamentals with which students of *Wilhelm Tell* are concerned. This great cry for freedom rings out today with all its original force and immediacy; and students will be quick to realize that there are in 1960, as in 1300 and in 1775, nations that need a Tell.

INTRODUCTION

I. SKETCH OF SCHILLER'S LIFE AND WORKS

There is no writer so well known, none so honored among the masses
of German people as Friedrich Schiller. Not Luther, nor Goethe, nor
anyone has ever got so close to the great, honest German _heart_ as he.
His name is a household word with every class. The rich and cultured
honor the genius with which he embodied his lofty ideals; the poor
and humble love him for his childlike simplicity and genuineness, for
his broad and tender human sympathies, for his noble life — in spite
of its sore trials and bitter disappointments, to them an inspiring example of all that is best and noblest in German character. His splendid
genius, his sterling manhood, his tireless energy, his unflinching courage
command the esteem and admiration of all men.

He descended from the sturdy stock of the middle classes. His ancestors were doughty village bakers and inn-keepers, holding office also
as magistrates. His father was first barber's apprentice, then surgeon,
soldier, and finally officer in the army of the Duke of Württemberg.
He was a man of some culture, of positive character, blunt and im-
perious in manner, but the soul of honor and kindness. The rugged
soldier found a fitting helpmeet in Elisabeth Dorothea Kodweiß, the
slender, blond-haired daughter of "mine host of the Golden Lion" in
Marbach in Württemberg — a glad-hearted girl of seventeen, whom
time soon developed into a noble, womanly woman of excellent tact
and judgment, of singularly gentle and happy disposition, of finest
sense and feeling. The eldest son and second of this worthy couple's
six children was Johann Christoph Friedrich Schiller, born in Marbach
on Saturday, Nov. 10, 1759 — thirty years after Lessing, ten years
after Goethe, two hundred and seventy-six years, to the day, after
Luther. Unlike the precocious wonder-child Goethe, Schiller was
an average boy, like other boys. Unlike Goethe, he inherited the
physique of his mother, even to her soft blue eyes and red-blond hair.
He combined the mental qualities of both parents — his father's restless energy and ambition and his mother's gentle dignity, happy disposition, refined feeling, and decided literary taste. The mother's influence, especially during his earlier years, when the father was away
with the army, cannot be overestimated in its wholesome effect upon

the boy's character. At the age of six he went to school in the neigh-
boring town of Lorch, where the family settled, in order to be near the
father. His first teacher was good old pastor Moser, whom the poet
afterward honored as the priest in *Die Räuber.*

By nature devout, inspired by the example of his teacher [1] and warmly
encouraged by his parents, the boy early decided to become a clergy-
man and devoted some time to preparatory classical studies in the
Latin School at Ludwigsburg. It is not strange that he chose biblical
themes for his (now forgotten) first dramatic sketches, inspired by
visits to the theater there. With his playmates for actors, himself as
director, and the chairs for audience, he played theater as eagerly as
he had preached. These cherished plans were broken up, however,
by Duke Karl Eugen, who wanted the already promising student for
his new military academy, the later Karlsschule, near his country
residence, "Solitude," where he made the boy's father superintendent
of the grounds. He offered a free education on condition that young
Schiller then devote himself to the service of Württemberg. Limited in
means and afraid to refuse, his parents reluctantly consented, and in Jan.
1773, not yet fourteen, the boy entered the school as a student of Law,
since Theology was not taught there. The step was soon bitterly re-
gretted, for the government of the school, a rigorous military discipline,
which made machines of the students, cut off the outside world, and
regulated work and play and even prayers and meals "by word of command," was in the highest degree galling to Schiller's impulsive, sensitive nature. The fault was partly his own, however. Having come
against his wish, he was prepared to be displeased. Expecting, as every
boy does, greater freedom at school than at home, he was disappointed
to find even more exacting rules. He naturally resented such restraint
and received only too ready encouragement from his fellows. He soon
developed decided aversion to Law, and within two years, on the removal of the school to Stuttgart, changed to Medicine. This was less
irksome, yet his heart was not in it. His chief interest centered in
literature, especially poetry, and, in spite of the rules, the works of
Rousseau, Ossian, Homer, Shakespeare (Wieland's translation), Klop-
stock's *Messias,* Goethe's *Götz* and *Werther,* and other foreign and
German classics, were eagerly devoured, like forbidden fruit, in secret
with a few chosen friends. Such reading at once awakened his own

[1] His sister tells us how he used to borrow her black kitchen apron, put it
around him as a clerical gown, mount a chair, and preach after the manner
of the pastor.

poetic impulse. He said later: "I would have gladly given my last shirt for a subject on which to practice my youthful, ambitious spirit." He did find themes for short poems, for epic and dramatic sketches — all more or less the extravagant expression of a morbidly sensitive imagination, and none of them important as literature, "but enough," says Carlyle, "to show that his mind had already dimly discovered its destination and was striving with restless vehemence to reach it, in spite of every obstacle."

These early efforts soon gave place to his first larger work, a revolutionary drama, *Die Räuber*, begun at eighteen and published, at his own expense, in 1781, after he had left the Karlsschule to become regimental surgeon, in the service of the Duke, at Stuttgart. At the instance of Dalberg, theater-manager at Mannheim, it was soon prepared for the stage and, in Jan. 1782, was performed. Eager to see his first drama played, but unable to go without special permission, which he knew would be refused, Schiller went secretly to see it. A second similar offense led to his arrest for a fortnight and to the Duke's positive command that in future he cease "all literary work and all communication with other countries." He pleaded in vain, endured for a while, and then, irritated beyond control by such senseless restraint, determined on flight as a last resort. In the night of Sept. 22, 1782, in company with his musician friend, Andreas Streicher, he left position, home, and country, and fled, under the assumed name of Dr. Ritter, to Mannheim. By repeated promises Dalberg had led him to hope for help towards pacifying the Duke and securing the post of theater-poet and critic. Dalberg had promised much, but, fearing the Duke's displeasure, did little, even refusing to accept *Fiesco*, a second drama Schiller had just finished and hoped soon to see performed. Disheartened, almost penniless, and fearing that, as a deserter, he was even in Mannheim not safe from the Duke's anger, he pawned his watch, changed his name again, and wandered about with the faithful Streicher, undecided what to do, seeking relief from his trouble in revising *Fiesco* and sketching another play, *Luise Millerin*, later called *Kabale und Liebe*.

Finally in his distress he turned to his friend, Frau von Wolzogen, the widowed mother of two of his Stuttgart fellow-students, who had offered him a home at her house in Bauerbach, near Meiningen. Kindly received there, he forgot his griefs, found leisure for work on *Kabale und Liebe*, and even planned another drama, *Don Carlos*. Too proud to accept longer the support of his hostess and unhappy in a love-affair with her daughter, he returned the next summer to Mannheim, where Dalberg, seeing that the Duke intended no persecution of Schiller or his family, now felt free to help by giving him the wished-for position of theater-poet, with small, but assured salary. Schiller contracted to furnish *Fiesco*, *Kabale und Liebe*, and one other play during the year. This agreement soon proved a burden: Dalberg refused his *Fiesco*, even in revised form, petty jealousies among the actors worked against him and rendered his position unpleasant. After one year he gave it up.

Again adrift, in great pecuniary distress, broken in health and out of heart, he turned next to journalism and founded a periodical — *Die Rheinische* (later *Die Neue*) *Thalia*, devoted to literature in general and drama in particular. The venture increased his literary influence, but was not a success financially. The future seemed darker than ever. Karl August, Grand-Duke of Weimar, had heard him read parts of *Don Carlos* and had made him *Hofrat* (Court Councilor); but such empty honor, however appreciated for the social prestige it gave, could not relieve his need or make Mannheim a congenial home. He keenly felt the narrowness of his sphere and yearned for better opportunities and conditions for work. With unalloyed pleasure, therefore, did he receive, after some exchange of letters, "the most glorious surprise in the world" — an invitation to visit in Leipzig one of several ardent admirers, Christian Gottfried Körner, later a high government official in Dresden and father of the poet, Theodor Körner.

In April 1785 he went to Leipzig and, generously helped by Körner, began the second "period" of his life. For two years, spent in Leipzig, Gohlis, Dresden, he was busy with many plans. He wrote for the *Thalia*, finished *Don Carlos*, and composed a number of fine lyrics, of which his *Ode to Joy* is especially popular. Beethoven's music has made it famous. Through *Don Carlos* he became interested also in history, and began his *Geschichte des Abfalls der Niederlande* (*Revolt of the Netherlands*), not a profound book in our sense, but one destined to exert a most wholesome influence on the literary style of German historians. In July 1787, unwilling to remain dependent on Körner, hoping to make influential connections, which might help to permanent position, he visited Weimar, the university town of Jena, and other places. He met prominent scholars and court officials, the dowager Duchess Amalia, and, in Rudolstadt, became acquainted in the family of Frau von Lengefeld, whose youngest daughter Charlotte (Schiller's 'Lotte') afterwards became his wife. Here, too, about a year later, he met Goethe, who, though not at once an intimate friend, felt interest in him and helped him to the chair of History, nominally Philosophy, in the University of Jena in May 1789. The position paid little at first (only students' fees), but soon, with a salary of two hundred thalers and a pension from the ever generous Karl August, he felt able to marry and have a home of his own. Feb. 22, 1790 is the date of the wedding. He owed much to Lotte. A noble heart, a sunny nature, a most lovable woman in heartiest sympathy with him and his plans, she was just the wife for him. With her help he soon found what he needed most — the quiet, contented happiness that only a happy home and settled work can bring. He devoted himself with enthusiasm to his history lectures, began his *Geschichte des dreißigjährigen Krieges*, and for once the future was all bright. His prospects were soon blighted, however. Within a year his health failed, tuberculosis laid hold of him, and long, serious illness brought direst need — and distress of mind as well, for, as a medical man, he knew that, sooner or later, he was doomed. Fortunately help came from the Prince of Holstein-Augustenburg and the Danish Minister, Count Schimmelmann, who "wishing to preserve to humanity one of her teachers," so generously and delicately offered him a thousand thalers a year for three years that he could not decline it. A trip to Karlsbad had benefited his health, and now a visit of nearly a year in his old Swabian home gave him rest and made glad his heart, but his enfeebled body was not restored to normal strength. It is characteristic of him that his splendid courage did not fail or falter and that he continued to study and to write. He finished his *Thirty Years' War*, read Kant, and occupied himself much with philosophy and esthetics, using this leisure "to learn, to gather material, and to work for eternity." At the close of this second period, he is no longer the impetuous revolutionist, but the calmer, riper critic, philosopher, historian, and poet, ready for still greater things.

May 1794 he returned to Jena, where he soon received a visit from Goethe, whom he had invited to become co-editor of a new periodical, *Die Horen*, for which arrangements had already been made with Cotta, the great South-German publisher. Goethe readily accepted, and from this time dates their intimate friendship, which grew ever closer till it became the pride of the nation and most fruitful of good to its literature. Schiller's enthusiasm inspired Goethe to effort, while

Goethe's calmer judgment had most wholesome influence on Schiller's impulsive nature. The world never saw anything like it before or since; they were not merely close personal friends, but each was also the confidant, critic, and adviser of the other in all that he planned and wrote. In spite of excellent prospects the *Horen* met a cold reception; many contributors lacked interest, and the public failed to appreciate its high standards of taste. Literary jealousy inspired attacks by mediocre writers, which injured the paper, and its issue was soon stopped. Retribution soon came in the *Xenien* (*Parting Gifts*), a collection of cutting epigrams, in which both poets took revenge upon the writers and critics of the day. In the *Horen*, and more especially in the *Musenalmanach*, his new annual, founded 1795, Schiller published many of his finest lyrics and ballads, written in friendly rivalry with Goethe: *Der Handschuh, Der Spaziergang, Der Ring des Polykrates, Der Taucher, Die Bürgschaft, Die Kraniche des Ibykus*, and many others, of which *Das Lied von der Glocke*, published in 1800, is the longest and best.

Meanwhile Schiller had "shut up the philosophy shop" and returned to the drama. He was busy with *Wallenstein*, the idea of which he had found in his studies for the *Thirty Years' War*, which had grown during his visit to Karlsbad in 1791, and finally took the form of the great trilogy which many call his masterpiece. He saw it performed in Weimar, and in Dec. 1799, wishing to be nearer Goethe and the theater, he moved permanently to Weimar, and spent there the last five years of his life. These last years were the happiest, busiest, and most successful of all, for in dramatic poetry he had found his work. Material affairs took a turn for the better; his pension was doubled; his income from his publishers was considerable; he bought a house; he became co-director of the theater with Goethe, and was happy in his home and in the brother poet, who had grown mentally, socially, and professionally so necessary to him. He was influential at court and among "such friends," says Bulwer, "as genius rarely finds — men alike dear to his heart and worthy of his intellect." After years of trial, he was at last honored as he deserved. Queen Luise of Prussia tried in vain to draw him to Berlin as director of a magnificent theater. In 1802 Franz II gave him a patent of nobility, a distinction he neither sought nor desired, but which he accepted "to please Lotte and the children." [1] At the height of his literary fame, just as he was ready to

[1] He had four: Fritz, Ernst, Karoline, Emilie. The last became the wife of Baron von Gleichen-Rußwurm; her grandson printed a biography of his illustrious ancestor.

live, he had to prepare to die. His feeble body grew rapidly weaker, yet with a mighty energy which no infirmity checked and no glory could satisfy, he worked on, for he knew his days were numbered. His persevering courage, his lofty poetic inspiration rose superior to every obstacle. Though his health was gone, he wrote in quick succession and, as it were, with his heart's blood, that splendid array of dramas, *Wallenstein*, *Maria Stuart*, *Die Jungfrau von Orleans*, *Die Braut von Messina*, and *Wilhelm Tell*, which made him Germany's greatest dramatist and made his name a household word in every German home. Important translations from French and classic authors engaged him, ambitious literary plans were going through his mind, when on May 9, 1805, death overtook him in the midst of what promised to be his greatest work thus far, a drama from Russian history, called *Demetrius*. He was cut off by consumption in the prime of his noble manhood, when not yet forty-six years old. His death was a profound shock, not only to near and dear ones, but to the whole German people, for in him that people had lost its best-loved poet and teacher and friend. Such an outpouring of a whole nation's sorrow would be hard to find elsewhere.

In personal appearance, to quote Carlyle in substance, "Schiller was tall, bony, very thin, with pale face, hollow cheeks, aquiline nose, and reddish hair. At no time handsome, his form and features were much wasted by disease and overwork, but his high, thoughtful brow, his finely shaped mouth, soft kindling eyes, and pale cheeks gave him withal an attractive appearance and a certain manly beauty. In manner he was plain and unassuming, modesty and childlike simplicity itself. Somewhat shy with strangers, he was, at home and among his friends, light-hearted and gay, everywhere patient, buoyant, calm, cheerful, never morose, never complaining. With no parade or display, he simply rated himself an honest man and a good citizen. He was the greater for having forgotten that he was great."

Schiller's literary career may be conveniently divided into three periods, determined largely by the external circumstances of his life: (1) the formative stage, from his first work to his removal to Leipzig-Dresden, 1777–1785, is devoted to drama and lyrics; (2) with greater maturity the author and professor writes history and is busy with esthetic and philosophical studies, 1785–1794; (3) his ripest years, spent in close friendship with Goethe; he returns to poetry and writes his greatest lyrics and dramas, 1794–1805.

His earliest important works were three plays, *Die Räuber* (1781), *Fiesco* (1783), and *Kabale und Liebe* (1784), all three written in prose and of decided revolutionary tendency. *Die Räuber*, he confesses, was the "product of his liberty-loving genius in union with the thraldom" of the Karlsschule, a true type of the "Storm and Stress" play, crude in plan, extravagant in expression, but intensely tragic, in spite of many unnatural scenes and distorted characters. In substance it is a violent, unreasoning attack upon existing social evils. Older people were scandalized, but the young were inspired to wildest enthusiasm by its stirring scenes. It was and has remained very popular and marks a distinct epoch in the poet's development, as well as in the literature of his time. *Fiesco* embodies a political revolution in Genoa, and though much less violent, it attempts by shrewdness and stratagem the same end, freedom, attained by brute force in *Die Räuber*. It is inferior in animation, yet is notable as Schiller's first historical drama. *Kabale und Liebe* protests against abuses in society, especially against the privileged position of the upper classes. Its greater simplicity and more natural tone make it dramatically and artistically far the best of the three. All show poetic fire and dramatic talent, but a talent that has not yet found its true path. The lyrics of this period are much like the dramas — boldly, vividly conceived, and full of "deep, though overdrawn, poetic feeling and impatient impulse."

The transition to the second period is *Don Carlos*, in which the extravagant, unreasoning passion of earlier plays becomes the calmer expression of riper thought. Though, as a result of long delay in its composition, 1784–1787, it lacks dramatic unity, it is notable as Schiller's first drama in verse, as the poet's own political confession of faith, and as marking a turning-point in his literary career. He is now a mature man, no longer a gifted youth. Based on important events in Spanish history in the reign of Philip II, it involved careful study of the political movements of those times. Such study soon led Schiller away from poetry, and for years he devoted himself almost entirely to prose and especially to history. Besides a number of shorter essays and sketches, he produced two larger works, the above-mentioned *Abfall der Niederlande* (1788) and *Die Geschichte des dreißigjährigen Krieges* (1792), both faithful, often vivid pictures of the times they describe, most remarkable, perhaps, for the characteristic epic method, by which details are conveniently grouped around well-drawn central characters, like Orange, Egmont, and Wallenstein. The philosophical and esthetic studies of this period resulted in a number of shorter essays, such as his *Ästhetische Erziehung des Menschen*, *Über Anmut und Würde*, and his later *Naive und sentimentalische Dichtung*.

His last ten years form a third period, blessed by domestic happiness, cheered by pleasant friendships, filled and inspired by his comradeship with Goethe, and one of great lyric and dramatic activity. His growing epic interest in Wallenstein, developed by his studies for the *Thirty Years' War*, brought him back to poetry. The Wallenstein trilogy (1798–99) — *Wallensteins Lager, Die Piccolomini, Wallensteins Tod* — is an historical drama in the best sense, based upon those great movements of the Thirty Years' War in which Wallenstein, at the close of his career, took part. Free from the faults of earlier plays, it is considered by some his best work. Its images are no longer distorted; they are faithful, vivid pictures from a master hand. After Schiller's removal to Weimar almost every year brought a new drama. *Wallenstein* was followed by *Maria Stuart* (1800), which deals with the imprisonment and death of Mary Queen of Scots, at the hands of Elizabeth. Turning then to France for a theme, he wrote *Die Jungfrau von Orleans* (1801), a classic account (half history, half miracle) of the career of the beautiful and terrible Joan of Arc, in her struggle against the English invaders of her country, in her tragic struggle with herself, when love for her enemy enters her heart. *Die Braut von Messina* (1803), called, though hardly correctly, a "drama of fate," is an unsuccessful attempt to combine the Classic and the Romantic, by bringing the Greek chorus into a modern play, thus giving it an antique dress; an awful destiny (which closer study shows to be the tragic guilt of secrecy) keeps two brothers at war with each other and results in ruin and death. There is but little action in the play, and the chorus is a disturbing element, so that it has never been popular on the stage, yet many of the lyric passages are of unrivaled beauty and tenderness. In his last drama, *Wilhelm Tell* (1804), Schiller "completes the circle," says Bulwer, "in which genius often seems to move and returns to those longings for liberty, now idealized and tempered by riper years, which once prompted the *Robbers*." It is the story of the Swiss struggle for liberty, and is in many respects the finest work of his life; many call it his greatest play. The lyrics and ballads of this last period are among the best in German literature. For bold conception, graphic description, deep poetic feeling, and rich fancy, Schiller is unsurpassed as a ballad-writer. Even Goethe acknowledged his own inferiority to him. In order to help supply the Weimar stage, Schiller was also busy during these last years with translations and adaptations, notably from Euripides, *Iphigenie in Aulis*, Shakespeare, *Macbeth*, Picard, *Der Parasit* and *Der Neffe als Onkel*, Gozzi, *Turandot*, and Racine, *Phädra*. His last complete work was a lyric festival-play, *Die Huldigung der Künste* (*Homage to the Arts*), containing "his poetic confession of faith," and written in honor of the marriage of the hereditary Grand-Duke of Weimar to a Russian princess, Nov. 1804.

In a review of Schiller's literary life we are surprised at the great amount of his work. He was allowed about twenty-five years, and into this time, by untiring industry and unparalleled devotion, he crowded the work of a long life. Again there is the greatest variety in his productions. As student, surgeon, theater-director and critic, editor, professor, historian, philosopher, essayist, dramatic and lyric poet, he was always busy, and despite the great amount and the great variety of his literary work, he attained a degree of excellence truly remarkable — and that in the face of poverty and life-long ill-health. He was denied all that he might have done and been during man's best and ripest years and yet he is one of the most imposing figures in the world of modern art. Dannecker, the sculptor, was right when he said: "I will make Schiller life-size — that is, *colossal*." The artist knew it then; the whole world knows it now.

II. HISTORICAL BACKGROUND — FACT AND FABLE

Since *Wilhelm Tell* has to do not only with the famous archer, but also, and especially, with the Swiss fight for freedom, the play has a certain historical background — but history so blended with tradition that separation is difficult. Schiller found his material in old Swiss chronicles, whose statements he may or may not have believed, though they were generally accepted in his day. To him it made no difference whether this material was fact or not, for he was writing drama, not history; he did not care whether given things were ever really done, but whether they might have been done by the given characters; for he knew a play may be very good, even if everything in it is fictitious, provided it is plausible. He was concerned that his picture be true to Swiss life and character and so took from local tradition what suited his purpose, without reference to historical accuracy of time or place or fact. The real history then is not in itself important, but it is essential to an understanding of the legends that grew out of it, and that form the substance of the play, for many situations are not clear at all unless we know the facts and figures to which they refer.

The story, as Schiller found it, is in substance as follows: The people of the Forest Cantons were descendants, tradition says, of Scandinavian ancestors, who were driven by famine from their northern home in Sweden, forced their way south, and settled the uninhabited shores of Lake Lucerne (*Tell*, 1167–1203). From the first they had been free men, acknowledging only the authority of the German emperor and giving voluntary allegiance in return for his royal protection (*Tell*, 1211–1227). They managed their own affairs, save in cases of murder, when an imperial delegate was called in (*Tell*, 1233–1242). All went well until a grasping Habsburg-Austrian emperor, Albrecht, ignoring their true relation to the Empire, endeavored, with the help of tyrannical bailiffs, whose cruelty is described in detail, to subjugate them and add the Forest Cantons to his own, Austrian, *private* possessions (*Tell*, 1257 ff.). After patient endurance and vain entreaty (*Tell*, 1325–1349), the people of Uri, Schwyz, and Unterwalden conspired against their governors (Act II, sc. 2) and, in open revolt on New Year's Day 1308, destroyed their castles (*Tell*, 2873 ff.), killed some and drove out others (*Tell*, 2903 ff.). The worst of the tyrants, Geßler von Bruneck, fell by the hand of Wilhelm Tell, a worthy man of Uri (Act IV, sc. 3). This union of the three cantons was the origin of the independent Swiss Confederation.

Thus in brief the legend. For the most part, however, these events are not founded on fact. The cantons were not settled by famine-stricken Swedes, nor were they free from obligation to Habsburg. They belonged to the German empire from the first and did not give their allegiance voluntarily. Albrecht did not send tyrants to grind the people, nor was any bailiff, Geßler, ever shot by a Tell. The Swiss Confederacy was not established by any sudden uprising, but by a long, stubborn struggle with Austria.

The Forest Cantons were settled not at once and by one great migration of Scandinavians, but very slowly and by straggling bands of Alamanni, who had occupied northern Switzerland in the fifth century and were gradually driven out of these lowlands by pressure from the north. They were conquered by the Franks and remained subject to the Carolingian kings until that empire was divided after the death of

Charlemagne. By the treaty of Verdun (843) eastern Switzerland became part of the dominions of Ludwig the German. Its permanent settlement, though begun in the sixth century, was not complete until the ninth. The population included various elements: some were free men, others serfs, attached to the soil; others owed more or less allegiance to individual lords, lay and clerical. Rich monasteries early acquired great power and the important privilege of exemption from all authority save that of the Emperor. Free towns and religious orders, as well as petty nobles and free peasants, enjoyed special rights, holding lands in fief directly from the Empire, paying nominal taxes, holding in common lands not covered by fief, and acting as a community, with a large measure of home rule, subject only in a general way to a governor chosen by the Crown. In the twelfth century this office was held by the Dukes of Zähringen, but, after the extinction of that House in 1218, passed to Rudolf the Elder, Count of Habsburg.

These ambitious princes, insatiably land-hungry, had forced themselves up with ceaseless effort and, in a century or so, by inheritance, by purchase, through mortgages, by well-planned marriages and political cunning had absorbed the power of others and gained virtual control, either as private landowners or *Reichsvögte*, rulers in the Emperor's name and stead, in the Forest Cantons and the surrounding country. In Uri their private possessions were small, for the canton was occupied in part by free nobles and peasants and chiefly by the dependents of the great Abbey of our Lady in Zürich (*die große Frau zu Zürch*, *Tell*, 1364), which in 853 Ludwig the German had endowed with large estates, rich rents, many serfs, and had exempted from all authority except his own. So great and so well founded, however, was the fear of Habsburg encroachment that the canton sought and in 1231 obtained through Heinrich, son of Friedrich II, a charter attesting its *Reichsunmittelbarkeit*.[1]

One great reason for the ready grant of Uri's charter was, no doubt, the opening of the Gotthard road, which had changed a dangerous

---

[1] That is — its *immediate* dependence on the Emperor himself, not *mediate* dependence on him through another feudal lord. With the Emperor for their overlord they would enjoy home rule, because often no imperial governor was appointed, affairs being administered by local magistrates, or in very special cases by an imperial delegate called in for the purpose. Moreover, since each new emperor was elected, this imperial overlordship could not become hereditary in one family, as it would have done, if a Habsburg prince had been their mediate feudal lord.

trail into the main highway between Germany and Italy.   As sovereign of both countries Friedrich II wished to keep control of this important link between these two parts of his vast dominion and, therefore, by purchase through his son, canceled the feudal grant to Habsburg, and Uri received the charter which gave her home rule, by her own *Landgemeinde* and native officials, and the assurance that none but the Emperor himself should ever be her overlord.   Because it was never afterwards seriously questioned, this charter has been called the corner-stone of Swiss liberty.   It was readily confirmed by Rudolf III of Habsburg after he was elected (1273) *Deutscher König*.[1]

Schwyz eagerly desired a similar charter.   Though most of her people were free, large estates and many serfs were owned by the monasteries and by the Habsburgs, who claimed, moreover, as Counts of the Zürichgau, to be "by lawful inheritance the rulers and protectors" of the canton.   Seeing her liberties thus endangered, she shrewdly seized her opportunity when Friedrich II, under the ban of the Pope and not on good terms with Habsburg, was besieging Faenza in northern Italy, sent him messengers and troops, and offered their service in return for the desired charter.   Though conflicting with certain Habsburg rights, it was granted, in vague terms at least, in Dec. 1240, and Schwyz was taken under the immediate protection of the Empire.

Unterwalden was not so fortunate.   Without organic union, with fewer free men, and owned largely by clerical and secular lords, it had no charter and was virtually controlled by the Habsburgs.   Watching their opportunity during the bitter conflict between Pope and Emperor, Schwyz and Unterwalden (i.e. Stanz and Sarnen) rose against the Papal partisan, their enemy, and in union with Luzern, in 1246–47, formed the first Swiss league for mutual defense, the *uralt Bündnis* of *Tell*, 1157. For years a bitter fight was kept up, in which secret meetings were held, castles destroyed, and officials driven out.   It is this conflict, no doubt, which furnished some historical basis for the tales of Habsburg cruelty told in *Tell*, in which Uri also was included (because she, too, was later menaced) and credited with similar resistance, such as the destruction of Zwing Uri and other castles built to guard the Gotthard road.

[1] This was the title of the newly elected emperor until he went to Rome to be crowned by the Pope (*Tell*, 1229 ff.) and receive the added title *Kaiser des Heiligen Römischen Reichs, deutscher Nation*.   Neither Rudolf nor his son, Albrecht, was ever thus crowned, yet both were called *Kaiser*, as well as *König*.

After the extinction of the Hohenstaufens and during the long inter-
regnum (1256–1273) the Habsburgs regained and even increased their
old authority in the cantons.   Ever alert in this *kaiserlose, schreckliche
Zeit* to meet encroachment from without and control dissension within,
Uri joined about 1260 with Schwyz and Nidwalden in a permanent
league for mutual help and defense; its text is not preserved, but we
know it was virtually the same as the compact of 1291, so it has been
called the germ of the later confederacy.

When Rudolf III of Habsburg was chosen emperor in 1273, the cantons suddenly found their *Vogt* and enemy become their sovereign.   As
such, in 1274, he confirmed the charter of Uri, but refused that of
Schwyz, because it was granted by an excommunicated emperor
(Friedrich II fell under the ban in 1239) and violated Habsburg private
rights.   As he did not send a governor, but, here and in Unterwalden,
was his own executive, these two cantons were as well off without
charters as Uri with one.   Fearful for the future, however, and bitter
over his increasing taxes, the cantons, on August 1, 1291, a few days
after his death, renewed their older league, with the significant added
pledge, evidently aimed at Habsburg, never to accept as judge anyone
not a native, or who had bought his office or received it as a reward.
This document, aptly called the Magna Charta of Swiss liberties, is
preserved with religious care in Schwyz.   Though independent in tone,
it is very conservative: it pledges resistance to "attacks from without
and dissensions within," but, far from seeking to establish any independent federal state, urges continued allegiance to their lawful sovereign, the Emperor.

In 1297 Rudolf's successor, Adolf of Nassau, gave charters to both
Schwyz and Uri, but these availed them little, since Adolf was soon
after killed in battle.   His rival, Albrecht of Austria,[1] refused charters
to both, because he was determined to keep them as private property,
even if, after his death, the new emperor should be chosen from some
other House.   Appeal to the Emperor for help against Austria was
thus useless, because the Emperor was that very Duke of Austria
against whom they wanted help.   He was a stern, grasping ruler, bent
on maintaining and increasing his private power, here using his imperial veto to that end, but not so bad as tradition makes him.   He did

---

[1] In 1278 Rudolf had given his sons the conquered duchy of Austria; hence
allegiance to *Östreich* (*Tell*, 184) meant submission to their hated enemies,
the Habsburgs.

refuse the charters (*Tell*, 1333 ff., 2078 ff.), yet all three cantons were practically free, being governed for a time at least by native magistrates. He was too busy elsewhere to send tyrannical bailiffs, nor was there any revolt during his reign.

Murdered May 1, 1308 by his nephew, Albrecht was succeeded by Heinrich (VII) of Luxemburg, the enemy and rival of the Dukes of Austria, Albrecht's sons. In 1309 he confirmed the charters of Schwyz and Uri and granted one also to Unterwalden. The next rivals for the crown were Ludwig of Bavaria and Friedrich of Austria, Albrecht's son. The Swiss naturally declared for Ludwig, who annulled all Habsburg rights in the cantons, whereupon Friedrich's brother, Leopold, with a splendid army set out to subdue them and restore all old claims. He was met Nov. 15, 1315 in the narrow pass of Morgarten and utterly defeated by the Swiss. Dec. 9, 1315 the old league of 1291 was renewed at Brunnen; other cantons admitted later and other victories won from Austria (Sempach, 1386; Näfels, 1388) only served to extend and strengthen the Confederation thus established.

Such the genuine history as drawn from the records preserved. Strange to say, nearly a hundred years pass by without even the slightest mention of Habsburg tyranny or Swiss resistance. Contemporary record says nothing of the events described in the later chronicles. The ancestry of the Swiss is mentioned about 1414 by Johann Puntiner of Uri, who makes his people descendants of Alaric's Goths; others, impelled by local prejudice, change the Goths to Swedes, Frisians, Saxons, etc. The dates vary from the fourth to the ninth century. The name, too (Swiss from Schwyz), is dragged through strange etymologies.[1] Of course, the similarity between Schweden and Schwyzer proves nothing. Such a Norse people, if not mentioned in the early records, would at least have left its impress on the language; but such is not the case. The fact seems to be that the Alamanni, driven south, very possibly by famine (a frequent cause of such migration), kept alive the memory of their northern home, which later legend purposely took to be Sweden or Frisia, lest the admission of their German descent should weaken their case in their quarrel with Habsburg.

Of bailiff tyranny and Swiss revolt the earliest records say nothing. Cruel governors are first mentioned about 1420 in Conrad Justinger's

[1] Cf. Rochholz: *Tell und Geßler*, pp. 64 ff. Oechsli derives the name from *Suites*, i.e. *The men of Suito*.

chronicle of Bern. With oral tradition as authority, he writes of old struggles with the Habsburgs as due to their attempts to assert and increase authority mortgaged to them by the Empire and insolent conduct towards worthy men and women; but his statement is perfectly general and lacks all detail of name and place and date. Such conduct of the governors, rather than any political or legal question involved, was naturally the thing best remembered by the people, and, as legend is ever ready to develop general statement into definite detail, we find that later accounts begin to record for each canton special acts of individual cruelty and gradually to assign name and place and time. These were then further embellished to suit the personal taste or local prejudice of each chronicler. Thus Hemmerlin of Zürich (1450) gives Tell no place at all; the *Tellenlied* (Lucerne, 1470) gives to him and to Uri all the credit for the Confederation. The "White Book" of Sarnen, an anonymous chronicle of about 1470, gives all five of the stories that appear in the play. Each canton has a share: Obwalden gets the clash between Landenberg and "a man in the Melchi" (*Tell*, 561 ff.); Nidwalden the later Baumgarten story (*Tell*, 68 ff.), though without names; Schwyz the story of Geßler, who "covets the stone house of Stoupacher," whose "wise wife" advises union with friends (*Tell*, 195–348; 656–745), that then meet at night "*im Rüdli*" (II, 2); Uri, neglected before, now gets the lion's share in the great story of *der Tall* in his clash with Geßler. This Tell story, no doubt already current in Uri, is thus quietly melted together with the *Rütlibund*, with which, at first, it had nothing to do. In the castles captured definite places begin to appear, but as yet no dates are attempted. Later chroniclers preserve essential features and add many minor details and especially names and dates.

The form of the legend used by Schiller is that given by Aegidius Tschudi, a learned man and high official of Glarus, who, about 1569 in his Chronicon Helveticum (publ. 1734–36), built up out of these old traditions an account so systematic, so vivid, so definite and plausible as to inspire the utmost confidence. It reads like a good historical novel. He changed details to suit himself, assigned definite names and exact dates, invented what he needed, and sent it out as authentic history.

Schiller's friend, the eminent Swiss historian, Johannes von Müller, further systematized and settled what had been handed down. He admitted his doubt of its truth, yet sacrificed critical method to patriotic and rhetorical ends, in order to please his people and promote his own republican views. Finally Schiller, with Tschudi and Müller as chief sources, made whatever changes suited his fancy or seemed required by dramatic expediency, freely invented what he needed, and wrought the whole into one of the great plays of all time.

While it would seem from this sketch that most of the things in the play never happened or, if so, at a much earlier time (1246 instead of 1307), yet no one should wish to deny that very similar things probably did happen to people and in places whose names are forgotten. The Baumgarten episode has nothing impossible about it; the lord had the right to be quartered in the homes of his dependents and in some case may have paid for insulting conduct with his life. Melchtal's oxen may well have been taken for unpaid taxes; his quarrel and flight would be only natural; the father's punishment may be the memory of actual fact, for such was not unusual in the Middle Ages. Stauffacher is an historical name, and one of the family may well have clashed with some governor, and been inspired by his wife to consult with friends; secret meetings were doubtless held — and why not in so good a place as the Rütli? The capture of several castles by force or stratagem is no less plausible, though the circumstances may never be known. It was probably during the revolt of 1246 and may well have been on Christmas Day, because tradition would remember such a day, though the year might easily be forgotten.

As to Tell himself, the Swiss have always loved him; to this day many firmly believe in him. Yet as early as 1607 scholars began to doubt his existence. During two centuries of bitter dispute zealous partisans resorted to every means possible, even to forgery (changing Trullo to Tello, Näll to Thäll), to establish his identity, but the searching investigations of modern scholars have shown that there is no proof of his being. To be sure important documents may have been lost. Among recent writers Bernouilli would have us see in the story of the hat on the pole a distorted memory of old legal custom, by which a judge whose authority was questioned, in the meeting under the village linden where court was held, asserted that authority by thrusting his staff in the ground and hanging his hat on it. At some trial under the linden in Altorf, some sturdy peasant may have clashed with the foreign judge and been required to respect the hat on the staff. Why may he not have suffered arrest, escaped, and later, possibly *long* afterwards, killed the judge? Such is possible, of course, though it is not easy to prove so much out of the mere protest of the league of 1291 against foreign governors — unless one is quite anxious to prove it. Even Bernouilli admits that this possible Swiss patriot, if he really existed, is closely bound up with the stories of the great archer so well known among all Germanic peoples, in Denmark, Norway, Sweden, Iceland, England, as well as in India, Persia, Greece, Italy, and even among the Turks and Mongolians. The target is not always an apple, but often a nut, ring, coin, laid on the head or held in the hand. The story most like Tell's is that of Toko (also Tokko, Palnatoki) first *recorded* by the Danish historian, Saxo Grammaticus (died 1204): Toko, having boasted great skill in archery, is ordered by his king, Harald Bluetooth (936–986), to shoot an apple from the head of his son. Allowed one shot, he is to die, if he misses. Taking three arrows, Toko commanded the boy to stand still, and hit the apple at the first shot. When asked the purpose of the other arrows, he said they were meant for the king, if he had killed the child. Toko is also an expert skater and is required by the king to skate down a steep mountain to a lake. Afterwards, during a revolt against Harald, Toko kills the king from ambush in the forest.

Such stories also found their way to England, where they still live in the legends of Robin Hood, Adam Bell, Clym of the Clough, and William of Cloudesly (cf. Percy's *Reliques*). The last is much like Tell, save that the shot is his own suggestion, not the king's order. Any connection between *William* Cloudesly and *Wilhelm* Tell is questionable. The name Tell (also Tall, Thall, Thell, Täll) has been variously explained. The author of the "White Book" took it to mean "foolish" (*Tell*, 1873), i.e. Wilhelm Tell is "William the Simple."

These widespread great-archer stories are thought by some to go back to a nature myth, by others to an actual occurrence of very remote date. It is impossible to know. But, whatever its origin, it seems likely that the story, in some crude form, was brought to the Alps by the Alamannic settlers from their home in the north, was developed and kept alive by oral tradition, and finally found its way into the chronicles and into Schiller's play.

Though we find no Tell in recorded history, we yet honor him and his people for the dauntless spirit he represents. Though he may never have existed, many heroic men very like him did live among that people. He may not be real, but all that he stands for was, so what difference does it make by what *name* it goes?   Tell never lived, but he will live, as long as such an ideal of manhood has a place in the hearts of men.

III. THE WRITING OF THE PLAY

Wilhelm Tell, Schiller's last finished drama, though composed in a few months, really occupied the poet's attention for several years.   His interest in the subject was due at first and indirectly to Goethe, who had once intended to use it himself.   On his third and last trip to Switzerland, late in 1797, he visited the Forest Cantons and wrote that he had found a theme, the story of Tell, which "he felt would suit for an epic poem."   Schiller was pleased and warmly encouraged this "very happy idea" of his friend.   Though much interested at first, Goethe made but little progress with his *Tell*.   He sketched the outlines of the first cantos, but, in doubt about the verse-form and soon busy with other things, he delayed work on it until, he confesses later, "it had lost the charm of novelty" and until *he* had lost that proper mood always so necessary to his success.   He gave it up, as he had given up other subjects neglected in the same way.

We hear no more of *Tell* until early in 1801, when the rumor went abroad that Schiller was writing a *Tell*, and not an epic but a drama. Many inquiries were made about it, though he had not yet thought of undertaking such a work.   It is to this false report that we owe the play.   Schiller admits as much in letters to various friends.   To his publisher, Cotta, he wrote (March 1802) asking for "a good map of Lake Lucerne and the adjacent cantons" and confessing that this "false rumor" had led him to read Tschudi's chronicle, which had so attracted him that he "now in all earnestness meant to write a *Wilhelm Tell*."

Though long delayed by other plans, he never lost interest and finally on Aug. 25, 1803, began the play.   He saw the peculiar difficulties of the task, especially for one who had never been in Switzerland and who yet felt obliged to embody purely local features as far as possible. Not in the least discouraged, however, he asked his friends again and again for maps, pictures, books, and other material with which to make himself familiar with Swiss life, history, scenery, manners, and character.   Patiently, though slowly at first, he gathered from every available source the information he needed.[1] Goethe tells us that he pasted all the maps he could find on the walls of his room and read Swiss travels until he was familiar in detail with the scene of the action. He also studied Swiss history, charters, laws, trades, customs, costumes, climate, houses, flowers, animals, and natural scenery in general and particular. His severer historical studies in other years, his history lectures in Jena, his *Thirty Years' War*, *Revolt of the Netherlands*, *Don Carlos*, and *Wallenstein* had given him great skill in using such material, while his native energy and enthusiastic sympathy with a subject so congenial to his own liberty-loving soul enabled him soon to get on faster. His intuitive genius was, moreover, inspired by the vivid descriptions of his wife, of Goethe, and of other friends, who had been in Switzerland and could tell him more of places and people than he could find in books. Oct. 1, 1803 he saw *Julius Caesar* played in Weimar and derived important indirect help and inspiration from it.

In spite of many interruptions, social and business engagements, the death of Herder, and the all too lengthy visit of Madame de Staël in Weimar, he was ready to send the first act, which then included also Act II, sc. 1, to Goethe on Jan. 12, 1804. The others followed soon, and on Feb. 18, 1804 the whole was finished. He began preparations at once to have it played before Easter. As far as poor health permitted he directed the rehearsals himself, and in his absence Goethe took his place. The first performance was in the Court Theater in Weimar, March 17, 1804, and during the next few months the play was given again and again in Berlin, Breslau, and other large cities. In Vienna it was barred by the censor as hostile to the reigning House, Habsburg, until 1827.

After all the labor and enthusiasm bestowed upon *Tell*, Schiller naturally expected much of the play. His hopes were more than realized,

---

[1] His notes show that, besides his maps, he studied: Ägidius Tschudi, *Chronicon Helveticum*, printed Basel, 1734–36; the chronicles of Petermann Etterlin (about 1507) ed. Spreng, Basel, 1752, and Johann Stumpff, Zürich, 1548; Johannes von Müller, *Der Geschichten schweizerischer Eidgenossenschaft erster Teil*, Leipzig, 1786; J. J. Scheuchzer, *Naturgeschichten des Schweizerlandes*, ed. Sulzer, Zürich, 1746; J. G. Ebel, *Schilderung der Gebirgsvölker der Schweiz*, Tübingen, 1798; J. K. Fäsi, *Staats- und Erdbeschreibung der ganzen Helvetischen Eidgenossenschaft*, Zürich, 1766; Michael Ignaz Schmidt, *Geschichte der Deutschen. Dritter Teil*, Ulm, 1779; Meiners, *Briefe über die Schweiz*, 1792. A few minor features he took from earlier Tell dramas by Le Mierre, Bodmer, and Am Bühel, who deserve no further mention.

for his friends were delighted, most of the critics were pleased and
praised especially its wonderful fidelity in the matter of local color. A
first edition of 7000 copies, issued Oct. 1804, was soon exhausted, and,
before the year was out, a second of 3000 copies was printed. On
sending out the first, Cotta wrote: "*Tell* now goes into all the world."
He spoke more wisely than he knew. In translations it has gone over
the whole civilized world and has done more than anything else to
spread the name and the fame of the Swiss and their hero as well as of
its author. The reason is that, while its setting and details are pe-
culiarly Swiss, its great themes of liberty and patriotism, its funda-
mental passions and conflicts of mind and heart are not more Swiss
than they are German — and human, for such devotion to the cause
of country, such spirit of union and sympathy and sacrifice are things
that belong to all the world. Schiller wrote not alone for the Swiss,
but especially for his own people and, though he doubtless did not
know it, for all men and all time. Germany has heard and heeded the
message; it has been sold by hundreds of thousands, far more widely
than any other German play; it is performed perhaps 200 times a
year; its striking lines are household words in every home. Its value
lies not alone in the poet's high purposes, but in what in the course of
time it has become. To the Swiss it is a sacred thing, to the Germans
their great teacher's legacy to his people, not only a masterpiece of
their literature, but the embodiment of their ideals, and a real working
force in their lives. In times of political unrest, as in the revolution of
1848, it rang out like a trumpet call proclaiming the rights of man as
against tyranny at home and during the wars with France (1813, 1870–
71) it was a great source of patriotic enthusiasm, an inspiring lesson to
the little German states to hold together — *fest und einig* — in resistance to their common enemy from without. And the future will
prize it no less than the past, for

> *Erzählen wird man von dem Schützen Tell,*
> *Solang' die Berge stehn auf ihrem Grunde.*

IV. THEME, TIME, PLACE, AND STRUCTURE

Closely following Tschudi, Schiller lays all the scenes of *Tell* on or near
the shores of Lake Lucerne. Tschudi's dates, however, — for the
Baumgarten story August, 1306; the Rütli oath Nov. 8, 1307; Geßler's
death Nov. 19, 1307; fall of Roßberg and Sarnen Jan. 1, 1308; the

murder of Albrecht May 1, 1308 — are so changed, in the interest of dramatic unity, that the events of the play occur on four different days at intervals in a period of about three weeks, as follows: Act I on Oct. 28, 1307; Act II on Nov. 7–8; Acts III and IV on *one* day, Nov. 20 (Tschudi says 18 and 19, by mistake for this year for 19 and 20); Act V on the morning on Nov. 22. Details are given in the Notes.

The Swiss fight for freedom naturally attracted the *Freiheitsdichter*, Schiller. The same love of liberty that had once prompted *The Robbers*, *Fiesco*, *Don Carlos*, and other plays, found here a most congenial, inspiring theme, and he devoted to it the last great effort of his life. His "object," of course, was not deliberately "to teach Germany the lesson of national unity" or any other "lesson," though many lessons have been drawn from it, but simply to write a great play, nobly to embody the noble theme, which had so strongly appealed to his own liberty-loving nature. Better than all the critics, he himself has expressed his purpose in the lines he wrote on sending a manuscript copy of *Tell* to Prince Elector Karl von Dalberg, Archbishop of Mainz and brother of his old friend, the theater manager in Mannheim:

> *Wenn rohe Kräfte feindlich sich entzweien*
> *Und blinde Wut die Kriegesflamme schürt;*
> *Wenn sich im Kampfe tobender Parteien*
> *Die Stimme der Gerechtigkeit verliert;*
> *Wenn alle Laster schamlos sich befreien,*
> *Wenn freche Willkür an das Heil'ge rührt,*
> *Den Anker löst, an dem die Staaten hängen:*
> *Da ist kein Stoff zu freudigen Gesängen.*
> *Doch wenn ein Volk, das fromm die Herden weidet,*
> *Sich selbst genug, nicht fremden Guts begehrt,*
> *Den Zwang abwirft, den es unwürdig leidet,*
> *Doch selbst im Zorn die Menschlichkeit noch ehrt,*
> *Im Glücke selbst, im Siege sich bescheidet:*
> *Das ist unsterblich und des Liedes wert.*
> *Und solch ein Lied darf ich dir freudig zeigen,*
> *Du kennst's, denn alles Große ist dein eigen.*

The theme of *Tell* then is the lawful and successful uprising of a united people against oppression. Therefore, the hero of the play is not Tell alone, but the whole Swiss people in close and faithful union against a common enemy. Though above all the most important factor, so that the play rightfully bears his name, Tell is but one individual element. Herein lay a great dramatic difficulty, and one not entirely overcome, namely to preserve the unity of the action, make it all seem cast in one mold, not several pieces merely fastened together, and yet to separate sufficiently the important individual cause of Tell from that of the whole people without giving it undue prominence. Such separation was necessary in order to justify the killing of Geßler; to make it not cowardly murder, but just and necessary self-defense in bitter personal feud, Tell must strike at the man Geßler, not at his political policy. Schiller felt, and so did Goethe, that "Tell must stand alone in the drama, that his cause is and must remain a private one, entirely without political character, till at the close it coincides with that of the people," in that by killing his own personal enemy he has also killed their political oppressor. For such dramatic reason, therefore, he made a quiet, unobtrusive man, unwilling to take any part in the councils of his friends, for that, of course, would have made his later action a political and patriotic, not a personal, thing.

Some critics urge that Schiller saw but did not solve his problem and that the play is not all one piece, but several separate, poorly fitted parts. If it might seem so at first sight, this view is not justified by closer study. Within the play there are three groups of characters, each with its own course of action, called for convenience the folk plot, the Tell plot, the nobles plot. The first two are found loosely connected in the poet's sources, the last is his own addition. The three are not carried forward together, but in succession, so that first the one advances, then another. The first begins with accounts of suffering in the three cantons (Act I), has its climax in the Rütli meeting (II, 2), and ends with sweeping away the last remnants of tyranny in Act V. The second, suggested in Tell's rescue of Baumgarten (I, 1) and in his talk with Stauffacher (I, 3), is developed in Hedwig's fears (III, 1), has its climax in the apple-shot (III, 3), its crisis in the death of Geßler (IV, 3), and its end in the homage paid to Tell in V, 3. The third, after vague mention (I, 1, 2, 4) begins with the turning of Rudenz to Austria (II, 1), is developed by Berta (III, 2), rises higher in Rudenz' defiance of Geßler (III, 3), reaches a climax in his bond with Melchtal (IV, 2) and its close in the storming of the castles (IV, 2) and his union with Berta (V, 3). The three are by no means so separate as might appear; Schiller unites them by giving each plot: (1) the same cause of action in the cruelty of the governors; (2) the same object, to get rid of this tyranny; (3) the same motive, self-defense; (4) by making them touch at important points; and (5) by joining them all at the end. Both Tell and Rudenz, in serving personal ends, secure the result sought by all; in killing Geßler Tell does the work specially dreaded by the Rütli men, and Rudenz does the rest, when he joins Melchtal and storms the castles in search of Berta, hidden from him because he had interfered between Geßler and Tell. Act I, 1 unites two of the plots; I, 3 all three; III, 3 all three; IV, 1 two; IV, 2 all three; IV, 3 two; V, 1 two; V, 3 all three. Attention is concentrated now on one, now on another, but there is very real dramatic unity in such interlocking action, that amply serves its purpose and does credit to the poet's skill. This unity becomes clearer, perhaps, when we see that the whole action is made up as follows:

1. "Exposition," or setting forth of time, place, and important characters, nature of the conflict, and plans for it (I–II, 1).

2. Progress of the conflict: in *action:* (a) by Wolfenschießen, I, 1; (b) by Geßler, I, 2, 3; (c) by Landenberg, I, 4; in *counter action:* (a) by Tell, I, 1; (b) by Gertrud and Stauffacher, I, 2; (c) by Melchtal-Stauffacher-Fürst, I, 4; (d) by the Rütli men, II, 2.

3. Climax of the conflict: in Geßler's cruelty and Tell's struggle in the scene of the apple-shot, III, 3.

4. Turn of the conflict: (a) in Rudenz' defiance, III, 3; (b) Tell's defiance, rearrest (III, 3), and escape, IV, 1; (c) Rudenz-Melchtal alliance, IV, 2; (d) Tell's monologue, IV, 3.

5. End of the conflict: (a) Geßler's death, IV, 3; (b) storming of the castles and expulsion of Landenberg, V, 1; (c) death of the Emperor, V, 1; (d) homage to Tell, betrothal of Berta, liberation of serfs, V, 3.

Whatever may be said of the unity of the whole plot, there can be no doubt whatever about the poet's skill in the blending of human nature and motive and action in the individual scenes. Almost without exception, as single scenes and whether the figures be few or many, they are pictures of rare charm and power. Goethe said the first act was "a whole play in itself, and a fine one at that." We might almost say that of the first scene, the overture for the whole. The Rütli meeting is most impressive, its many characters most skillfully handled, its setting grand as the majestic Nature in which it is laid. Only he who has seen the Alps by moonlight and at dawn can feel its power or appreciate the genius that painted it — without having seen it himself. In contrast Tell's little family gives us a home idyll of singular charm. The alliance of Melchtal, Fürst, and Stauffacher has a pathos that will touch and a fervor that will fire any heart. Attinghausen's pleading alone with Rudenz and his message to the assembled confederates at his death are the inspired gospel of that patriotism that makes a country worth fighting for. The great scene of the apple-shot, one of the finest things on the stage, runs the scale of human feeling from whimsical humor through fearful suffering to frozen horror and melting joy, the whole range of human nature from the sweet trustfulness of innocent childhood to the iron control of tortured manhood and the fiendish cruelty of inhuman tyranny, from the boy's faith in his father to the strong man's faith in his God; it has a host of characters of every age, sex, rank, and walk in life, yet they stand out as individuals and are not lost in the crowd; it has a dramatic tension, whose grip grows ever stronger and relaxes only at the end. The death of Geßler is another of those master-scenes that have made the play famous, another *ensemble* with life-like individual figures, full of vivid character-drawing, dramatic suspense and surprises, and telling contrasts: the monologue of the avenger, alone with his awful purpose of death, and the chorus of the Brothers of Mercy with its warning of the uncertainty of life; the grim and silent Tell and the inquisitive, talkative Stüssi; the threatening Geßler and the stricken governor; the murder and music, the pleas and curses, the marrying and burying that come together, the innocent children and the dying tyrant. Each picture is good in itself and all the better for its contrast with the other. Whole scenes are also contrasted with each other: the death of Geßler with that of Attinghausen; the killing of Geßler with that of the Emperor; the arrest of Tell with his escape; the lazy sunshine that smiles on the meadows of Schwyz with the ghostly moonlight that broods over the Rütli and the wild storms that sweep down on the lake.

V. THE CHARACTERS

But the crowning glory of the play is Schiller's portrayal of character. A Swiss critic in 1805 writes: "We cannot say of them that they are invented, for . . . they are taken right out of nature. One would swear that Schiller had lived the greatest part of his life in Schwyz or Uri with this simple, unassuming, yet sturdy shepherd race. Such *are* these little known mountaineers in their hour of need, *thus* do they think, thus act."

Tell is one of Nature's own heroes, notable for self-reliant strength, independent manhood, and persistent individualism. His profession has taught him to love the solitude of the mountains and the silence of his own thoughts, to shun the crowd and its secret plans and counsels. The wild Nature in which he lives and of which he has in a sense become a part has given him a clear eye, a steady hand, a daring spirit, a heart without fear; has trained him with quick decision to meet emergency when it comes, not to deliberate about it before or after. As his life is lonely, his views are narrow and lack the breadth that only contact with others can give. Forced to fight his own battles, he knows and trusts his own strength and judgment, and is quick to do, with the wisdom of experience, the common-sense thing the moment demands, without discussion with others. Familiar with danger, he is daring and unafraid, even heedless, acting not on impulse, but by instinct. He is also as kind and gentle as he is big and brave and strong. In his quiet way he loves his wife and children with all his heart. With ready sympathy he springs to the help of another in distress, just because he *is* in distress, without asking who or how or wherefore. There is no selfishness about him, he is modest almost to shyness, keeps his own counsel, and is loath to tell his exploits even to his wife. His trust in God is the absolute faith of a child in its father. His skillful hand, his generous heart, his blameless life win him the love of all who know him: *Es gibt nicht zwei wie der ist im Gebirge!*

Some, for instance such a man as Prince Bismarck, object to Tell as "unnatural," because no such father *could* shoot at his own child. The very idea is dreadful, of course; but we must remember that without this shot Tell would cease to be the Tell of the legend and would become somebody else; just as Rip Van Winkle without his long nap would no longer be Rip. But even for one not familiar with the legend and not aware that just this shot is part of the very idea of a Tell, Schiller has made it seem natural and inevitable, for Tell must shoot or die with the boy. It is very natural, even if he were not a great marksman, that he should risk his only chance to save them both. To aim wide of the mark meant his death (1890); to shoot Geßler instead would have meant the wholesale slaughter of himself, his boy, and his friends by the body-guard. When the offer of his own life is twice made and twice refused and all intercession proves vain, Tell knows there is no other way out, and it is the struggle born of that knowledge that makes the scene so intensely dramatic.

Again some cannot forgive Tell's desertion of Geßler in the storm. Yet why should he save one, whose inhuman cruelty has cost him all claim to human sympathy, one no longer his judge, but the ruthless, relentless foe he has so rightly sworn to kill? Tell promised to help, and did help over the worst danger, but not to save. Even if he had, we could not call it binding, for we have no faith in Geßler's promise. This is war, and Tell did what any red-blooded man would do, if he could.

Similar objection is made to the killing of Geßler from ambush by those, Bismarck again among them, who forget that it is Tell's only way. In this conflict the question is simply: which can destroy the other first? Unless Tell and his loved ones are to die, he must kill. No one denies his right to do so or doubts that the deed is done in lawful self-defense. It is as necessary as the apple-shot, for without it Tell is no longer Tell; it is, moreover, justified by the logic of the monologue and the Parricida scene, as well as by every human instinct. Before we condemn the ambush let us remember that he cannot risk failure, because he will never have another chance; an attack in the open might well kill Geßler, but would leave Tell at the mercy of his body-guard; a challenge to fair fight would have been laughed at (even Rudenz could not demand it) and would have left Tell a hunted man. The ambush may not be high-minded chivalry, but it is longheaded common sense.

The other characters, rather typical than strongly individual, are simpler. They give us examples of various classes, occupations, ranks, and ages, from child to patriarch, from serf to nobleman, among the Swiss people. The three leaders, Melchtal, Stauffacher, and Fürst all belong to the higher class, but, in intended contrast, each stands for a different canton and for a different age and temperament. Melchtal's *rasche Jugend* is prone to act on impulse, but yields to the wiser counsel of experience, sinks his own in the common cause, learns to tame his fiery spirit, and is ripened by suffering. An outspoken democrat, he shrinks from alliance with the nobleman, but soon sees his mistake and joins him in a union that means so much for his people and the future. He is one of that younger generation of yeomen that is to rule when the old patrician class (Attinghausen) is gone, one of those "other forces" by which real liberty is to be maintained, from which in later time a new prosperity for the burgher is to rise out of the ruins of a crumbling feudalism.

Stauffacher, with all his hesitation the real leader, is the solid citizen of wealth and standing, respected for his simple life, his enlightened public spirit, his generous charity and hospitality. He is well informed as to his country's history and legal rights, a sober thinker and farseeing student of affairs, moderate in his judgments, convincing in his speech, calm in a crisis, meeting an issue squarely, brave but prudent — the conservative force in the community, that restrains the extremes of others less thoughtful. He has well been called the spokesman of Schiller's views on the rights of man in his relation to government.

Fürst, the beloved old grandfather, with all the wisdom of rich experience and none of the boldness of conscious strength, is no less patriotic, but much more cautious and careful, hesitating even when he knows the time for action has come. He is the ultraconservative whose virtues have become his weakness, who sees that conditions are intolerable, yet shrinks from the violent measures needed to better them.

Rudenz and Attinghausen are more or less types as well as individuals among the young and old native nobility; the latter a loved patriarch among his people, inspiring example of all that was best in the elder age, and prophet of the future, who sinks to his rest in the glow of a sunset that makes way for the dawn of a better day; the former young and ambitious, without the chastening of experience, with mistaken views of the real values, coquetting with Austria to gain his selfish ends, but finally awakening to his real duty and character, and supporting his people against a common foe.

The women are especially well-drawn types. Gertrud is the social leader, well born and well trained for the place she fills, the "pleasant hostess" and able homemaker, the brave and patriotic, childless matron, a woman of rare breadth of view and depth of insight, with time and temper for the concerns of her country as well as the affairs of her home. She follows her head as well as her heart and uses them both to inspire her less confident husband to sacrifice all, if need be, for her people's sake. In striking contrast, Hedwig is the anxious wife, the loving mother, deaf to the voice of reason, following only her heart and her intuitive feeling, bound up in the little world of her home, concerned only for the welfare of her husband and children, suffering needlessly from her too vivid imagination, hasty in her censure of Tell, yet trembling for his safety, and proud as a queen of him and his part in the liberation of the country. Berta is the high-minded fearless girl, who, though not of Swiss birth, noble in rank, and related to Geßler, gives her sympathy to this people and her heart to the lover whom she wins back to his country and his duty. All three and in them all the better classes of women, maidens, wives, and mothers, noble and peasant, native and foreign alike, resent the tyrant's oppression.

Geßler, the worst of the governors because the ablest, is a thorough tyrant, cruel and cowardly, faithless and vindictive, a stranger to every impulse of kindness. He is the stern, inflexible ruler, loyal to his master, with great plans for extending the power of Habsburg, and determined to carry them out, though it means stifling every impulse of liberty in this people. Angered by their stubbornness, he resorts to the most unreasonable means to enforce his authority. To his haughty sternness as judge he adds a personal hatred and private vengeance, which lead him from mere severity to ruthless, fiendish, inhuman cruelty.

The lower classes, too, hunters, herdsmen, laborers, and even serfs, men, women, and children all have their types, well drawn and true to nature, in Werni, Ruodi, Kuoni, and the rest, and all making common cause against their common enemy. This union of all classes only makes the justice of their cause the more evident. It is not the rash hotheadedness of youth, not the protest of fanatical reformers, not the revolt of the rabble — it is the common uprising of a whole people, whose most sacred rights have been ruthlessly outraged.

Among the characters of the play, for it is as well portrayed and as vital as any, one is almost tempted to include Swiss Nature, scenery, "atmosphere," "local color," whatever we care to call it — that something that makes the play so really Swiss, that takes us to the Forest Cantons as the curtain goes up, keeps us there till it falls, and remains among our most abiding memories. Little short of marvelous is the skill with which Schiller succeeded in this most difficult part of his task, the painting of purely local features of Swiss Nature and character and the harmonizing of that character with that environment. These men are what they are, because they are the product of that Nature; they are simple and rugged as their mountains, their souls as free as the winds on their snow peaks; they love their liberty because *Das Haus der Freiheit hat uns Gott gegründet.* Schiller was never in the

Alps, knew Swiss scenes and people only through the accounts of others, yet his pictures are vivid and faithful and full of "those precious little touches" that make them unmistakably Swiss. The glowing descriptions of others were helpful, but the secret of his success lies rather in his patient study of even the smallest details, in his intuitive understanding of his sources, and in his sheer genius in using this material. His rich imagination freely supplied what he could not find elsewhere, but in many places he follows his sources so closely as to transfer to his play not only the subject matter of whole passages, but even the old and peculiar words and all the quaint simplicity of Swiss dialect, thus securing the most genuine local color and almost always that harmony of speech with speaker which makes a character so lifelike. It is easy to forgive him his few and unimportant mistakes — in the meaning of a word, his estimate of distance, his confusion of scenery — for usually we know no better ourselves and can see such mistakes, as we do the spots on the sun, only through glasses that are smoked over the midnight lamp of some pedantic scholar. But even then our illusion is not destroyed, for "one who reads Tell and then visits Switzerland, feels as if he had already seen it all, and that which seemed an ideal picture of the imagination, becomes actual and living reality" (Carriere).

In its dramatic character the play is, of course, not comedy, nor is it tragedy, for it ends happily; its theme is, moreover, too epic and its personal action and passion too often secondary to the general welfare. Schiller wisely called it *ein Schauspiel*, "an epic drama, in which the force of outward circumstances and conditions as well as of innate character determines the action" (Carriere).

As one of the faults of the play it is urged that the *Rütlibund*, after all its solemn council, gets no further, that Melchtal, when he breaks away and follows Rudenz, is the only one of the confederates who does anything, and that the *Bund* thus loses in dignity and importance. Yet we must remember that the confederates are bound by oath not to act before a given time. Tyranny, however, does not wait, and when the wave of events lifts Tell into the crisis and he acts as he must, there is little left for the *Bund* to do. In doing that little Rudenz is joined by many others (not named) besides Melchtal, for it is absurd to think Schiller meant the castles to be taken by these two men alone.

The so called "Berta-Rudenz episode," Schiller's own invention, has been condemned as unnecessary, as lacking in force, and as unimportant for the action. True, it is weaker than other things in the play, but it is much more than a response to the conventional demand for a love story in a drama, much more than an episode, for it is woven into the action of the whole play. The lyric charm of the love idyll brightens and relieves the seriousness of the action, even though, at times, its speech is rhetorical and forced. But its importance lies in what it leads to. Though she was the reason for the apparent desertion of Rudenz, Berta wins him back to his duty, is responsible for his defiance of Geßler, and inspires the young nobleman's alliance with the fiery democrat, which completes the union of the whole people, renders such service in securing their liberty, and symbolizes the new order prophesied by the dying patriarch. To this love affair is also due the interview of Rudenz with his uncle, not only one of the best things in the play, but the inspired gospel of patriotism, whose ringing words are an impelling force even to-day. Surely this is no mere romantic episode; it is vital.

The addition of Act V, with its less animated action and more epic character, has been called a mistake. Some think the play should end with Geßler's death. Yet Act V is necessary, for, in the capture of the castles, it shows the further results of the struggle for liberty, the theme of the whole play, and the certainty that this liberty is complete, while in the Emperor's death it brings the assurance that this liberty is permanently safe from outside interference. It is satisfying also to see Tell again after his deed of death and to observe its effect upon him and his people after both have had time to think about it. The interview with Parricida, the Emperor's murderer, was intended by sharp contrast to justify the one and condemn the other; yet it seems unnecessary and out of harmony with the rest of the Act. The provocation of Tell's deed is its own defense; he needs no further justification. Indeed it is an open question whether this second defense does not do more harm than good, by rousing latent doubt in the reader's mind as to the correctness of his first intuitive judgment. At any rate the holier-than-thou tone of Tell's condemnation of Parricida is most unfortunate and unnatural in the greathearted Tell of the play.

One or two other matters seem to have escaped the attention of the poet, whose mind is bent on larger things. At the end of Act IV, sc. 2, when the Rudenz party starts off, Tell's friends think he is in prison (though the spectator knows he is not); that is Melchtal's reason for breaking his Rütli oath, and the anxious Hedwig has been assured that he shall be set free; yet nothing is done or even suggested to capture Küßnacht or keep the promise, though the matter is so vital. Perhaps we are to suppose that the expedition means to *begin* with the nearest castles and go to Küßnacht later — and then finds it does not need to do so. The matter is not made clear or even referred to. Again, why should Ruodi (IV, 1) see in the death of Attinghausen such a loss to the confederates, when the Baron had never even heard of them or their plans, much less helped them in any way? The reference is apparently to the Baron's sympathy in general with his oppressed people.

As the poet of freedom, Schiller achieved in *Tell* his greatest triumph. More than any other of his plays does it appeal to the great masses of German people; more than any other has it furnished favorite sayings, almost become proverbs, ever remembered and quoted by prince and peasant alike; in it the prose of his early dramas has given place to his noblest poetry; the extravagant rhetoric and unreasonable theories of the young enthusiast have here become the calmer thought, the riper convictions of the mature man; the narrower social or political or personal freedom which was the theme of *Die Räuber, Fiesco, Kabale und Liebe, Don Carlos*, and others has been broadened, till freedom everywhere, in the home, in society, in government, the freedom of a whole people is the theme of *Tell;* the effort of individual fanatics or revolutionists in earlier plays to overthrow all law and order in attaining an imaginary freedom has here become the uprising of a whole brave and patient people to defend and preserve their real liberty from the attacks of foreign tyrants.

The deeper significance of *Tell* lies not alone in what Schiller made it, the beautiful, inspiring story of a brave fight for freedom, but also in that which in a hundred years it has become, in that which a century and more of further human progress has found in it and got out of it, in those lessons of plain living and high thinking, of service and suffering and sacrifice which the centuries to come will learn from it. It is not merely Swiss, but belongs to the Germans as well; is their great poet's last inspired message, their national drama as no other has ever become. It is more than that, for Schiller overstepped the bounds of mere nationality and became a great apostle of all that is best in all modern life. Like all great artists he did impress his own individuality and nationality upon his work, but he did still more; he knew that art has to do with universal truth and beauty, and he, therefore, subordinated the merely local and ephemeral and made his appeal to all time

and all men.   He is gone these many years, but, in a work like this, still
lives, for

> "They do not die who leave their thought
>   Imprinted on some deathless page;
> Themselves may pass; the spell they wrought
>   Endures on earth from age to age."

PERSONEN

Hermann Geßler, Reichsvogt in Schwyz und Uri
Werner, Freiherr von Attinghausen, Bannerherr
Ulrich von Rudenz, sein Neffe
Werner Stauffacher
Konrad Hunn
Itel Reding
Hans auf der Mauer } Landleute aus Schwyz
Jörg im Hofe
Ulrich der Schmied
Jost von Weiler
Walter Fürst
Wilhelm Tell
Rösselmann, der Pfarrer
Petermann, der Sigrist } aus Uri
Kuoni, der Hirte
Werni, der Jäger
Ruodi, der Fischer
Arnold vom Melchtal
Konrad Baumgarten
Meier von Sarnen
Struth von Winkelried } aus Unterwalden
Klaus von der Flüe
Burkhard am Bühel
Arnold von Sewa
Pfeifer von Luzern
Kunz von Gersau
Jenni, Fischerknabe
Seppi, Hirtenknabe
Gertrud, Stauffachers Gattin
Hedwig, Tells Gattin, Fürsts Tochter
Berta von Bruneck, eine reiche Erbin
Armgard
Mechthild } Bäuerinnen
Elsbet
Hildegard
Walter } Tells Knaben
Wilhelm
Frießhard } Söldner
Leuthold
Rudolf der Harras, Geßlers Stallmeister
Johannes Parricida, Herzog von Schwaben
Stüssi, der Flurschütz
Der Stier von Uri
Ein Reichsbote
Fronvogt
Meister Steinmetz, Gesellen und Handlanger
Öffentliche Ausrufer
Barmherzige Brüder
Geßlerische und Landenbergische Reiter
Viele Landleute, Männer und Weiber aus den Waldstätten

ERSTER AUFZUG

ERSTE SZENE

(Hohes Felsenufer des Vierwaldstättersees, Schwyz gegenüber. Der
See macht eine Bucht ins Land, eine Hütte ist unweit dem Ufer,
Fischerknabe fährt sich in einem Kahn. Über den See hinweg sieht
man die grünen Matten, Dörfer und Höfe von Schwyz im hellen
Sonnenschein liegen. Zur Linken des Zuschauers zeigen sich die
Spitzen des Haken, mit Wolken umgeben; zur Rechten im fernen
Hintergrund sieht man die Eisgebirge. Noch ehe der Vorhang
aufgeht, hört man den Kuhreihen und das harmonische Geläut' der
Herdenglocken, welches sich auch bei eröffneter Szene noch eine
Zeitlang fortsetzt.)

Fischerknabe

(singt im Kahn)
(Melodie des Kuhreihens)

Es lächelt der See, er ladet zum Bade,
Der Knabe schlief ein am grünen Gestade,
    Da hört er ein Klingen,
    Wie Flöten so süß,
5   Wie Stimmen der Engel
    Im Paradies.
Und wie er erwachet in seliger Lust,
Da spülen die Wasser ihm um die Brust,
    Und es ruft aus den Tiefen:
10   Lieb Knabe, bist m e i n !
    Ich locke den Schläfer,
    Ich zieh' ihn herein.

Hirte

(auf dem Berge)
(Variation des Kuhreihens)

Ihr Matten, lebt wohl,
Ihr sonnigen Weiden!

3

15   Der Senne muß scheiden,
      Der Sommer ist hin.
      Wir fahren zu Berg, wir kommen wieder,
      Wenn der Kuckuck ruft, wenn erwachen die Lieder,
      Wenn mit Blumen die Erde sich kleidet neu,
20   Wenn die Brünnlein fließen im lieblichen Mai.
      Ihr Matten, lebt wohl,
      Ihr sonnigen Weiden!
      Der Senne muß scheiden,
      Der Sommer ist hin.

Alpenjäger

(erscheint gegenüber auf der Höhe des Felsens)
(Zweite Variation)

25   Es donnern die Höhen, es zittert der Steg,
      Nicht grauet dem Schützen auf schwindlichtem Weg;
      Er schreitet verwegen
      Auf Feldern von Eis;
      Da pranget kein Frühling,
30   Da grünet kein Reis;
      Und unter den Füßen ein neblichtes Meer,
      Erkennt er die Städte der Menschen nicht mehr;
      Durch den Riß nur der Wolken
      Erblickt er die Welt,
35   Tief unter den Wassern
      Das grünende Feld.

(Die Landschaft verändert sich, man hört ein dumpfes Krachen von den
Bergen, Schatten von Wolken laufen über die Gegend. *Ruodi, der
Fischer*, kommt aus der Hütte. *Werni, der Jäger*, steigt vom Felsen.
Kuoni, der Hirte, kommt mit dem Melknapf auf der Schulter. *Seppi,
sein Handbube*, folgt ihm.)

Ruodi

Mach' hurtig, Jenni! Zieh die Naue ein!
Der graue Talvogt kommt, dumpf brüllt der Firn,

Der Mythenstein zieht seine Haube an,
40   Und kalt her bläst es aus dem Wetterloch;
Der Sturm, ich mein', wird da sein, eh' wir's denken.

Kuoni

's kommt Regen, Fährmann. Meine Schafe fressen
Mit Begierde Gras, und Wächter scharrt die Erde.

Werni

Die Fische springen, und das Wasserhuhn
45   Taucht unter. Ein Gewitter ist im Anzug.

Kuoni

(zum Buben)

Lug', Seppi, ob das Vieh sich nicht verlaufen.

Seppi

Die braune Lisel kenn' ich am Geläut'.

Kuoni

So fehlt uns keine mehr, d i e geht am weitsten.

Ruodi

Ihr habt ein schön Geläute, Meister Hirt.

Werni

50   Und schmuckes Vieh — Ist's Euer eignes, Landsmann?

Kuoni

Bin nit so reich — 's ist meines gnäd'gen Herrn,
Des Attinghäusers, und mir zugezählt.

Ruodi

Wie schön der Kuh das Band zu Halse steht!

Kuoni

Das weiß sie auch, daß sie den Reihen führt,
55 Und nähm' ich ihr's, sie hörte auf zu fressen.

Ruodi

Ihr seid nicht klug! Ein unvernünft'ges Vieh —

Werni

Ist bald gesagt. Das Tier hat auch Vernunft;
Das wissen w i r , die wir die Gemsen jagen.
Die stellen klug, wo sie zur Weide gehn,
60 'ne Vorhut aus, die spitzt das Ohr und warnet
Mit heller Pfeife, wenn der Jäger naht.

Ruodi

(zum Hirten)

Treibt Ihr jetzt heim?

Kuoni

Die Alp ist abgeweidet.

Werni

Glückse 'ge Heimkehr, Senn!

Kuoni

Die wünsch' ich E u c h ;
Von E u r e r Fahrt kehrt sich's nicht immer wieder.

Ruodi

65 Dort kommt ein Mann in voller Hast gelaufen.

Werni

Ich kenn' ihn, 's ist der Baumgart von Alzellen.

(*Konrad Baumgarten* atemlos hereinstürzend)

Baumgarten

Um Gottes willen, Fährmann, Euren Kahn!

Ruodi

Nun, nun, was gibt's so eilig?

Baumgarten

Bindet los!
Ihr rettet mich von Tode! Setzt mich über!

Kuoni

70 Landsmann, was habt Ihr?

Werni

Wer verfolgt Euch denn?

Baumgarten

(zum Fischer)

Eilt, eilt, sie sind mir dicht schon an den Fersen!
Des Landvogts Reiter kommen hinter mir;
Ich bin ein Mann des Tods, wenn sie mich greifen.

Ruodi

Warum verfolgen Euch die Reisigen?

Baumgarten

75 Erst rettet mich, und dann steh' ich Euch Rede.

Werni

Ihr seid mit Blut befleckt, was hat's gegeben?

Baumgarten

Des Kaisers Burgvogt, der auf Roßberg saß —

Kuoni

Der Wolfenschießen! Läßt Euch d e r verfolgen?

Baumgarten

D e r schadet nicht mehr, ich hab' ihn erschlagen.

Alle

(fahren zurück)

80   Gott sei Euch gnädig! Was habt Ihr getan?

Baumgarten

Was jeder freie Mann an meinem Platz!
Mein gutes Hausrecht hab' ich ausgeübt
Am Schänder meiner Ehr' und meines Weibes.

Kuoni

Hat Euch der Burgvogt an der Ehr' geschädigt?

Baumgarten

85   Daß er sein bös Gelüsten nicht vollbracht,
Hat Gott und meine gute Axt verhütet.

Werni

Ihr habt ihm mit der Axt den Kopf zerspalten?

Kuoni

O laßt uns alles hören; Ihr habt Zeit,
Bis er den Kahn vom Ufer losgebunden.

Baumgarten

90   Ich hatte Holz gefällt im Wald, da kommt
Mein Weib gelaufen in der Angst des Todes.
Der Burgvogt lieg' in meinem Haus; er hab'

Ihr anbefohlen, ihm ein Bad zu rüsten.
Drauf hab' er Ungebührliches von ihr
95 Verlangt; sie sei entsprungen, mich zu suchen.
Da lief ich frisch hinzu, so wie ich war,
Und mit der Axt hab' ich ihm 's Bad gesegnet.

Werni

Ihr tatet wohl, kein Mensch kann Euch drum schelten.

Kuoni

Der Wüterich! Der hat nun seinen Lohn!
100 Hat's lang' verdient ums Volk von Unterwalden.

Baumgarten

Die Tat ward ruchtbar; mir wird nachgesetzt —
Indem wir sprechen — Gott — verrinnt die Zeit —

(Es fängt an zu donnern.)

Kuoni

Frisch, Fährmann — schaff' den Biedermann hinüber!

Ruodi

Geht nicht. Ein schweres Ungewitter ist
105 Im Anzug. Ihr müßt warten.

Baumgarten

Heil'ger Gott!
Ich kann nicht warten. Jeder Aufschub tötet —

Kuoni

(zum Fischer)

Greif an mit Gott! Dem Nächsten muß man helfen;
Es kann uns allen Gleiches ja begegnen.

(Brausen und Donnern)

Ruodi

Der Föhn ist los; ihr seht, wie hoch der See geht;
110 Ich kann nicht steuern gegen Sturm und Wellen.

Baumgarten

(umfaßt seine Knie)

So helf' Euch Gott, wie Ihr Euch mein erbarmet —

Werni

Es geht ums Leben. Sei barmherzig, Fährmann!

Kuoni

's ist ein Hausvater und hat Weib und Kinder!

(Wiederholte Donnerschläge)

Ruodi

Was? Ich hab' auch ein Leben zu verlieren,
115 Hab' Weib und Kind daheim, wie er — Seht hin,
Wie's brandet, wie es wogt und Wirbel zieht
Und alle Wasser aufrührt in der Tiefe.
— Ich wollte gern den Biedermann erretten;
Doch es ist rein unmöglich, ihr seht selbst.

Baumgarten

(noch auf den Knien)

120 So muß ich fallen in des Feindes Hand,
Das nahe Rettungsufer im Gesichte!
— Dort liegt's! Ich kann's erreichen mit den Augen,
Hinüberdringen kann der Stimme Schall;
Da ist der Kahn, der mich hinübertrüge,
125 Und muß hier liegen, hilflos, und verzagen!

Kuoni

Seht, wer da kommt!

Werni

Es ist Tell aus Bürglen.

(Tell mit der Armbrust)

Tell

Wer ist der Mann, der hier um Hilfe fleht?

Kuoni

's ist ein Alzeller Mann; er hat sein' Ehr'
Verteidigt und den Wolfenschieß erschlagen,
130   Des Königs Burgvogt, der auf Roßberg saß —
Des Landvogts Reiter sind ihm auf den Fersen;
Er fleht den Schiffer um die Überfahrt;
Der fürcht't sich vor dem Sturm und will nicht fahren.

Ruodi

Da ist der Tell, er führt das Ruder auch,
135   Der soll mir's zeugen, ob die Fahrt zu wagen.

Tell

Wo's not tut, Fährmann, läßt sich alles wagen.

(Heftige Donnerschläge, der See rauscht auf.)

Ruodi

Ich soll mich in den Höllenrachen stürzen?
Das täte keiner, der bei Sinnen ist.

Tell

Der brave Mann denkt an sich selbst zuletzt.
140   Vertrau' auf Gott und rette den Bedrängten!

Ruodi

Vom sichern Port läßt sich's gemächlich raten.
Da ist der Kahn und dort der See! Versucht's!

Tell

Der See kann sich, der Landvogt nicht erbarmen.
Versuch' es, Fährmann!

Hirten und Jäger

Rett' ihn! Rett' ihn! Rett' ihn!

Ruodi

145 Und wär's mein Bruder und mein leiblich Kind,
Es kann nicht sein; 's ist heut' Simons und Judä,
Da rast der See und will sein Opfer haben.

Tell

Mit eitler Rede wird hier nichts geschafft;
Die Stunde dringt, dem Mann muß Hilfe werden.
150 Sprich, Fährmann, willst du fahren?

Ruodi

Nein, nicht ich!

Tell

In Gottes Namen denn! Gib her den Kahn!
Ich will's mit meiner schwachen Kraft versuchen.

Kuoni

Ha, wackrer Tell!

Werni

Das gleicht dem Weidgesellen!

Baumgarten

Mein Retter seid Ihr und mein Engel, Tell!

Tell

155 Wohl aus des Vogts Gewalt errett' ich Euch,
Aus Sturmes Nöten muß ein Andrer helfen.
Doch besser ist's, Ihr fallt in Gottes Hand
Als in der Menschen!

(Zu dem Hirten)

Landsmann, tröstet Ihr
Mein Weib, wenn mir was Menschliches begegnet.
160 Ich hab' getan, was ich nicht lassen konnte.

(Er springt in den Kahn)

Kuoni

(zum Fischer)

Ihr seid ein Meister Steuermann. Was sich
Der Tell getraut, das konntet I h r nicht wagen?

Ruodi

Wohl beßre Männer tun's dem Tell nicht nach,
Es gibt nicht zwei, wie der ist, im Gebirge.

Werni

(ist auf den Fels gestiegen)

165 Er stößt schon ab. Gott helf' dir, braver Schwimmer!
Sieh, wie das Schifflein auf den Wellen schwankt!

Kuoni

(am Ufer)

Die Flut geht drüber weg — Ich seh's nicht mehr.
Doch halt, da ist es wieder! Kräftiglich
Arbeitet sich der Wackre durch die Brandung.

Seppi

170 Des Landvogts Reiter kommen angesprengt.

Kuoni

Weiß Gott, sie sind's!   Das war Hilf' in der Not.

(Ein Trupp Landenbergischer Reiter)

Erster Reiter

Den Mörder gebt heraus, den ihr verborgen!

Zweiter

D e s Wegs kam er, umsonst verhehlt ihr ihn.

Kuoni und Ruodi

Wen meint ihr, Reiter?

Erster Reiter

(entdeckt den Nachen)

Ha, was seh' ich!   Teufel!

Werni

(oben)

175   Ist's d e r im Nachen, den ihr sucht? — Reit zu!
Wenn ihr frisch beilegt, holt ihr ihn noch ein.

Zweiter

Verwünscht!   Er ist entwischt.

Erster

(zum Hirten und Fischer)

Ihr habt ihm fortgeholfen,
Ihr sollt uns büßen — Fallt in ihre Herde!
Die Hütte reißet ein, brennt und schlagt nieder!

(Eilen fort)

Seppi

(stürzt nach)

180 O meine Lämmer!

Kuoni

(folgt)

Weh mir! meine Herde!

Werni

Die Wütriche!

Ruodi

(ringt die Hände)

Gerechtigkeit des Himmels!
Wann wird der Retter kommen diesem Lande?

(Folgt ihnen)

ZWEITE SZENE

(Zu Steinen in Schwyz. Eine Linde vor des Stauffachers Hause an der Landstraße, nächst der Brücke. *Werner Stauffacher, Pfeifer von Luzern* kommen im Gespräch.)

Pfeifer

Ja, ja, Herr Stauffacher, wie ich Euch sagte,
Schwört nicht zu Östreich, wenn ihr's könnt vermeiden,
185 Haltet fest am Reich und wacker, wie bisher.
Gott schirme euch bei eurer alten Freiheit!

(Drückt ihm herzlich die Hand und will gehen)

Stauffacher

Bleibt doch, bis meine Wirtin kommt — Ihr seid
Mein Gast zu Schwyz, ich in Luzern der Eure.

Pfeifer

Viel Dank! Muß heute Gersau noch erreichen.
190 — Was ihr auch Schweres mögt zu leiden haben
Von eurer Vögte Geiz und Übermut,
Tragt's in Geduld! Es kann sich ändern, schnell,
Ein andrer Kaiser kann ans Reich gelangen.
S e i d ihr erst Österreichs, seid ihr's auf immer.

(Er geht ab. Stauffacher setzt sich kummervoll auf eine Bank unter der
Linde. So findet ihn *Gertrud*, seine Frau, die sich neben ihn stellt und
ihn eine Zeitlang schweigend betrachtet.)

Gertrud

195 So ernst, mein Freund? Ich kenne dich nicht mehr.
Schon viele Tage seh' ich's schweigend an,
Wie finstrer Trübsinn deine Stirne furcht.
Auf deinem Herzen drückt ein still Gebresten;
Vertrau' es mir; ich bin dein treues Weib,
200 Und meine Hälfte fordr' ich deines Grams.

(Stauffacher reicht ihr die Hand und schweigt)

Was kann dein Herz beklemmen? Sag' es mir.
Gesegnet ist dein Fleiß, dein Glücksstand blüht,
Voll sind die Scheunen, und der Rinder Scharen,
Der glatten Pferde wohlgenährte Zucht
205 Ist von den Bergen glücklich heimgebracht
Zur Winterung in den bequemen Ställen.
— Da steht dein Haus, reich wie ein Edelsitz;
Von schönem Stammholz ist es neu gezimmert
Und nach dem Richtmaß ordentlich gefügt;
210 Von vielen Fenstern glänzt es wohnlich hell;
Mit bunten Wappenschildern ist's bemalt
Und weisen Sprüchen, die der Wandersmann
Verweilend liest und ihren Sinn bewundert.

Stauffacher

Wohl steht das Haus gezimmert und gefügt,
215 Doch ach — es wankt der Grund, auf dem wir bauten.

Gertrud

Mein Werner, sage, wie verstehst du das?

Stauffacher

Vor dieser Linde saß ich jüngst wie heut',
Das schön Vollbrachte freudig überdenkend,
Da kam daher von Küßnacht, seiner Burg,
220 Der Vogt mit seinen Reisigen geritten.
Vor diesem Hause hielt er wundernd an;
Doch ich erhub mich schnell, und unterwürfig,
Wie sich's gebührt, trat ich dem Herrn entgegen,
Der uns des Kaisers richterliche Macht
225 Vorstellt im Lande. „Wessen ist dies Haus?"
Fragt' er bösmeinend, denn er wußt' es wohl.
Doch schnell besonnen ich entgegn' ihm so:
„Dies Haus, Herr Vogt, ist meines Herrn, des Kaisers,
Und Eures, und mein Lehen" — Da versetzt' er:
230 „Ich bin Regent im Land an Kaisers Statt
Und will nicht, daß der Bauer Häuser baue
Auf seine eigne Hand und also frei
Hinleb', als ob er Herr wär' in dem Lande;
Ich werd' mich unterstehn, euch das zu wehren."
235 Dies sagend, ritt er trutziglich von dannen,
Ich aber blieb mit kummervoller Seele,
Das Wort bedenkend, das der Böse sprach.

Gertrud

Mein lieber Herr und Ehewirt! Magst du
Ein redlich Wort von deinem Weib vernehmen?
240 Des edeln Ibergs Tochter rühm' ich mich,

Des vielerfahrnen Manns. Wir Schwestern saßen,
Die Wolle spinnend, in den langen Nächten,
Wenn bei dem Vater sich des Volkes Häupter
Versammelten, die Pergamente lasen
245 Der alten Kaiser, und des Landes Wohl
Bedachten in vernünftigem Gespräch.
Aufmerkend hört' ich da manch kluges Wort,
Was der Verständ'ge denkt, der Gute wünscht,
Und still im Herzen hab' ich mir's bewahrt.
250 So höre denn und acht' auf meine Rede!
Denn, was dich preßte, sieh, das wußt' ich längst.
— Dir grollt der Landvogt, möchte gern dir schaden,
Denn du bist ihm ein Hindernis, daß sich
Der Schwyzer nicht dem neuen Fürstenhaus
255 Will unterwerfen, sondern treu und fest
Beim Reich beharren, wie die würdigen
Altvordern es gehalten und getan. —
Ist's nicht so, Werner? Sag es, wenn ich lüge!

Stauffacher

So ist's, das ist des Geßlers Groll auf mich.

Gertrud

260 Er ist dir neidisch, weil du glücklich wohnst,
Ein freier Mann auf deinem eignen Erb';
— Denn er hat keins. Vom Kaiser selbst und Reich
Trägst du dies Haus zu Lehn; du darfst es zeigen,
So gut der Reichsfürst seine Länder zeigt;
265 Denn über dir erkennst du keinen Herrn
Als nur den Höchsten in der Christenheit —
Er ist ein jüngrer Sohn nur seines Hauses,
Nichts nennt er sein als seinen Rittermantel;
Drum sieht er jedes Biedermannes Glück
270 Mit scheelen Augen gift'ger Mißgunst an.
D i r hat er längst den Untergang geschworen —

Noch stehst du unversehrt — Willst du erwarten,
Bis er die böse Lust an dir gebüßt?
Der kluge Mann baut vor.

Stauffacher

Was ist zu tun?

Gertrud

(tritt näher)

275 So höre meinen Rat! Du weißt, wie hier
Zu Schwyz sich alle Redlichen beklagen
Ob dieses Landvogts Geiz und Wüterei.
So zweifle nicht, daß sie dort drüben auch
In Unterwalden und im Urner Land
280 Des Dranges müd' sind und des harten Jochs —
Denn wie der Geßler hier, so schafft es frech
Der Landenberger drüben überm See —
Es kommt kein Fischerkahn zu uns herüber,
Der nicht ein neues Unheil und Gewalt-
285 Beginnen von den Vögten uns verkündet.
Drum tät' es gut, daß euer etliche,
Die's redlich meinen, still zu Rate gingen,
Wie man des Drucks sich möcht' erledigen;
So acht' ich wohl, Gott würd' euch nicht verlassen
290 Und der gerechten Sache gnädig sein —
Hast du in Uri keinen Gastfreund, sprich,
Dem du dein Herz magst redlich offenbaren?

Stauffacher

Der wackern Männer kenn' ich viele dort
Und angesehen große Herrenleute,
295 Die mir geheim sind und gar wohl vertraut.
(Er steht auf.)
Frau, welchen Sturm gefährlicher Gedanken
Weckst du mir in der stillen Brust! Mein Innerstes

Kehrst du ans Licht des Tages mir entgegen,
Und was ich mir zu denken still verbot,
300 Du sprichst's mit leichter Zunge kecklich aus.
— Hast du auch wohl bedacht, was du mir rätst?
Die wilde Zwietracht und den Klang der Waffen
Rufst du in dieses friedgewohnte Tal —
Wir wagten es, ein schwaches Volk der Hirten,
305 In Kampf zu gehen mit dem Herrn der Welt?
Der gute Schein nur ist's, worauf sie warten,
Um loszulassen auf dies arme Land
Die wilden Horden ihrer Kriegesmacht,
Darin zu schalten mit des Siegers Rechten
310 Und unterm Schein gerechter Züchtigung
Die alten Freiheitsbriefe zu vertilgen.

Gertrud

Ihr seid a u c h Männer, wisset eure Axt
Zu führen, und dem Mutigen hilft Gott!

Stauffacher

O Weib! Ein furchtbar wütend Schrecknis ist
315 Der Krieg; die Herde schlägt er und den Hirten.

Gertrud

Ertragen muß man, was der Himmel sendet;
Unbilliges erträgt kein edles Herz.

Stauffacher

Dies Haus erfreut dich, das wir neu erbauten.
Der Krieg, der ungeheure, brennt es nieder.

Gertrud

320 Wüßt' ich mein Herz an zeitlich Gut gefesselt,
Den Brand würf' ich hinein mit eigner Hand.

Stauffacher

Du glaubst an Menschlichkeit! Es schont der Krieg
Auch nicht das zarte Kindlein in der Wiege.

Gertrud

Die Unschuld hat im Himmel einen Freund!
325 — Sieh vorwärts, Werner, und nicht hinter dich!

Stauffacher

Wir Männer können tapfer fechtend sterben;
Welch Schicksal aber wird das eure sein?

Gertrud

Die letzte Wahl steht auch dem Schwächsten offen,
Ein Sprung von dieser Brücke macht mich frei.

Stauffacher

(stürzt in ihre Arme)

330 Wer solch ein Herz an seinen Busen drückt,
Der kann für Herd und Hof mit Freuden fechten,
Und keines Königs Heermacht fürchtet er —
Nach Uri fahr' ich stehnden Fußes gleich;
Dort lebt ein Gastfreund mir, Herr Walter Fürst,
335 Der über diese Zeiten denkt wie ich.
Auch find' ich dort den edeln Bannerherrn
Von Attinghaus — obgleich von hohem Stamm,
Liebt er das Volk und ehrt die alten Sitten.
Mit ihnen beiden pfleg' ich Rats, wie man
340 Der Landesfeinde mutig sich erwehrt —
Leb' wohl — und, weil ich fern bin, führe du˘
Mit klugem Sinn das Regiment des Hauses —
Dem Pilger, der zum Gotteshause wallt,
Dem frommen Mönch, der für sein Kloster sammelt,
345 Gib reichlich und entlaß ihn wohlgepflegt.

Stauffachers Haus verbirgt sich nicht. Zu äußerst
Am offnen Heerweg steht's, ein wirtlich Dach
Für alle Wandrer, die des Weges fahren.

(Indem sie nach dem Hintergrund abgehen, tritt *Wilhelm Tell* mit *Baumgarten* vorn auf die Szene.)

Tell

(zu Baumgarten)

Ihr habt jetzt meiner weiter nicht vonnöten.
350   Zu jenem Hause gehet ein; dort wohnt
Der Stauffacher, ein Vater der Bedrängten.
— Doch sieh, da ist er selber — Folgt mir, kommt!

(Gehen auf ihn zu; die Szene verwandelt sich.)

DRITTE SZENE

(Öffentlicher Platz bei Altorf. Auf einer Anhöhe im Hintergrund sieht man eine Feste bauen, welche schon so weit gediehen, daß sich die Form des Ganzen darstellt. Die hintere Seite ist fertig, an der vordern wird eben gebaut, das Gerüste steht noch, an welchem die Werkleute auf und nieder steigen; auf dem höchsten Dach hängt der Schieferdecker — Alles ist in Bewegung und Arbeit. *Fronvogt. Meister Steinmetz. Gesellen* und *Handlanger.*)

Fronvogt

(mit dem Stabe, treibt die Arbeiter)

Nicht lang' gefeiert! Frisch! Die Mauersteine
Herbei! Den Kalk, den Mörtel zugefahren!
355   Wenn der Herr Landvogt kommt, daß er das Werk
Gewachsen sieht — Das schlendert wie die Schnecken.

(Zu zwei Handlangern, welche tragen)

Heißt das geladen? Gleich das Doppelte!
Wie die Tagdiebe ihre Pflicht bestehlen!

Erster Gesell

360 Das ist doch hart, daß wir die Steine selbst
Zu unserm Twing und Kerker sollen fahren!

Fronvogt

Was murret ihr? Das ist ein schlechtes Volk,
Zu nichts anstellig, als das Vieh zu melken
Und faul herumzuschlendern auf den Bergen.

Alter Mann

(ruht aus)

Ich kann nicht mehr.

Fronvogt

(schüttelt ihn)

Frisch, Alter, an die Arbeit!

Erster Gesell

365 Habt Ihr denn gar kein Eingeweid', daß Ihr
Den Greis, der kaum sich selber schleppen kann,
Zum harten Frondienst treibt?

Meister Steinmetz und Gesellen

's ist himmelschreiend!

Fronvogt

Sorgt ihr für euch; ich tu', was meines Amts.

Zweiter Gesell

Fronvogt, wie wird die Feste denn sich nennen,
370 Die wir da baun?

Fronvogt

Z w i n g   U r i soll sie heißen;
Denn unter dieses Joch wird man euch beugen.

Gesellen

Zwing Uri!

Fronvogt

Nun, was gibt's dabei zu lachen?

Zweiter Gesell

Mit diesem Häuslein wollt ihr Uri zwingen?

Erster Gesell

Laß sehn, wie viel man solcher Maulwurfshaufen
375 Muß über 'nander setzen, bis ein Berg
Draus wird, wie der geringste nur in Uri!

(Fronvogt geht nach dem Hintergrund.)

Meister Steinmetz

Den Hammer werf' ich in den tiefsten See,
Der mir gedient bei diesem Fluchgebäude!

(*Tell* und *Stauffacher* kommen.)

Stauffacher

O, hätt' ich nie gelebt, um das zu schauen!

Tell

380 Hier ist nicht gut sein. Laßt uns weitergehn.

Stauffacher

Bin ich zu Uri, in der Freiheit Land?

Meister Steinmetz

O Herr, wenn Ihr die Keller erst gesehn
Unter den Türmen! Ja, wer d i e bewohnt,
Der wird den Hahn nicht fürder krähen hören.

Stauffacher

385 O Gott!

Steinmetz

Seht diese Flanken, diese Strebepfeiler,
Die stehn, wie für die Ewigkeit gebaut!

Tell

Was Hände bauten, können Hände stürzen.

(Nach den Bergen zeigend)

Das Haus der Freiheit hat uns Gott gegründet.

(Man hört eine Trommel, es kommen Leute, die einen Hut auf einer
Stange tragen, ein *Ausrufer* folgt ihnen, Weiber und Kinder dringen
tumultuarisch nach.)

Erster Gesell

390 Was will die Trommel? Gebet acht!

Meister Steinmetz

Was für
Ein Fastnachtsaufzug, und was soll der Hut?

Ausrufer

In des Kaisers Namen! Höret!

Gesellen

Still doch! Höret!

Ausrufer

Ihr sehet diesen Hut, Männer von Uri!
Aufrichten wird man ihn auf hoher Säule,
395 Mitten in Altorf, an dem höchsten Ort,
Und dieses ist des Landvogts Will' und Meinung:

Dem Hut soll gleiche Ehre wie ihm selbst geschehn.
Man soll ihn mit gebognem Knie und mit
Entblößtem Haupt verehren — Daran will
400 Der König die Gehorsamen erkennen.
Verfallen ist mit seinem Leib und Gut
Dem Könige, wer das Gebot verachtet.

(Das Volk lacht laut auf, die Trommel wird gerührt, sie gehen vorüber.)

Erster Gesell

Welch neues Unerhörtes hat der Vogt
Sich ausgesonnen! Wir 'nen H u t verehren!
405 Sagt! Hat man je vernommen von dergleichen?

Meister Steinmetz

Wir unsre Knie beugen einem Hut!
Treibt er sein Spiel mit ernsthaft würd'gen Leuten?

Erster Gesell

Wär's noch die kaiserliche Kron'! So ist's
Der Hut von Österreich; ich sah ihn hangen
410 Über dem Thron, wo man die Lehen gibt!

Meister Steinmetz

Der Hut von Österreich! Gebt acht, es ist
Ein Fallstrick, uns an Östreich zu verraten!

Gesellen

Kein Ehrenmann wird sich der Schmach bequemen.

Meister Steinmetz

Kommt, laßt uns mit den andern Abred' nehmen.

(Sie gehen nach der Tiefe.)

Tell

(zum Stauffacher)

415 Ihr wisset nun Bescheid. Lebt wohl, Herr Werner!

Stauffacher

Wo wollt Ihr hin? O, eilt nicht so von dannen!

Tell

Mein Haus entbehrt des Vaters. Lebet wohl!

Stauffacher

Mir ist das Herz so voll, mit Euch zu reden.

Tell

Das schwere Herz wird nicht durch Worte leicht.

Stauffacher

420 Doch könnten Worte uns zu Taten führen.

Tell

Die einz'ge Tat ist jetzt Geduld und Schweigen.

Stauffacher

Soll man ertragen, was unleidlich ist?

Tell

Die schnellen Herrscher sind's, die kurz regieren.
— Wenn sich der Föhn erhebt aus seinen Schlünden,
425 Löscht man die Feuer aus, die Schiffe suchen
Eilends den Hafen, und der mächt'ge Geist
Geht ohne Schaden spurlos über die Erde.
Ein jeder lebe still bei sich daheim;
Dem Friedlichen gewährt man gern den Frieden.

Stauffacher

430 Meint Ihr?

Tell

Die Schlange sticht nicht ungereizt.
Sie werden endlich doch von selbst ermüden,
Wenn sie die Lande ruhig bleiben sehn.

Stauffacher

Wir könnten viel, wenn wir zusammenstünden.

Tell

Beim Schiffbruch hilft der Einzelne sich leichter.

Stauffacher

435 So kalt verlaßt Ihr die gemeine Sache?

Tell

Ein jeder zählt nur sicher auf sich selbst.

Stauffacher

Verbunden werden auch die Schwachen mächtig.

Tell

Der Starke ist am mächtigsten a l l e i n .

Stauffacher

So kann das Vaterland auf Euch nicht zählen,
440 Wenn es verzweiflungsvoll zur Notwehr greift?

Tell

(gibt ihm die Hand)

Der Tell holt ein verlornes Lamm vom Abgrund
Und sollte seinen Freunden sich entziehen?
Doch, w a s ihr tut, laßt mich aus eurem R a t !

Ich kann nicht lange prüfen oder wählen;
445 Bedürft ihr meiner zu bestimmter Tat,
Dann ruft den Tell, es soll an mir nicht fehlen.

(Gehen ab zu verschiedenen Seiten. Ein plötzlicher Auflauf entsteht um das Gerüste.)

Meister Steinmetz

(eilt hin)

Was gibt's?

Erster Gesell

(kommt vor, rufend)

Der Schieferdecker ist vom Dach gestürzt.

(*Berta* mit *Gefolge*)

Berta

(stürzt herein)

Ist er zerschmettert? Rennet, rettet, helft —
450 Wenn Hilfe möglich, rettet, hier ist Gold —

(Wirft ihr Geschmeide unter das Volk)

Meister

Mit eurem Golde! — Alles ist euch feil
Um Gold; wenn ihr den Vater von den Kindern
Gerissen und den Mann von seinem Weibe,
Und Jammer habt gebracht über die Welt,
455 Denkt ihr's mit Golde zu vergüten — Geht!
Wir waren frohe Menschen, eh' ihr kamt;
Mit euch ist die Verzweiflung eingezogen.

Berta

(zu dem Fronvogt, der zurückkommt)

Lebt er?

(Fronvogt gibt ein Zeichen des Gegenteils.)

O unglücksel'ges Schloß, mit Flüchen
Erbaut, und Flüche werden dich bewohnen!

(Geht ab)

VIERTE SZENE

(Walter Fürsts Wohnung. *Walter Fürst* und *Arnold vom Melchtal* treten
zugleich ein von verschiedenen Seiten.)

Melchtal

460   Herr Walter Fürst —

Walter Fürst

                    Wenn man uns überraschte!
Bleibt, wo Ihr seid. Wir sind umringt von Spähern.

Melchtal

Bringt Ihr mir nichts von Unterwalden? nichts
Von meinem Vater? Nicht ertrag' ich's länger,
Als ein Gefangner müßig hier zu liegen.
465   Was hab' ich denn so Sträfliches getan,
Um mich gleich einem Mörder zu verbergen?
Dem frechen Buben, der die Ochsen mir,
Das trefflichste Gespann, vor meinen Augen
Weg wollte treiben auf des Vogts Geheiß,
470   Hab' ich den Finger mit dem Stab gebrochen.

Walter Fürst

Ihr seid zu rasch. Der Bube war des Vogts;
Von Eurer Obrigkeit war er gesendet.
Ihr wart in Straf' gefallen, mußtet Euch,
Wie schwer sie war, der Buße schweigend fügen.

Melchtal

475 Ertragen sollt' ich die leichfert'ge Rede
Des Unverschämten, wenn der Bauer Brot
Wollt' essen, mög' er selbst am Pfluge ziehn!
In die Seele schnitt mir's, als der Bub die Ochsen,
Die schönen Tiere, von dem Pfluge spannte;
480 Dumpf brüllten sie, als hätten sie Gefühl
Der Ungebühr, und stießen mit den Hörnern;
Da übernahm mich der gerechte Zorn,
Und meiner selbst nicht Herr, schlug ich den Boten.

Walter Fürst

O, kaum bezwingen wir das eigne Herz;
485 Wie soll die rasche Jugend sich bezähmen!

Melchtal

Mich jammert nur der Vater — Er bedarf
So sehr der Pflege, und sein Sohn ist fern.
Der Vogt ist ihm gehässig, weil er stets
Für Recht und Freiheit redlich hat gestritten.
490 Drum werden sie den alten Mann bedrängen,
Und niemand ist, der ihn vor Unglimpf schütze.
— Werde mit mir, was will, ich muß hinüber.

Walter Fürst

Erwartet nur und faßt Euch in Geduld,
Bis Nachricht uns herüberkommt vom Walde.
495 — Ich höre klopfen, geht — Vielleicht ein Bote
Vom Landvogt — Geht hinein — Ihr seid in Uri
Nicht sicher vor des Landenbergers Arm;
Denn die Tyrannen reichen sich die Hände.

Melchtal

Sie lehren uns, was w i r tun sollten.

Walter Fürst

Geht!
500 Ich ruf' Euch wieder, wenn's hier sicher ist.

(Melchtal geht hinein.)

Der Unglückselige, ich darf ihm nicht
Gestehen, was mir Böses schwant — Wer klopft?
So oft die Türe rauscht, erwart' ich Unglück.
Verrat und Argwohn lauscht in allen Ecken;
505 Bis in das Innerste der Häuser dringen
Die Boten der Gewalt; bald tät' es not,
Wir hätten Schloß und Riegel an den Türen.

(Er öffnet und tritt erstaunt zurück, da *Werner Stauffacher* hereintritt.)

Was seh' ich? Ihr, Herr Werner! Nun, bei Gott!
Ein werter, teurer Gast — Kein beßrer Mann
510 Ist über diese Schwelle noch gegangen.
Seid hoch willkommen unter meinem Dach!
Was führt Euch her? Was sucht Ihr hier in Uri?

Stauffacher

(ihm die Hand reichend)

Die alten Zeiten und die alte Schweiz.

Walter Fürst

Die bringt Ihr mit Euch — Sieh, mir wird so wohl,
515 Warm geht das Herz mir auf bei Eurem Anblick.
— Setzt Euch, Herr Werner — Wie verließet Ihr
Frau Gertrud, Eure angenehme Wirtin,
Des weisen Ibergs hochverständ'ge Tochter?
Von allen Wandrern aus dem deutschen Land,
520 Die über Meinrads Zell nach Welschland fahren,
Rühmt jeder Euer gastlich Haus — Doch sagt,
Kommt Ihr soeben frisch von Flüelen her

Und habt Euch nirgend sonst noch umgesehn,
Eh' Ihr den Fuß gesetzt auf diese Schwelle?

Stauffacher

(setzt sich)

525 Wohl ein erstaunlich neues Werk hab' ich
Bereiten sehen, das mich nicht erfreute.

Walter Fürst

O Freund, da habt Ihr's gleich mit e i n e m Blicke!

Stauffacher

Ein solches ist in Uri nie gewesen —
Seit Menschendenken war kein Twinghof hier,
530 Und fest war keine Wohnung als das Grab.

Walter Fürst

Ein Grab der Freiheit ist's. Ihr nennt's mit Namen.

Stauffacher

Herr Walter Fürst, ich will Euch nicht verhalten,
Nicht eine müß'ge Neugier führt mich her;
Mich drücken schwere Sorgen — Drangsal hab' ich
535 Zu Haus verlassen, Drangsal find' ich hier.
Denn ganz unleidlich ist's, was wir erdulden,
Und dieses Dranges ist kein Ziel zu sehn.
Frei war der Schweizer von uralters her,
Wir sind's gewohnt, daß man uns gut begegnet.
540 Ein solches war im Lande nie erlebt,
Solang ein Hirte trieb auf diesen Bergen.

Walter Fürst

Ja, es ist ohne Beispiel, wie sie's treiben!
Auch unser edler Herr von Attinghausen,

Der noch die alten Zeiten hat gesehn,
545   Meint selber, es sei nicht mehr zu ertragen.

Stauffacher

Auch drüben unterm Wald geht Schweres vor,
Und blutig wird's gebüßt — Der Wolfenschießen,
Des Kaisers Vogt, der auf dem Roßberg hauste,
Gelüsten trug er nach verbotner Frucht;
550   Baumgartens Weib, der haushält zu Alzellen,
Wollt' er zu frecher Ungebühr mißbrauchen,
Und mit der Axt hat ihn der Mann erschlagen.

Walter Fürst

O, die Gerichte Gottes sind gerecht!
— Baumgarten, sagt Ihr? Ein bescheidner Mann!
555   Er ist gerettet doch und wohl geborgen?

Stauffacher

Euer Eidam hat ihn übern See geflüchtet;
Bei mir zu Steinen halt' ich ihn verborgen —
— Noch Greulichers hat mir derselbe Mann
Berichtet, was zu Sarnen ist geschehn.
560   Das Herz muß jedem Biedermanne bluten.

Walter Fürst

(aufmerksam)

Sagt an, was ist's?

Stauffacher

Im M e l c h t a l , da, wo man
Eintritt bei K e r n s , wohnt ein gerechter Mann,
Sie nennen ihn den H e i n r i c h von der H a l d e n ,
Und seine Stimm' gilt was in der Gemeinde.

Walter Fürst

565 Wer kennt ihn nicht! Was ist's mit ihm? Vollendet!

Stauffacher

Der Landenberger büßte seinen Sohn
Um kleinen Fehlers willen, ließ die Ochsen,
Das beste Paar, ihm aus dem Pfluge spannen;
Da schlug der Knab' den Knecht und wurde flüchtig.

Walter Fürst

(in höchster Spannung)

570 Der Vater aber — sagt, wie steht's um den?

Stauffacher

Den Vater läßt der Landenberger fordern,
Zur Stelle schaffen soll er ihm den Sohn,
Und da der alte Mann mit Wahrheit schwört,
Er habe von dem Flüchtling keine Kunde,
575 Da läßt der Vogt die Folterknechte kommen —

Walter Fürst

(springt auf und will ihn auf die andere Seite führen)

O still, nichts mehr!

Stauffacher

(mit steigendem Ton)

„Ist mir der Sohn entgangen,
So hab' ich d i c h !" — Läßt ihn zu Boden werfen,
Den spitz'gen Stahl ihm in die Augen bohren —

Walter Fürst

Barmherz'ger Himmel!

Melchtal

(stürzt heraus)

In die Augen, sagt Ihr?

Stauffacher

(erstaunt zu Walter Fürst)

580 Wer ist der Jüngling?

Melchtal

(faßt ihn mit krampfhafter Heftigkeit)

In die Augen? Redet!

Walter Fürst

O der Bejammernswürdige!

Stauffacher

Wer ist's?

(Da Walter Fürst ihm ein Zeichen gibt)

Der Sohn ist's? Allgerechter Gott!

Melchtal

Und ich

Muß ferne sein! — In seine beiden Augen?

Walter Fürst

Bezwinget Euch! Ertragt es wie ein Mann!

Melchtal

585 Um m e i n e r Schuld, um m e i n e s Frevels willen!
— Blind also? Wirklich b l i n d , und g a n z geblendet?

Stauffacher

Ich sagt's. Der Quell des Sehns ist ausgeflossen,
Das Licht der Sonne schaut er niemals wieder.

Walter Fürst

Schont seines Schmerzens!

Melchtal

Niemals! niemals wieder!

(Er drückt die Hand vor die Augen und schweigt einige Momente, dann
wendet er sich von dem einen zu dem andern und spricht mit sanfter,
von Tränen erstickter Stimme.)

590 O, eine edle Himmelsgabe ist
Das Licht des Auges — Alle Wesen leben
Vom Lichte, jedes glückliche Geschöpf —
Die Pflanze selbst kehrt freudig sich zum Lichte.
Und e r muß sitzen, fühlend, in der Nacht,
595 Im ewig Finstern — ihn erquickt nicht mehr
Der Matten warmes Grün, der Blumen Schmelz;
Die roten Firnen kann er nicht mehr schauen —
Sterben ist nichts — doch l e b e n und nicht s e h e n ,
Das ist ein Unglück — Warum seht ihr mich
600 So jammernd an? Ich hab' zwei frische Augen
Und kann dem blinden Vater keines geben,
Nicht einen Schimmer von dem Meer des Lichts,
Das glanzvoll, blendend mir ins Auge dringt.

Stauffacher

Ach, ich muß Euren Jammer noch vergrößern,
605 Statt ihn zu heilen — Er bedarf noch mehr!
Denn alles hat der Landvogt ihm geraubt;
Nichts hat er ihm gelassen als den Stab,
Um nackt und blind von Tür zu Tür zu wandern.

Melchtal

Nichts als den Stab dem augenlosen Greis!
610 Alles geraubt und auch das Licht der Sonne,
Des Ärmsten allgemeines Gut — Jetzt rede
Mir keiner mehr von Bleiben, von Verbergen!
Was für ein feiger Elender bin ich,
Daß ich auf m e i n e Sicherheit gedacht
615 Und nicht auf deine! — Dein geliebtes Haupt
Als Pfand gelassen in des Wütrichs Händen!
Feigherz'ge Vorsicht, fahre hin — Auf nichts
Als blutige Vergeltung will ich denken.
Hinüber will ich — Keiner soll mich halten —
620 Des Vaters Auge von dem Landvogt fordern —
Aus allen seinen Reisigen heraus
Will ich ihn finden — Nichts liegt mir am Leben,
Wenn ich den heißen, ungeheuren Schmerz
In seinem Lebensblute kühle.

(Er will gehen.)

Walter Fürst

Bleibt!
625 Was könnt Ihr gegen ihn? Er sitzt zu Sarnen
Auf seiner hohen Herrenburg und spottet
Ohnmächt'gen Zorns in seiner sichern Feste.

Melchtal

Und wohnt' er droben auf dem Eispalast
Des S c h r e c k h o r n s oder höher, wo die J u n g f r a u
630 Seit Ewigkeit verschleiert sitzt — ich mache
Mir Bahn zu ihm; mit zwanzig Jünglingen,
Gesinnt wie ich, zerbrech' ich seine Feste.
Und wenn mir niemand folgt, und wenn ihr alle,
Für eure Hütten bang und eure Herden,
635 Euch dem Tyrannenjoche beugt — die Hirten

Will ich zusammenrufen im Gebirg,
Dort, unterm freien Himmelsdache, wo
Der Sinn noch frisch ist und das Herz gesund,
Das ungeheuer Gräßliche erzählen.

Stauffacher

(zu Walter Fürst)

640 Es ist auf seinem Gipfel — Wollen wir
Erwarten, bis das Äußerste —

Melchtal

Welch Äußerstes
Ist noch zu fürchten, wenn der Stern des Auges
In seiner Höhle nicht mehr sicher ist?
— Sind wir denn wehrlos? Wozu lernten wir
645 Die Armbrust spannen und die schwere Wucht
Der Streitaxt schwingen? Jedem Wesen ward
Ein Notgewehr in der Verzweiflungsangst.
Es stellt sich der erschöpfte Hirsch und zeigt
Der Meute sein gefürchtetes Geweih;
650 Die Gemse reißt den Jäger in den Abgrund —
Der Pflugstier selbst, der sanfte Hausgenoß
Des Menschen, der die ungeheure Kraft
Des Halses duldsam unters Joch gebogen,
Springt auf, gereizt, wetzt sein gewaltig Horn
655 Und schleudert seinen Feind den Wolken zu.

Walter Fürst

Wenn die drei Lande dächten wie wir drei,
So möchten wir vielleicht etwas vermögen.

Stauffacher

Wenn Uri ruft, wenn Unterwalden hilft,
Der Schwyzer wird die alten Bünde ehren.

Melchtal

660 Groß ist in Unterwalden meine Freundschaft,
Und jeder wagt mit Freuden Leib und Blut,
Wenn er am andern einen Rücken hat
Und Schirm — O fromme Väter dieses Landes!
Ich stehe nur ein Jüngling zwischen euch,
665 Den Vielerfahrnen — meine Stimme muß
Bescheiden schweigen in der Landsgemeinde.
Nicht, weil ich jung bin und nicht viel erlebte,
Verachtet meinen Rat und meine Rede!
Nicht lüstern jugendliches Blut, mich treibt
670 Des höchsten Jammers schmerzliche Gewalt,
Was auch den Stein des Felsen muß erbarmen.
Ihr selbst seid Väter, Häupter eines Hauses,
Und wünscht euch einen tugendhaften Sohn,
Der eures Hauptes heil'ge Locken ehre
675 Und euch den Stern des Auges fromm bewache.
O, weil ihr selbst an eurem Leib und Gut
Noch nichts erlitten, eure Augen sich
Noch frisch und hell in ihren Kreisen regen,
So sei euch darum unsre Not nicht fremd.
680 Auch über euch hängt das Tyrannenschwert,
Ihr habt das Land von Östreich abgewendet;
Kein anderes war meines Vaters Unrecht,
Ihr seid in gleicher Mitschuld und Verdammnis.

Stauffacher

(zu Walter Fürst)

Beschließet I h r ! Ich bin bereit, zu folgen.

Walter Fürst

685 Wir wollen hören, was die edeln Herrn
Von Sillinen, von Attinghausen raten —
Ihr Name, denk' ich, wird uns Freunde werben.

Melchtal

Wo ist ein Name in dem Waldgebirg'
Ehrwürdiger als Eurer und der Eure?
690 An solcher Namen echte Währung glaubt
Das Volk, sie haben guten Klang im Lande.
Ihr habt ein reiches Erb' von Vätertugend
Und habt es selber reich vermehrt — Was braucht's
Des Edelmanns? Laßt's uns allein vollenden!
695 Wären wir doch allein im Land! Ich meine,
Wir wollten uns schon selbst zu schirmen wissen.

Stauffacher

Die Edeln drängt nicht gleiche Not mit uns;
Der Strom, der in den Niederungen wütet,
Bis jetzt hat er die Höhn noch nicht erreicht —
700 Doch ihre Hilfe wird uns nicht entstehn,
Wenn sie das Land in Waffen erst erblicken.

Walter Fürst

Wäre ein Obmann zwischen uns und Östreich,
So möchte Recht entscheiden und Gesetz.
Doch der uns unterdrückt, ist unser Kaiser
705 Und höchster Richter — so muß G o t t   u n s   h e l f e n
D u r c h   u n s e r n   A r m — Erforschet I h r die Männer
Von Schwyz, ich will in Uri Freunde werben;
Wen aber senden wir nach Unterwalden? —

Melchtal

Mich sendet hin — Wem läg' es näher an? —

Walter Fürst

710 Ich geb's nicht zu; Ihr seid mein Gast, ich muß
Für Eure Sicherheit gewähren!

Melchtal

Laßt mich!
Die Schliche kenn' ich und die Felsensteige;
Auch Freunde find' ich g'nug, die mich dem Feind
Verhehlen und ein Obdach gern gewähren.

Stauffacher

715 Laßt ihn mit Gott hinübergehn! Dort drüben
Ist kein Verräter — So verabscheut ist
Die Tyrannei, daß sie kein Werkzeug findet.
Auch der Alzeller soll uns nid dem Wald
Genossen werben und das Land erregen.

Melchtal

720 Wie bringen wir uns sichre Kunde zu,
Daß wir den Argwohn der Tyrannen täuschen?

Stauffacher

Wir könnten uns zu B r u n n e n oder T r e i b
Versammeln, wo die Kaufmannsschiffe landen.

Walter Fürst

So offen dürfen wir das Werk nicht treiben.
725 — Hört meine Meinung: Links am See, wenn man
Nach Brunnen fährt, dem Mythenstein grad' über,
Liegt eine Matte heimlich im Gehölz,
Das R ü t l i heißt sie bei dem Volk der Hirten,
Weil dort die Waldung ausgereutet ward.
730 Dort ist's, wo unsre Landmark und die Eure

(Zu Melchtal)

Zusammengrenzen, und in kurzer Fahrt

(Zu Stauffacher)

Trägt Euch der leichte Kahn von Schwyz herüber.
Auf öden Pfaden können wir dahin
Bei Nachtzeit wandern und uns still beraten.
735 Dahin mag jeder zehn vertraute Männer
Mitbringen, die herzeinig sind mit uns,
So können wir gemeinsam das Gemeine
Besprechen und mit Gott es frisch beschließen.

Stauffacher

So sei's! Jetzt reicht mir Eure biedre Rechte,
740 Reicht Ihr die Eure her, und so wie wir
D r e i M ä n n e r jetzo unter uns die Hände
Zusammenflechten, redlich, ohne Falsch,
So wollen wir d r e i L ä n d e r auch zu Schutz
und Trutz zusammenstehn auf Tod und Leben.

Walter Fürst und Melchtal

745 Auf Tod und Leben!

(Sie halten die Hände noch einige Pausen lang zusammengeflochten
und schweigen.)

Melchtal

Blinder, alter Vater!
Du kannst den Tag der Freiheit nicht mehr s c h a u e n ,
Du sollst ihn h ö r e n — Wenn von Alp zu Alp
Die Feuerzeichen flammend sich erheben,
Die festen Schlösser der Tyrannen fallen,
750 In deine Hütte soll der Schweizer wallen,
Zu deinem Ohr die Freudenkunde tragen,
Und hell in deiner Nacht soll es dir tagen!

(Sie gehen auseinander.)

ZWEITER AUFZUG

ERSTE SZENE

(Edelhof des Freiherrn von Attinghausen. Ein gotischer Saal, mit Wappenschildern und Helmen verziert. *Der Freiherr*, ein Greis von fünfundachtzig Jahren, von hoher, edler Statur, an einem Stabe, worauf ein Gemsenhorn, und in ein Pelzwams gekleidet. *Kuoni* und noch *sechs Knechte* stehen um ihn her mit Rechen und Sensen. — *Ulrich von Rudenz* tritt ein in Ritterkleidung.)

Rudenz

Hier bin ich, Oheim — Was ist Euer Wille?

Attinghausen

Erlaubt, daß ich nach altem Hausgebrauch,
755   Den Frühtrunk erst mit meinen Knechten teile.

(Er trinkt aus einem Becher, der dann in der Reihe herumgeht.)

Sonst war ich selber mit in Feld und Wald,
Mit meinem Auge ihren Fleiß regierend,
Wie sie mein Banner führte in der Schlacht;
Jetzt kann ich nichts mehr, als den Schaffner machen,
760   Und kommt die warme Sonne nicht zu mir,
Ich kann sie nicht mehr suchen auf den Bergen.
Und so in enger stets und engerm Kreis,
Beweg' ich mich dem engsten und letzten,
Wo alles Leben still steht, langsam zu.
765   Mein Schatten bin ich nur, bald nur mein Name.

Kuoni

(zu Rudenz mit dem Becher)

Ich bring's Euch, Junker.

(Da Rudenz zaudert, den Becher zu nehmen)

44

Trinket frisch! Es geht
Aus e i n e m Becher und aus e i n e m Herzen.

Attinghausen

Geht, Kinder, und wenn's Feierabend ist,
Dann reden wir auch von des Lands Geschäften.

(Knechte gehen ab. *Attinghausen* und *Rudenz*)

Attinghausen

770   Ich sehe dich gegürtet und gerüstet,
Du willst nach Altorf in die Herrenburg?

Rudenz

Ja, Oheim, und ich darf nicht länger säumen —

Attinghausen

(setzt sich)

Hast du's so eilig? Wie? Ist deiner Jugend
Die Zeit so karg gemessen, daß du sie
775   An deinem alten Oheim mußt ersparen?

Rudenz

Ich sehe, daß Ihr meiner nicht bedürft,
Ich bin ein Fremdling nur in diesem Hause.

Attinghausen

(hat ihn lange mit den Augen gemustert)

Ja, leider bist du's. Leider ist die Heimat
Zur Fremde dir geworden! — Uli! Uli!
780   Ich kenne dich nicht mehr. In Seide prangst du,
Die Pfauenfeder trägst du stolz zur Schau
Und schlägst den Purpurmantel um die Schultern;
Den Landmann blickst du mit Verachtung an
Und schämst dich seiner traulichen Begrüßung.

Rudenz

785 Die Ehr', die ihm gebührt, geb' ich ihm gern;
Das Recht, das er sich nimmt, verweigr' ich ihm.

Attinghausen

Das ganze Land liegt unterm schweren Zorn
Des Königs — Jedes Biedermannes Herz
Ist kummervoll ob der tyrannischen Gewalt,
790 Die wir erdulden — Dich allein rührt nicht
Der allgemeine Schmerz — Dich siehet man
Abtrünnig von den Deinen auf der Seite
Des Landesfeindes stehen, unsrer Not
Hohnsprechend nach der leichten Freude jagen
795 Und buhlen um die Fürstengunst, indes
Dein Vaterland von schwerer Geißel blutet.

Rudenz

Das Land ist schwer bedrängt — Warum, mein Oheim?
Wer ist's, der es gestürzt in diese Not?
Es kostete ein einzig leichtes Wort,
800 Um augenblicks des Dranges los zu sein
Und einen gnäd'gen Kaiser zu gewinnen.
Weh ihnen, die dem Volk die Augen halten,
Daß es dem wahren Besten widerstrebt!
Um eignen Vorteils willen hindern sie,
805 Daß die Waldstätte nicht zu Östreich schwören,
Wie ringsum alle Lande doch getan.
Wohl tut es ihnen, auf der Herrenbank
Zu sitzen mit dem Edelmann — den K a i s e r
Will man zum Herrn, um k e i n e n Herrn zu haben.

Attinghausen

810 Muß ich d a s hören und aus deinem Munde!

Rudenz

Ihr habt mich aufgefordert, laßt mich enden!
— Welche Person ist's, Oheim, die Ihr selbst
Hier spielt? Habt Ihr nicht höhern Stolz, als hier
Landammann oder Bannerherr zu sein
815 Und neben diesen Hirten zu regieren?
Wie? Ist's nicht eine rühmlichere Wahl,
Zu huldigen dem königlichen Herrn,
Sich an sein glänzend Lager anzuschließen,
Als Eurer eignen Knechte Pair zu sein
820 Und zu Gericht zu sitzen mit dem Bauer?

Attinghausen

Ach Uli! Uli! Ich erkenne sie,
Die Stimme der Verführung! Sie ergriff
Dein offnes Ohr, sie hat dein Herz vergiftet.

Rudenz

Ja, ich verberg' es nicht — in tiefer Seele
825 Schmerzt mich der Spott der Fremdlinge, die uns
Den B a u e r n a d e l schelten — Nicht ertrag' ich's,
Indes die edle Jugend ringsumher
Sich Ehre sammelt unter Habsburgs Fahnen,
Auf meinem Erb' hier müßig still zu liegen,
830 Und bei gemeinem Tagewerk den Lenz
Des Lebens zu verlieren — Anderswo
Geschehen Taten, eine Welt des Ruhms
Bewegt sich glänzend jenseits dieser Berge —
M i r rosten in der Halle Helm und Schild;
835 Der Kriegsdrommete mutiges Getön,
Der Heroldsruf, der zum Turniere ladet,
Er dringt in diese Täler nicht herein;
Nichts als den K u h r e i h n und der Herdeglocken
Einförmiges Geläut' vernehm' ich hier.

Attinghausen

840　Verblendeter, vom eiteln Glanz verführt!
Verachte dein Geburtsland! Schäme dich
Der uralt frommen Sitte deiner Väter!
Mit heißen Tränen wirst du dich dereinst
Heimsehnen nach den väterlichen Bergen,
845　Und dieses Herdenreihens Melodie,
Die du in stolzem Überdruß verschmähst,
Mit Schmerzenssehnsucht wird sie dich ergreifen,
Wenn sie dir anklingt auf der fremden Erde.
O, mächtig ist der Trieb des Vaterlands!
850　Die fremde, falsche Welt ist nicht für dich;
Dort an dem stolzen Kaiserhof bleibst du
Dir ewig fremd mit deinem treuen Herzen!
Die Welt, sie fordert andre Tugenden,
Als du in diesen Tälern dir erworben.
855　— Geh hin, verkaufe deine freie Seele,
Nimm Land zu Lehen, werd' ein Fürstenknecht,
Da du ein Selbstherr sein kannst und ein Fürst
Auf deinem eignen Erb' und freien Boden.
Ach Uli! Uli! Bleibe bei den Deinen!
860　Geh nicht nach Altorf — O, verlaß sie nicht,
Die heil'ge Sache deines Vaterlands!
— Ich bin der Letzte meines Stamms — Mein Name
Endet mit mir. Da hängen Helm und Schild;
Die werden sie mir in das Grab mitgeben.
865　Und muß ich denken bei dem letzten Hauch,
Daß du mein brechend Auge nur erwartest,
Um hinzugehn vor diesen neuen Lehenhof
Und meine edeln Güter, die ich frei
Von Gott empfing, von Östreich zu empfangen!

Rudenz

870　Vergebens widerstreben wir dem König;
Die Welt gehört ihm; wollen wir allein

Uns eigensinnig steifen und verstocken,
Die Länderkette ihm zu unterbrechen,
Die er gewaltig rings um uns gezogen?
875 S e i n sind die Märkte, die Gerichte, s e i n
Die Kaufmannsstraßen, und das Saumroß selbst,
Das auf dem Gotthard ziehet, muß ihm zollen.
Von seinen Ländern wie mit einem Netz
Sind wir umgarnet rings und eingeschlossen.
880 — Wird uns das Reich beschützen? Kann es selbst
Sich schützen gegen Östreichs wachsende Gewalt?
Hilft Gott uns nicht, kein Kaiser kann uns helfen.
Was ist zu geben auf der Kaiser Wort,
Wenn sie in Geld- und Kriegesnot die Städte,
885 Die untern Schirm des Adlers sich geflüchtet,
Verpfänden dürfen und dem Reich veräußern?
— Nein, Oheim! Wohltat ist's und weise Vorsicht,
In diesen schweren Zeiten der Parteiung,
Sich anzuschließen an ein mächtig Haupt.
890 Die Kaiserkrone geht von Stamm zu Stamm,
D i e hat für treue Dienste kein Gedächtnis;
Doch um den mächt'gen Erbherrn wohl verdienen,
Heißt Saaten in die Zukunft streun.

Attinghausen

Bist du so weise?
Willst heller sehn als deine edeln Väter,
895 Die um der Freiheit kostbarn Edelstein
Mit Gut und Blut und Heldenkraft gestritten?
— Schiff' nach L u z e r n hinunter, frage d o r t,
Wie Östreichs Herrschaft lastet auf den Ländern!
Sie werden kommen, unsre Schaf' und Rinder
900 Zu zählen, unsre Alpen abzumessen,
Den Hochflug und das Hochgewilde bannen
In unsern freien Wäldern, ihren Schlagbaum
An unsre Brücken, unsre Tore setzen,

Mit unsrer Armut ihre Länderkäufe,
905 Mit unserm Blute ihre Kriege zahlen —
Nein, wenn wir unser Blut dran setzen sollen,
So sei's f ü r u n s — wohlfeiler kaufen wir
Die Freiheit als die Knechtschaft ein!

Rudenz

Was können wir,
Ein Volk der Hirten, gegen Albrechts Heere!

Attinghausen

910 Lern' dieses Volk der Hirten kennen, Knabe!
Ich kenn's, ich hab' es angeführt in Schlachten,
Ich hab' es fechten sehen bei Favenz.
Sie sollen kommen, uns ein Joch aufzwingen,
Das wir entschlossen sind, n i c h t zu ertragen!
915 — O, lerne fühlen, welches Stamms du bist!
Wirf nicht für eiteln Glanz und Flitterschein
Die echte Perle deines Wertes hin —
Das Haupt zu heißen eines f r e i e n Volks,
Das dir aus Liebe nur sich herzlich weiht,
920 Das treulich zu dir steht in Kampf und Tod —
D a s sei dein Stolz, d e s Adels rühme dich —
Die angebornen Bande knüpfe fest,
Ans Vaterland, ans teure, schließ dich an,
Das halte fest mit deinem ganzen Herzen!
925 Hier sind die starken Wurzeln deiner Kraft;
Dort in der fremden Welt stehst du allein,
Ein schwankes Rohr, das jeder Sturm zerknickt.
O komm, du hast uns lang' nicht mehr gesehn,
Versuch's mit uns nur e i n e n Tag — nur heute
930 Geh nicht nach Altorf — Hörst du? Heute nicht;
Den e i n e n Tag nur schenke dich den Deinen!

(Er faßt seine Hand.)

Rudenz

Ich gab mein Wort — Laßt mich — Ich bin gebunden.

Attinghausen

(läßt seine Hand los, mit Ernst)

Du bist gebunden — Ja, Unglücklicher!
Du bist's, doch nicht durch Wort und Schwur,
935 Gebunden bist du durch der Liebe Seile!

(Rudenz wendet sich weg.)

— Verbirg dich, wie du willst. Das Fräulein ist's,
Berta von Bruneck, die zur Herrenburg
Dich zieht, dich fesselt an des Kaisers Dienst.
Das Ritterfräulein willst du dir erwerben
940 Mit deinem Abfall von dem Land — Betrüg' dich nicht!
Dich anzulocken, zeigt man dir die Braut;
Doch deiner Unschuld ist sie nicht beschieden.

Rudenz

Genug hab' ich gehört. Gehabt Euch wohl!

(Er geht ab.)

Attinghausen

Wahnsinn'ger Jüngling, bleib! — Er geht dahin!
945 Ich kann ihn nicht erhalten, nicht erretten —
So ist der Wolfenschießen abgefallen
Von seinem Land — so werden andre folgen;
Der fremde Zauber reißt die Jugend fort,
Gewaltsam strebend über unsre Berge.
950 — O unglücksel'ge Stunde, da das Fremde
In diese still beglückten Täler kam,
Der Sitten fromme Unschuld zu zerstören!
Das Neue dringt herein mit Macht, das Alte,
Das Würd'ge scheidet, andre Zeiten kommen,

955   Es lebt ein andersdenkendes Geschlecht!
Was tu' ich hier? Sie sind begraben alle,
Mit denen ich gewaltet und gelebt.
Unter der Erde schon liegt m e i n e Zeit;
Wohl dem, der mit der n e u e n nicht mehr braucht zu
leben!

(Geht ab)

ZWEITE SZENE

(Eine Wiese, von hohen Felsen und Wald umgeben. Auf den Felsen
sind Steige mit Geländern, auch Leitern, von denen man nachher die
Landleute herabsteigen sieht. Im Hintergrunde zeigt sich der See,
über welchem anfangs ein Mondregenbogen zu sehen ist. Den Prospekt
schließen hohe Berge, hinter welchen noch höhere Eisgebirge ragen.
Es ist völlig Nacht auf der Szene, nur der See und die weißen Gletscher
leuchten im Mondlicht. *Melchtal, Baumgarten, Winkelried, Meier
von Sarnen, Burkhard am Bühel, Arnold von Sewa, Klaus von der Flüe*
und noch vier andere *Landleute*, alle bewaffnet.)

Melchtal

(noch hinter der Szene)

960   Der Bergweg öffnet sich, nur frisch m i r nach!
Den Fels erkenn' ich und das Kreuzlein drauf;
Wir sind am Ziel, hier ist das Rütli.

(Treten auf mit Windlichtern)

Winkelried

Horch!

Sewa

Ganz leer.

Meier

's ist noch kein Landmann da. Wir sind
Die ersten auf dem Platz, wir Unterwaldner.

Melchtal

965 Wie weit ist's in der Nacht?

Baumgarten

Der Feuerwächter
Vom Selisberg hat eben zwei gerufen.

(Man hört in der Ferne Läuten.)

Meier

Still! Horch!

Am Bühel

Das Mettenglöcklein in der Waldkapelle
Klingt hell herüber aus dem Schwyzerland.

Von der Flüe

Die Luft ist rein und trägt den Schall so weit.

Melchtal

970 Gehn einige und zünden Reisholz an,
Daß es loh brenne, wenn die Männer kommen.

(Zwei Landleute gehen.)

Sewa

's ist eine schöne Mondennacht.   Der See
Liegt ruhig da als wie ein ebner Spiegel.

Am Bühel

Sie haben eine leichte Fahrt.

Winkelried

(zeigt nach dem See)

Ha, seht!
975 Seht dorthin!   Seht ihr nichts?

Meier

Was denn? — Ja, wahrlich!
Ein Regenbogen mitten in der Nacht!

Melchtal

Es ist das Licht des Mondes, das ihn bildet.

Von der Flüe

Das ist ein seltsam wunderbares Zeichen!
Es leben viele, die das nicht gesehn.

Sewa

980   Er ist doppelt; seht, ein blässerer steht drüber.

Baumgarten

Ein Nachen fährt soeben drunter weg.

Melchtal

Das ist der Stauffacher mit seinem Kahn,
Der Biedermann läßt sich nicht lang' erwarten.

(Geht mit Baumgarten nach dem Ufer)

Meier

Die Urner sind es, die am längsten säumen.

Am Bühel

985   Sie müssen weit umgehen durchs Gebirg',
Daß sie des Landvogts Kundschaft hintergehen.

(Unterdessen haben die zwei Landleute in der Mitte des Platzes ein
Feuer angezündet.)

Melchtal

(am Ufer)

Wer ist da? Gebt das Wort!

Stauffacher

(von unten)

Freunde des Landes.

(Alle gehen nach der Tiefe, den Kommenden entgegen. Aus dem Kahn steigen *Stauffacher, Itel Reding, Hans auf der Mauer, Jörg im Hofe, Konrad Hunn, Ulrich der Schmied, Jost von Weiler* und noch drei andere *Landleute*, gleichfalls bewaffnet.)

Alle

(rufen)

Willkommen!

(Indem die übrigen in der Tiefe verweilen und sich begrüßen, kommt *Melchtal* mit *Stauffacher* vorwärts.)

Melchtal

O Herr Stauffacher! Ich hab' ihn
Gesehn, der m i c h nicht wiedersehen konnte!
990 Die Hand hab' ich gelegt auf seine Augen,
Und glühend Rachgefühl hab' ich gesogen
Aus der erloschnen Sonne seines Blicks.

Stauffacher

Sprecht nicht von Rache. Nicht Geschehnes rächen,
Gedrohtem Übel wollen wir begegnen.
995 — Jetzt sagt, was Ihr im Unterwaldner Land
Geschafft und für gemeine Sach' geworben,
Wie die Landleute denken, wie Ihr selbst
Den Stricken des Verrats entgangen seid.

Melchtal

Durch der Surennen furchtbares Gebirg',
1000 Auf weit verbreitet öden Eisesfeldern,
Wo nur der heisre Lämmergeier krächzt,
Gelangt' ich zu der Alpentrift, wo sich
Aus Uri und vom Engelberg die Hirten

Anrufend grüßen und gemeinsam weiden,
1005 Den Durst mir stillend mit der Gletscher Milch,
Die in den Runsen schäumend niederquillt.
In den einsamen Sennhütten kehrt' ich ein,
Mein eigner Wirt und Gast, bis daß ich kam
Zu Wohnungen gesellig lebender Menschen.
1010 — Erschollen war in diesen Tälern schon
Der Ruf des neuen Greuels, der geschehn,
Und fromme Ehrfurcht schaffte mir mein Unglück
Vor jeder Pforte, wo ich wandernd klopfte.
Entrüstet fand ich diese graden Seelen
1015 Ob dem gewaltsam neuen Regiment;
Denn so wie ihre Alpen fort und fort
Dieselben Kräuter nähren, ihre Brunnen
Gleichförmig fließen, Wolken selbst und Winde
Den gleichen Strich unwandelbar befolgen,
1020 So hat die alte Sitte hier vom Ahn
Zum Enkel unverändert fortbestanden.
Nicht tragen sie verwegne Neuerung
Im altgewohnten gleichen Gang des Lebens.
— Die harten Hände reichten sie mir dar,
1025 Von den Wänden langten sie die rost'gen Schwerter,
Und aus den Augen blitzte freudiges
Gefühl des Muts, als ich die Namen nannte,
Die im Gebirg' dem Landmann heilig sind,
Den Eurigen und Walter Fürsts — Was euch
1030 Recht würde dünken, schwuren sie zu tun,
Euch schwuren sie, bis in den Tod zu folgen.
— So eilt' ich sicher unterm heil'gen Schirm
Des Gastrechts von Gehöfte zu Gehöfte —
Und als ich kam ins heimatliche Tal,
1035 Wo mir die Vettern viel verbreitet wohnen —
Als ich den Vater fand, beraubt und blind,
Auf fremdem Stroh, von der Barmherzigkeit
Mildtät'ger Menschen lebend —

Stauffacher

Herr im Himmel!

Melchtal

Da weint' ich nicht! Nicht in ohnmächt'gen Tränen
1040 Goß ich die Kraft des heißen Schmerzens aus;
In tiefer Brust, wie einen teuren Schatz,
Verschloß ich ihn und dachte nur auf Taten.
Ich kroch durch alle Krümmen des Gebirgs,
Kein Tal war so versteckt, ich späht' es aus;
1045 Bis an der Gletscher eisbedeckten Fuß
Erwartet' ich und fand bewohnte Hütten,
Und überall, wohin mein Fuß mich trug,
Fand ich den gleichen Haß der Tyrannei;
Denn bis an diese letzte Grenze selbst
1050 Belebter Schöpfung, wo der starre Boden
Aufhört zu geben, raubt der Vögte Geiz —
Die Herzen alle dieses biedern Volks
Erregt' ich mit dem Stachel meiner Worte,
Und unser sind sie all' mit Herz und Mund.

Stauffacher

1055 Großes habt Ihr in kurzer Frist geleistet.

Melchtal

Ich tat noch mehr. Die beiden Festen sind's,
R o ß b e r g und S a r n e n , die der Landmann fürchtet;
Denn hinter ihren Felsenwällen schirmt
Der Feind sich leicht und schädiget das Land.
1060 Mit eignen Augen wollt' ich es erkunden,
Ich war zu Sarnen und besah die Burg.

Stauffacher

Ihr wagtet Euch bis in des Tigers Höhle?

Melchtal

Ich war verkleidet dort in Pilgerstracht,
Ich sah den Landvogt an der Tafel schwelgen —
1065 Urteilt, ob ich mein Herz bezwingen kann;
Ich sah den Feind, und ich erschlug ihn nicht.

Stauffacher

Fürwahr, das Glück war Eurer Kühnheit hold.

(Unterdessen sind die andern Landleute vorwärts gekommen und nähern sich den beiden.)

Doch jetzo sagt mir, wer die Freunde sind
Und die gerechten Männer, die Euch folgten?
1070 Macht mich bekannt mit ihnen, daß wir uns
Zutraulich nahen und die Herzen öffnen.

Meier

Wer kennte E u c h nicht, Herr, in den drei Landen?
Ich bin der Mei'r von Sarnen; dies hier ist
Mein Schwestersohn, der Struth von Winkelried.

Stauffacher

1075 Ihr nennt mir keinen unbekannten Namen.
Ein Winkelried war's, der den Drachen schlug
Im Sumpf bei Weiler und sein Leben ließ
In diesem Strauß.

Winkelried

Das war mein Ahn, Herr Werner.

Melchtal

(zeigt auf zwei Landleute)

D i e wohnen hinterm Wald, sind Klosterleute
1080 Vom Engelberg — Ihr werdet sie drum nicht

Verachten, weil sie e i g n e Leute sind,
Und nicht wie wir frei sitzen auf dem Erbe —
Sie lieben's Land, sind sonst auch wohl berufen.

Stauffacher

(zu den beiden)

Gebt mir die Hand! Es preise sich, wer keinem
1085 Mit seinem Leibe pflichtig ist auf Erden;
Doch Redlichkeit gedeiht in jedem Stande.

Konrad Hunn

Das ist Herr Reding, unser Altlandammann.

Meier

Ich kenn' ihn wohl. Er ist mein Widerpart,
Der um ein altes Erbstück mit mir rechtet.
1090 — Herr Reding, wir sind Feinde vor Gericht;
Hier sind wir einig.

(Schüttelt ihm die Hand)

Stauffacher

Das ist brav gesprochen.

Winkelried

Hört ihr? Sie kommen. Hört das Horn von Uri!

(Rechts und links sieht man bewaffnete Männer mit Windlichtern die
Felsen herabsteigen.)

Auf der Mauer

Seht! Steigt nicht selbst der fromme Diener Gottes,
Der würd'ge Pfarrer mit herab? Nicht scheut er
1095 Des Weges Mühen und das Graun der Nacht,
Ein treuer Hirte, für das Volk zu sorgen.

Baumgarten

Der Sigrist folgt ihm und Herr Walter Fürst;
Doch nicht den Tell erblick' ich in der Menge.

(*Walter Fürst, Rösselmann der Pfarrer, Petermann der Sigrist, Kuoni der Hirt, Werni der Jäger, Ruodi der Fischer* und noch fünf andere *Landleute*. Alle zusammen, dreiunddreißig an der Zahl, treten vorwärts und stellen sich um das Feuer.)

Walter Fürst

So müssen wir auf unserm eignen Erb'
1100 Und väterlichen Boden uns verstohlen
Zusammenschleichen, wie die Mörder tun,
Und bei der Nacht, die ihren schwarzen Mantel
Nur dem Verbrechen und der sonnenscheuen
Verschwörung leihet, unser gutes Recht
1105 Uns holen, das doch lauter ist und klar
Gleichwie der glanzvoll offne Schoß des Tages.

Melchtal

Laßt's gut sein! Was die dunkle Nacht gesponnen,
Soll frei und fröhlich an das Licht der Sonnen.

Rösselmann

Hört, was mir Gott ins Herz gibt, Eidgenossen!
1110 Wir stehen hier statt einer Landsgemeinde
Und können gelten für ein ganzes Volk.
So laßt uns tagen nach den alten Bräuchen
Des Lands, wie wir's in ruhigen Zeiten pflegen;
Was ungesetzlich ist in der Versammlung,
1115 Entschuldige die Not der Zeit. Doch Gott
Ist überall, wo man das Recht verwaltet,
Und unter seinem Himmel stehen wir.

Stauffacher

Wohl, laßt uns tagen nach der alten Sitte!
Ist es gleich Nacht, so leuchtet unser Recht.

Melchtal

1120 Ist gleich die Zahl nicht voll, das H e r z ist hier
Des ganzen Volks, die B e s t e n sind zugegen.

Konrad Hunn

Sind auch die alten Bücher nicht zur Hand,
Sie sind in unsre Herzen eingeschrieben.

Rösselmann

Wohlan, so sei der Ring sogleich gebildet!
1125 Man pflanze auf die Schwerter der Gewalt!

Auf der Mauer

Der Landesammann nehme seinen Platz,
Und seine Weibel stehen ihm zur Seite!

Sigrist

Es sind der Völker dreie. Welchem nun
Gebührt's, das Haupt zu geben der Gemeinde?

Meier

1130 Um diese Ehr' mag Schwyz mit Uri streiten;
Wir Unterwaldner stehen frei zurück.

Melchtal

Wir stehn zurück; wir sind die Flehenden,
Die Hilfe heischen von den mächt'gen Freunden.

Stauffacher

So nehme Uri denn das Schwert; sein Banner
1135 Zieht bei den Römerzügen uns voran.

Walter Fürst

Des Schwertes Ehre werde Schwyz zuteil;
Denn seines Stammes rühmen wir uns alle.

Rösselmann

Den edeln Wettstreit laßt mich freundlich schlichten;
Schwyz soll im Rat, Uri im Felde führen.

Walter Fürst

(reicht dem Stauffacher die Schwerter)

1140 So nehmt!

Stauffacher

Nicht mir, dem Alter sei die Ehre.

Im Hofe

Die meisten Jahre zählt Ulrich der Schmied.

Auf der Mauer

Der Mann ist wacker, doch nicht freien Stands;
Kein eigner Mann kann Richter sein in Schwyz.

Stauffacher

Steht nicht Herr Reding hier, der Altlandammann?
1145 Was suchen wir noch einen Würdigern?

Walter Fürst

Er sei der Ammann und des Tages Haupt!
Wer dazu stimmt, erhebe seine Hände!

(Alle heben die rechte Hand auf.)

Reding

(tritt in die Mitte)

Ich kann die Hand nicht auf die Bücher legen,
So schwör' ich droben bei den ew'gen Sternen,
1150 Daß ich mich nimmer will vom Recht entfernen.

(Man richtet die zwei Schwerter vor ihm auf, der Ring bildet sich um ihn her, Schwyz hält die Mitte, rechts stellt sich Uri und links Unterwalden. Er steht auf sein Schlachtschwert gestützt.)

Was ist's, das die drei Völker des Gebirgs
Hier an des Sees unwirtlichem Gestade
Zusammenführte in der Geisterstunde?
Was soll der Inhalt sein des neuen Bunds,
1155 Den wir hier unterm Sternenhimmel stiften?

Stauffacher

(tritt in den Ring)

Wir stiften keinen neuen Bund; es ist
Ein uralt Bündnis nur von Väter Zeit,
Das wir erneuern. Wisset, Eidgenossen!
Ob uns der See, ob uns die Berge scheiden,
1160 Und jedes Volk sich für sich selbst regiert,
So sind wir e i n e s Stammes doch und Bluts,
Und e i n e Heimat ist's, aus der wir zogen.

Winkelried

So ist es wahr, wie's in den Liedern lautet,
Daß wir von fern her in das Land gewallt?
1165 O, teilt's uns mit, was Euch davon bekannt,
Daß sich der neue Bund am alten stärke.

Stauffacher

Hört, was die alten Hirten sich erzählen.
— Es war ein großes Volk, hinten im Lande
Nach Mitternacht, das litt von schwerer Teurung.
1170 In dieser Not beschloß die Landsgemeinde,
Daß je der zehnte Bürger nach dem Los
Der Väter Land verlasse — Das geschah.
Und zogen aus, wehklagend, Männer und Weiber,

Ein großer Heerzug, nach der Mittagsonne,
1175　Mit dem Schwert sich schlagend durch das deutsche Land,
Bis an das Hochland dieser Waldgebirge.
Und eher nicht ermüdete der Zug,
Bis daß sie kamen in das wilde Tal,
Wo jetzt die Muotta zwischen Wiesen rinnt —
1180　Nicht Menschenspuren waren hier zu sehen,
Nur eine Hütte stand am Ufer einsam.
Da saß ein Mann und wartete der Fähre —
Doch heftig wogete der See und war
Nicht fahrbar; da besahen sie das Land
1185　Sich näher und gewahrten schöne Fülle
Des Holzes und entdeckten gute Brunnen
Und meinten, sich im lieben Vaterland
Zu finden — Da beschlossen sie zu bleiben,
Erbaueten den alten Flecken S c h w y z
1190　Und hatten manchen sauren Tag, den Wald
Mit weit verschlungnen Wurzeln auszuroden —
Drauf, als der Boden nicht mehr Gnügen tat
Der Zahl des Volks, da zogen sie hinüber
Zum schwarzen Berg, ja bis ans Weißland hin,
1195　Wo, hinter ew'gem Eiseswall verborgen,
Ein andres Volk in andern Zungen spricht.
Den Flecken S t a n z erbauten sie am Kernwald,
Den Flecken A l t o r f in dem Tal der Reuß —
Doch blieben sie des Ursprungs stets gedenk;
1200　Aus all den fremden Stämmen, die seitdem
In Mitte ihres Lands sich angesiedelt,
Finden die Schwyzer Männer sich heraus;
Es gibt das Herz, das Blut sich zu erkennen.

(Reicht rechts und links die Hand hin)

Auf der Mauer

Ja, wir sind e i n e s Herzens, e i n e s Bluts!

Alle

(sich die Hände reichend)

1205 Wir sind e i n Volk, und einig wollen wir handeln.

Stauffacher

Die andern Völker tragen fremdes Joch,
Sie haben sich dem Sieger unterworfen.
Es leben selbst in unsern Landesmarken
Der Sassen viel, die fremde Pflichten tragen,
1210 Und ihre Knechtschaft erbt auf ihre Kinder.
Doch w i r , der alten Schweizer echter Stamm,
Wir haben stets die Freiheit uns bewahrt.
Nicht unter Fürsten bogen wir das Knie,
Freiwillig wählten wir den Schirm der Kaiser.

Rösselmann

1215 Frei wählten wir des Reiches Schutz und Schirm;
So steht's bemerkt in Kaiser Friedrichs Brief.

Stauffacher

Denn herrenlos ist auch der Freiste nicht.
Ein Oberhaupt muß sein, ein höchster Richter,
Wo man das Recht mag schöpfen in dem Streit.
1220 Drum haben unsre Väter für den Boden,
Den sie der alten Wildnis abgewonnen,
Die Ehr' gegönnt dem Kaiser, der den Herrn
Sich nennt der deutschen und der welschen Erde,
Und, wie die andern Freien seines Reichs,
1225 Sich ihm zu edelm Waffendienst gelobt;
Denn dieses ist der Freien einz'ge Pflicht,
Das Reich zu schirmen, das sie selbst beschirmt.

Melchtal

Was drüber ist, ist Merkmal eines Knechts.

Stauffacher

Sie folgten, wenn der Heribann erging,
1230 Dem Reichspanier und schlugen seine Schlachten.
Nach Welschland zogen sie gewappnet mit,
Die Römerkron' ihm auf das Haupt zu setzen.
Daheim regierten sie sich fröhlich selbst
Nach altem Brauch und eigenem Gesetz;
1235 Der höchste Blutbann war allein des Kaisers.
Und dazu ward bestellt ein großer Graf,
Der hatte seinen Sitz nicht in dem Lande.
Wenn Blutschuld kam, so rief man ihn herein,
Und unter offnem Himmel, schlicht und klar,
1240 Sprach er das Recht und ohne Furcht der Menschen.
Wo sind hier Spuren, daß wir Knechte sind?
Ist einer, der es anders weiß, der rede!

Im Hofe

Nein, so verhält sich alles, wie Ihr sprecht,
Gewaltherrschaft ward nie bei uns geduldet.

Stauffacher

1245 Dem Kaiser selbst versagten wir Gehorsam,
Da er das Recht zu Gunst der Pfaffen bog.
Denn als die Leute von dem Gotteshaus
E i n s i e d e l n uns die Alp in Anspruch nahmen,
Die wir beweidet seit der Väter Zeit,
1250 Der Abt herfürzog einen alten Brief,
Der ihm die herrenlose Wüste schenkte —
Denn unser Dasein hatte man verhehlt —
Da sprachen wir: „Erschlichen ist der Brief!
Kein Kaiser kann, was unser ist, verschenken;
1255 Und wird uns Recht versagt vom Reich, wir können
In unsern Bergen auch des Reichs entbehren."

— So sprachen unsre Väter! Sollen w i r
Des neuen Joches Schändlichkeit erdulden,
Erleiden von dem fremden Knecht, was uns
1260 In seiner Macht kein Kaiser durfte bieten?
— Wir haben diesen Boden uns e r s c h a f f e n
Durch unsrer Hände Fleiß, den alten Wald,
Der sonst der Bären wilde Wohnung war,
Zu einem Sitz für Menschen umgewandelt;
1265 Die Brut des Drachen haben wir getötet,
Der aus den Sümpfen giftgeschwollen stieg;
Die Nebeldecke haben wir zerrissen,
Die ewig grau um diese Wildnis hing,
Den harten Fels gesprengt, über den Abgrund
1270 Dem Wandersmann den sichern Steg geleitet;
Unser ist durch tausendjährigen Besitz
Der Boden — und der fremde Herrenknecht
Soll kommen dürfen und uns Ketten schmieden
Und Schmach antun auf unsrer eignen Erde?
1275 Ist keine Hilfe gegen solchen Drang?

     (Eine große Bewegung unter den Landleuten)

Nein, eine Grenze hat Tyrannenmacht:
Wenn der Gedrückte nirgends Recht kann finden,
Wenn unerträglich wird die Last — greift er
Hinauf getrosten Mutes in den Himmel
1280 Und holt herunter seine ew'gen Rechte,
Die droben hangen unveräußerlich
Und unzerbrechlich wie die Sterne selbst —
Der alte Urstand der Natur kehrt wieder,
Wo Mensch dem Menschen gegenüber steht —
1285 Zum letzten Mittel, wenn kein andres mehr
Verfangen will, ist ihm das Schwert gegeben —
Der Güter höchstes dürfen wir verteid'gen
Gegen Gewalt. — Wir stehn für unser Land,
Wir stehn für unsre Weiber, unsre Kinder!

Alle

(an ihre Schwerter schlagend)

1290 Wir stehn für unsre Weiber, unsre Kinder!

Rösselmann

(tritt in den Ring)

Eh' ihr zum Schwerte greift, bedenkt es wohl!
Ihr könnt es friedlich mit dem Kaiser schlichten.
Es kostet euch ein Wort, und die Tyrannen,
Die euch jetzt schwer bedrängen, schmeicheln euch.

1295 — Ergreift, was man euch oft geboten hat,
Trennt euch vom Reich, erkennet Östreichs Hoheit —

Auf der Mauer

Was sagt der Pfarrer? Wir zu Östreich schwören!

Am Bühel

Hört ihn nicht an!

Winkelried

Das rät uns ein Verräter,
Ein Feind des Landes!

Reding

Ruhig, Eidgenossen!

Sewa

1300 Wir Östreich huldigen, nach solcher Schmach!

Von der Flüe

Wir uns abtrotzen lassen durch Gewalt,
Was wir der Güte weigerten!

Meier

Dann wären
Wir Sklaven und verdienten, es zu sein!

Auf der Mauer

Der sei gestoßen aus dem Recht der Schweizer,
1305 Wer von Ergebung spricht an Österreich!
— Landammann, ich bestehe drauf; dies sei
Das erste Landsgesetz, das wir hier geben.

Melchtal

So sei's! Wer von Ergebung spricht an Östreich,
Soll rechtlos sein und aller Ehren bar.
1310 Kein Landmann nehm' ihn auf an seinem Feuer.

Alle

(heben die rechte Hand auf)

Wir wollen es, das sei Gesetz!

Reding

(nach einer Pause)

Es ist's.

Rösselmann

Jetzt seid ihr frei, ihr seid's durch dies Gesetz.
Nicht durch Gewalt soll Österreich ertrotzen,
Was es durch freundlich Werben nicht erhielt —

Jost von Weiler

1315 Zur Tagesordnung, weiter!

Reding

Eidgenossen!
Sind alle sanften Mittel auch versucht?

Vielleicht weiß es der König nicht; es ist
Wohl gar se n Wille nicht, was wir erdulden.
Auch dieses Letzte sollten wir versuchen,
1320 Erst unsre Klage bringen vor sein Ohr,
Eh' wir zum Schwerte greifen. Schrecklich immer,
Auch in gerechter Sache, ist Gewalt.
Gott hilft nur dann, wenn Menschen nicht mehr helfen.

Stauffacher

(zu Konrad Hunn)

Nun ist's an Euch, Bericht zu geben. Redet!

Konrad Hunn

1325 Ich war zu Rheinfeld an des Kaisers Pfalz,
Wider der Vögte harten Druck zu klagen,
Den Brief zu holen unsrer alten Freiheit,
Den jeder neue König sonst bestätigt.
Die Boten vieler Städte fand ich dort,
1330 Vom schwäb'schen Lande und vom Lauf des Rheins,
Die all' erhielten ihre Pergamente
Und kehrten freudig wieder in ihr Land.
Mich, e u r e n Boten, wies man an die Räte,
Und die entließen mich mit leerem Trost:
1335 Der Kaiser habe diesmal keine Zeit;
Er würde sonst einmal wohl an uns denken.
— Und als ich traurig durch die Säle ging
Der Königsburg, da sah ich Herzog Hansen
In einem Erker weinend stehn, um ihn
1340 Die edeln Herrn von Wart und Tegerfeld,
Die riefen mir und sagten: „Helft euch selbst!
Gerechtigkeit erwartet nicht vom König!
Beraubt er nicht des eignen Bruders Kind
Und hinterhält ihm sein gerechtes Erbe?
1345 Der Herzog fleht ihn um sein Mütterliches,

Er habe seine Jahre voll, es wäre
Nun Zeit, auch Land und Leute zu regieren.
Was ward ihm zum Bescheid? Ein Kränzlein setzt' ihm
Der Kaiser auf: das sei die Zier der Jugend."

Auf der Mauer

1350 Ihr habt's gehört. Recht und Gerechtigkeit
Erwartet nicht vom Kaiser! Helft euch selbst!

Reding

Nichts anders bleibt uns übrig. Nun gebt Rat,
Wie wir es klug zum frohen Ende leiten.

Walter Fürst

(tritt in den Ring)

Abtreiben wollen wir verhaßten Zwang;
1355 Die alten Rechte, wie wir sie ererbt
Von unsern Vätern, wollen wir bewahren,
Nicht ungezügelt nach dem Neuen greifen.
Dem Kaiser bleibe, was des Kaisers ist;
Wer einen Herrn hat, dien' ihm pflichtgemäß.

Meier

1360 Ich trage Gut von Österreich zu Lehen.

Walter Fürst

Ihr fahret fort, Östreich die Pflicht zu leisten.

Jost von Weiler

Ich steure an die Herrn von Rappersweil.

Walter Fürst

Ihr fahret fort, zu zinsen und zu steuern.

Rösselmann

Der großen Frau zu Zürch bin ich vereidet.

Walter Fürst

1365   Ihr gebt dem Kloster, was des Klosters ist.

Stauffacher

Ich trage keine Lehen als des Reichs.

Walter Fürst

Was sein muß, das geschehe, doch nicht drüber!
Die Vögte wollen wir mit ihren Knechten
Verjagen und die festen Schlösser brechen;
1370   Doch, wenn es sein mag, ohne Blut.   Es sehe
Der Kaiser, daß wir notgedrungen nur
Der Ehrfurcht fromme Pflichten abgeworfen.
Und sieht er uns in unsern Schranken bleiben,
Vielleicht besiegt er staatsklug seinen Zorn;
1375   Denn bill'ge Furcht erwecket sich ein Volk,
Das mit dem Schwerte in der Faust sich mäßigt.

Reding

Doch lasset hören!   Wie vollenden wir's?
Es hat der Feind die Waffen in der Hand,
Und nicht fürwahr in Frieden wird er weichen.

Stauffacher

1380   Er wird's, wenn er in Waffen uns erblickt;
Wir überraschen ihn, eh' er sich rüstet.

Meier

Ist bald gesprochen, aber schwer getan.
Uns ragen in dem Land zwei feste Schlösser,
Die geben Schirm dem Feind und werden furchtbar,

1385 Wenn uns der König in das Land sollt' fallen.
Roßberg und Sarnen muß bezwungen sein,
Eh' man ein Schwert erhebt in den drei Landen.

Stauffacher

Säumt man so lang, so wird der Feind gewarnt;
Zu viele sind's, die das Geheimnis teilen.

Meier

1390 In den Waldstätten find't sich kein Verräter.

Rösselmann

Der Eifer auch, der gute, kann verraten.

Walter Fürst

Schiebt man es auf, so wird der Twing vollendet
In Altorf, und der Vogt befestigt sich.

Meier

Ihr denkt an euch.

Sigrist

Und ihr seid ungerecht.

Meier

(auffahrend)

1395 Wir ungerecht! Das darf uns Uri bieten!

Reding

Bei eurem Eide! Ruh'!

Meier

Ja, wenn sich Schwyz
Versteht mit Uri, müssen w i r wohl schweigen.

Reding

Ich muß euch weisen vor der Landsgemeinde,
Daß ihr mit heft'gem Sinn den Frieden stört!
1400 Stehn wir nicht alle für dieselbe Sache?

Winkelried

Wenn wir's verschieben bis zum Fest des Herrn,
Dann bringt's die Sitte mit, daß alle Sassen
Dem Vogt Geschenke bringen auf das Schloß;
So können zehen Männer oder zwölf
1405 Sich unverdächtig in der Burg versammeln,
Die führen heimlich spitz'ge Eisen mit,
Die man geschwind kann an die Stäbe stecken;
Denn niemand kommt mit Waffen in die Burg.
Zunächst im Wald hält dann der große Haufe,
1410 Und wenn die andern glücklich sich des Tors
Ermächtiget, so wird ein Horn geblasen,
Und jene brechen aus dem Hinterhalt;
So wird das Schloß mit leichter Arbeit unser.

Melchtal

Den Roßberg übernehm' ich zu ersteigen,
1415 Denn eine Dirn' des Schlosses ist mir hold,
Und leicht betör' ich sie, zum nächtlichen
Besuch die schwanke Leiter mir zu reichen;
Bin ich droben erst, zieh' ich die Freunde nach.

Reding

Ist's aller Wille, daß verschoben werde?
(Die Mehrheit erhebt die Hand.)

Stauffacher

(zählt die Stimmen)

1420 Es ist ein Mehr von zwanzig gegen zwölf!

Walter Fürst

Wenn am bestimmten Tag die Burgen fallen,
So geben wir von einem Berg zum andern
Das Zeichen mit dem Rauch; der Landsturm wird
Aufgeboten, schnell, im Hauptort jedes Landes.
1425 Wenn dann die Vögte sehn der Waffen Ernst,
Glaubt mir, sie werden sich des Streits begeben
Und gern ergreifen friedliches Geleit,
Aus unsern Landesmarken zu entweichen.

Stauffacher

Nur mit dem Geßler fürcht' ich schweren Stand:
1430 Furchtbar ist er mit Reisigen umgeben,
Nicht ohne Blut räumt er das Feld, ja selbst
Vertrieben bleibt er furchtbar noch dem Land;
Schwer ist's und fast gefährlich, ihn zu schonen.

Baumgarten

Wo's halsgefährlich ist, da stellt m i c h hin!
1435 Dem Tell verdank' ich mein gerettet Leben,
Gern schlag' ich's in die Schanze für das Land;
Mein' Ehr' hab' ich beschützt, mein Herz befriedigt.

Reding

Die Zeit bringt Rat. Erwartet's in Geduld!
Man muß dem Augenblick auch was vertrauen.
1440 — Doch seht, indes wir nächtlich hier noch tagen,
Stellt auf den höchsten Bergen schon der Morgen
Die glüh'nde Hochwacht aus — Kommt, laßt uns scheiden,
Eh' uns des Tages Leuchten überrascht.

Walter Fürst

Sorgt nicht, die Nacht weicht langsam aus den Tälern.

(Alle haben unwillkürlich die Hüte abgenommen und betrachten mit
stiller Sammlung die Morgenröte.)

Rösselmann

1445 Bei diesem Licht, das uns zuerst begrüßt
Von allen Völkern, die tief unter uns
Schwer atmend wohnen in dem Qualm der Städte,
Laßt uns den Eid des neuen Bundes schwören!
— Wir wollen sein ein einzig Volk von Brüdern,
1450 In keiner Not uns trennen und Gefahr!

(Alle sprechen es nach mit erhobenen drei Fingern.)

— Wir wollen frei sein, wie die Väter waren,
Eher den Tod, als in der Knechtschaft leben!

(Wie oben)

— Wir wollen trauen auf den höchsten Gott
Und uns nicht fürchten vor der Macht der Menschen!

(Wie oben.   Die Landleute umarmen einander.)

Stauffacher

1455 Jetzt gehe jeder seines Weges still
Zu seiner Freundschaft und Genoßsame!
Wer Hirt ist, wintre ruhig seine Herde
Und werb' im Stillen Freunde für den Bund!
— W a s   noch bis dahin muß erduldet werden,
1460 Erduldet's!   Laßt die Rechnung der Tyrannen
Anwachsen, bis   e i n   Tag die allgemeine
Und die besondre Schuld auf einmal zahlt.
Bezähme jeder die gerechte Wut
Und spare für das Ganze seine Rache;

1465 Denn Raub begeht am allgemeinen Gut,
Wer selbst sich hilft in seiner eignen Sache.

(Indem sie zu drei verschiedenen Seiten in größter Ruhe abgehen, fällt
das Orchester mit einem prachtvollen Schwung ein; die leere Szene
bleibt noch eine Zeitlang offen und zeigt das Schauspiel der aufgehenden
Sonne über den Eisgebirgen.)

Jägerliedchen für
    Walther Tell
womit Actus III. anzufangen.

Mit dem Pfeil, dem Bogen
Durch Gebirg und Thal
Kommt der Schütz gezogen,
Früh im Morgenstrahl!

Wie im Reich der Lüfte
König ist der Weih
Durch Gebirg und Klüfte
Herrscht der Schütze frei.

Ihm gehört das Weite,
Was sein Pfeil erreicht,
Das ist seine Beute,
Was da fleugt und kreucht.

DRITTER AUFZUG

ERSTE SZENE

(Hof vor Tells Hause. *Tell* ist mit der Zimmeraxt, *Hedwig* mit einer häuslichen Arbeit beschäftigt. *Walter* und *Wilhelm* in der Tiefe spielen mit einer kleinen Armbrust.)

Walter

(singt)

Mit dem Pfeil, dem Bogen
Durch Gebirg' und Tal
Kommt der Schütz gezogen
1470   Früh am Morgenstrahl.

Wie im Reich der Lüfte
König ist der Weih —
Durch Gebirg' und Klüfte
Herrscht der Schütze frei.

1475   Ihm gehört das Weite,
Was sein Pfeil erreicht,
Das ist seine Beute,
Was da kreucht und fleugt.

(Kommt gesprungen)

Der Strang ist mir entzwei. Mach' mir ihn, Vater.

Tell

1480 Ich nicht. Ein rechter Schütze hilft sich selbst.

(Knaben entfernen sich.)

Hedwig

Die Knaben fangen zeitig an zu schießen.

79

Tell

Früh übt sich, was ein Meister werden will.

Hedwig

Ach, wollte Gott, sie lernten's nie!

Tell

Sie sollen alles lernen. Wer durch's Leben
1485 Sich frisch will schlagen, muß zu Schutz und Trutz
Gerüstet sein.

Hedwig

   Ach, es wird keiner seine Ruh'
Zu Hause finden.

Tell

   Mutter, ich kann's auch nicht.
Zum Hirten hat Natur mich nicht gebildet;
Rastlos muß ich ein flüchtig Ziel verfolgen.
1490 Dann erst genieß' ich meines Lebens recht,
Wenn ich mir's jeden Tag aufs neu' erbeute.

Hedwig

Und an die Angst der Hausfrau denkst du nicht,
Die sich indessen, deiner wartend, härmt.
Denn mich erfüllt's mit Grausen, was die Knechte
1495 Von euren Wagefahrten sich erzählen;
Bei jedem Abschied zittert mir das Herz,
Daß du mir nimmer werdest wiederkehren.
Ich sehe dich, im wilden Eisgebirg'
Verirrt, von einer Klippe zu der andern
1500 Den Fehlsprung tun, seh', wie die Gemse dich
Rückspringend mit sich in den Abgrund reißt,
Wie eine Windlawine dich verschüttet,

Wie unter dir der trügerische Firn
Einbricht, und du hinabsinkst, ein lebendig
1505 Begrabner, in die schauerliche Gruft —
Ach, den verwegnen Alpenjäger hascht
Der Tod in hundert wechselnden Gestalten!
Das ist ein unglückseliges Gewerb',
Das halsgefährlich führt am Abgrund hin!

Tell

1510 Wer frisch umherspäht mit gesunden Sinnen,
Auf Gott vertraut und die gelenke Kraft,
Der ringt sich leicht aus jeder Fahr und Not;
Den schreckt der Berg nicht, der darauf geboren.

(Er hat seine Arbeit vollendet, legt das Gerät hinweg.)

Jetzt, mein' ich, hält das Tor auf Jahr und Tag.
1515 Die Axt im Haus erspart den Zimmermann.

(Nimmt den Hut)

Hedwig

Wo gehst du hin?

Tell

Nach Altorf, zu dem Vater.

Hedwig

Sinnst du auch nichts Gefährliches? Gesteh mir's!

Tell

Wie kommst du darauf, Frau?

Hedwig

Es spinnt sich etwas
Gegen die Vögte — Auf dem Rütli ward
1520 Getagt, ich weiß, und du bist auch im Bunde.

Tell

Ich war nicht mit dabei — doch werd' ich mich
Dem Lande nicht entziehen, wenn es ruft.

Hedwig

Sie werden dich hinstellen, wo Gefahr ist;
Das Schwerste w rd dein Anteil sein, wie immer.

Tell

1525 Ein jeder wird besteuert nach Vermögen.

Hedwig

Den Unterwaldner hast du auch im Sturme
Über den See geschafft — Ein Wunder war's,
Daß ihr entkommen — Dachtest du denn gar nicht
An Kind und Weib?

Tell

        Lieb Weib, ich dacht' an euch!
1530 Drum rettet' ich den Vater seinen Kindern.

Hedwig

Zu schiffen in dem wüt'gen See! Das heißt
Nicht Gott vertrauen! Das heißt Gott versuchen!

Tell

Wer gar zu viel bedenkt, wird wenig leisten.

Hedwig

Ja, du bist gut und hilfreich, dienest allen,
1535 Und wenn du selbst in Not kommst, hilft dir keiner.

Tell

Verhüt' es Gott, daß ich nicht Hilfe brauche!

      (Er nimmt die Armbrust und Pfeile.)

Hedwig

Was willst du mit der Armbrust? Laß sie hier!

Tell

Mir fehlt der Arm, wenn mir die Waffe fehlt.

(Die Knaben kommen zurück.)

Walter

Vater, wo gehst du hin?

Tell

Nach Altorf, Knabe,
1540 Zum Ehni — Willst du mit?

Walter

Ja freilich will ich.

Hedwig

Der Landvogt ist jetzt dort. Bleib weg von Altorf!

Tell

Er g e h t , noch heute.

Hedwig

Drum laß ihn erst fort sein!
Gemahn' ihn nicht an dich; du weißt, er grollt uns.

Tell

Mir soll sein böser Wille nicht viel schaden,
1545 Ich tue recht und scheue keinen Feind.

Hedwig

Die recht tun, eben die haßt er am meisten.

Tell

Weil er nicht an sie kommen kann — M i c h wird
Der Ritter wohl in Frieden lassen, mein' ich.

Hedwig

So, weißt du das?

Tell

   Es ist nicht lange her,
1550 Da ging ich jagen durch die wilden Gründe
Des Schächentals auf menschenleerer Spur,
Und da ich einsam einen Felsensteig
Verfolgte, wo nicht auszuweichen war,
Denn über mir hing schroff die Felswand her,
1555 Und unten rauschte fürchterlich der Schächen,

(Die Knaben drängen sich rechts und links an ihn und sehen mit
gespannter Neugier zu ihm hinauf.)

   Da kam der Landvogt gegen mich daher,
Er ganz allein mit mir, der auch allein war,
Bloß Mensch zu Mensch, und neben uns der Abgrund.
Und als der Herre mein ansichtig ward
1560 Und mich erkannte, den er kurz zuvor
Um kleiner Ursach' willen schwer gebüßt,
Und sah mich mit dem stattlichen Gewehr
Daher geschritten kommen, da verblaßt' er,
Die Knie versagten ihm, ich sah es kommen,
1565 Daß er jetzt an die Felswand würde sinken.
  — Da jammerte mich sein, ich trat zu ihm
Bescheidentlich und sprach: „Ich bin's, Herr Landvogt."
Er aber konnte keinen armen Laut
Aus seinem Munde geben — Mit der Hand nur
1570 Winkt' er mir schweigend, meines Wegs zu gehn;
Da ging ich fort und sandt' ihm sein Gefolge.

Hedwig

Er hat vor dir gezittert — Wehe dir!
Daß du ihn schwach gesehn, vergibt er nie.

Tell

Drum meid' ich ihn, und er wird mich nicht suchen.

Hedwig

1575 Bleib heute nur dort weg. Geh lieber jagen!

Tell

Was fällt dir ein?

Hedwig

Mich ängstigt's. Bleibe weg!

Tell

Wie kannst du dich so ohne Ursach' quälen?

Hedwig

W e i l ' s keine Ursach' hat — Tell, bleibe hier!

Tell

Ich hab's versprochen, liebes Weib, zu kommen.

Hedwig

1580 M u ß t du, so geh — nur lasse mir den Knaben!

Walter

Nein, Mütterchen. Ich gehe mit dem Vater.

Hedwig

Wälti, verlassen willst du deine Mutter?

Walter

Ich bring' dir auch was Hübsches mit vom Ehni.

(Geht mit dem Vater)

Wilhelm

Mutter, ich bleibe bei dir!

Hedwig

(umarmt ihn)

Ja, du bist

1585 Mein liebes Kind, du bleibst mir noch allein!

(Sie geht an das Hoftor und folgt den Abgehenden lange mit den Augen.)

ZWEITE SZENE

(Eine eingeschlossene wilde Waldgegend. Staubbäche stürzen von den Felsen. *Berta* im Jagdkleid. Gleich darauf *Rudenz.*)

Berta

Er folgt mir. Endlich kann ich mich erklären.

Rudenz

(tritt rasch ein)

Fräulein, ˙etzt endlich find' ich Euch allein,
Abgründe schließen ringsumher uns ein;
In dieser Wildnis fürcht' ich keinen Zeugen,
1590 Vom Herzen wälz' ich dieses lange Schweigen —

Berta

Seid Ihr gewiß, daß uns die Jagd nicht folgt?

Rudenz

Die Jagd ist dort hinaus — Jetzt oder nie!
Ich muß den teuren Augenblick ergreifen —
Entschieden sehen muß ich mein Geschick,
1595 Und sollt' es mich auf ewig von Euch scheiden.
— O, waffnet Eure güt'gen Blicke nicht
Mit dieser finstern Strenge — W e r bin ich,
Daß ich den kühnen Wunsch zu Euch erhebe?
Mich hat der Ruhm noch nicht genannt; ich darf
1600 Mich in die Reih' nicht stellen mit den Rittern,
Die siegberühmt und glänzend Euch umwerben.
Nichts hab' ich als mein Herz voll Treu' und Liebe —

Berta

(ernst und streng)

Dürft Ihr von Liebe reden und von Treue,
Der treulos wird an seinen nächsten Pflichten?

(*Rudenz* tritt zurück.)

1605 Der Sklave Österreichs, der sich dem Fremdling
Verkauft, dem Unterdrücker seines Volks?

Rudenz

Von Euch, mein Fräulein, hör' ich diesen Vorwurf?
Wen such' ich denn als Euch auf jener Seite?

Berta

Mich denkt Ihr auf der Seite des Verrats
1610 Zu finden? Eher wollt' ich meine Hand
Dem Geßler selbst, dem Unterdrücker, schenken,
Als dem naturvergeßnen Sohn der Schweiz,
Der sich zu seinem Werkzeug machen kann!

Rudenz

O Gott, was muß ich hören!

Berta

Wie? Was liegt
1615 Dem guten Menschen näher als die Seinen?
Gibt's schönre Pflichten für ein edles Herz,
Als ein Verteidiger der Unschuld sein,
Das Recht des Unterdrückten zu beschirmen?
— Die Seele blutet mir um Euer Volk;
1620 Ich leide m i t ihm, denn ich muß es lieben,
Das so bescheiden ist und doch voll Kraft;
Es zieht mein ganzes Herz mich zu ihm hin,
Mit jedem Tage lern' ich's mehr verehren.
— Ihr aber, den Natur und Ritterpflicht
1625 Ihm zum geborenen Beschützer gaben,
Und der's v e r l ä ß t , der treulos übertritt
Zum Feind und Ketten schmiedet seinem Land,
Ihr seid's, der mich verletzt und kränkt; ich muß
Mein Herz bezwingen, daß ich Euch nicht hasse.

Rudenz

1630 Will ich denn nicht das Beste meines Volks?
Ihm unter Östreichs mächt'gem Zepter nicht
Den Frieden —

Berta

Knechtschaft wollt Ihr ihm bereiten!
Die Freiheit wollt Ihr aus dem letzten Schloß,
Das ihr noch auf der Erde blieb, verjagen.
1635 Das Volk versteht sich besser auf sein Glück;
Kein Schein verführt sein sicheres Gefühl.
Euch haben sie das Netz ums Haupt geworfen —

Rudenz

Berta! Ihr haßt mich, Ihr verachtet mich!

Berta

Tät' ich's, mir wäre besser — Aber den
1640 Verachtet s e h e n und verachtungswert,
Den man gern lieben möchte —

Rudenz

Berta! Berta!
Ihr zeiget mir das höchste Himmelsglück
Und stürzt mich tief in e i n e m Augenblick.

Berta

Nein, nein, das Edle ist nicht ganz erstickt
1645 In Euch! Es schlummert nur, ich will es wecken.
Ihr müßt Gewalt ausüben an Euch selbst,
Die angestammte Tugend zu ertöten;
Doch wohl Euch, sie ist mächtiger als Ihr,
Und trotz Euch selber seid Ihr gut und edel!

Rudenz

1650 Ihr glaubt an mich! O Berta, alles läßt
Mich Eure Liebe sein und werden!

Berta

Seid,
Wozu die herrliche Natur Euch machte!
Erfüllt den Platz, wohin sie Euch gestellt,
Zu Eurem Volke steht und Eurem Lande,
1655 Und kämpft für Euer heilig Recht!

Rudenz

Weh mir!
Wie kann ich Euch erringen, Euch besitzen,
Wenn ich der Macht des Kaisers widerstrebe?
Ist's der Verwandten mächt'ger Wille nicht,
Der über Eure Hand tyrannisch waltet?

Berta

1660   In den Waldstätten liegen meine Güter,
Und ist der Schweizer frei, so bin auch ich's.

Rudenz

Berta! welch einen Blick tut Ihr mir auf!

Berta

Hofft nicht durch Östreichs Gunst mich zu erringen;
Nach meinem Erbe strecken sie die Hand,
1665   Das will man mit dem großen Erb' vereinen.
Dieselbe Ländergier, die Eure Freiheit
Verschlingen will, sie drohet auch der meinen!
— O Freund, zum Opfer bin ich ausersehn,
Vielleicht, um einen Günstling zu belohnen —
1670   Dort, wo die Falschheit und die Ränke wohnen,
Hin an den Kaiserhof will man mich ziehn,
Dort harren mein verhaßter Ehe Ketten;
Die Liebe nur — die Eure kann mich retten!

Rudenz

Ihr könntet Euch entschließen, hier zu leben,
1675   In meinem Vaterlande mein zu sein?
O Berta, all mein Sehnen in das Weite,
Was war es, als ein Streben nur nach Euch?
Euch sucht' ich einzig auf dem Weg des Ruhms,
Und all mein Ehrgeiz war nur meine Liebe.
1680   Könnt Ihr mit mir Euch in dies stille Tal
Einschließen und der Erde Glanz entsagen —
O, dann ist meines Strebens Ziel gefunden;
Dann mag der Strom der wildbewegten Welt
Ans sichre Ufer dieser Berge schlagen —
1685   Kein flüchtiges Verlangen hab' ich mehr
Hinauszusenden in des Lebens Weiten —

Dann mögen diese Felsen um uns her
Die undurchdringlich feste Mauer breiten,
Und dies verschloßne sel'ge Tal allein
1690 Zum Himmel offen und gelichtet sein!

Berta

Jetzt bist du ganz, wie dich mein ahnend Herz
Geträumt, mich hat mein Glaube nicht betrogen!

Rudenz

Fahr hin, du eitler Wahn, der mich betört!
Ich soll das Glück in meiner Heimat finden.
1695 Hier, wo der Knabe fröhlich aufgeblüht,
Wo tausend Freudespuren mich umgeben,
Wo alle Quellen mir und Bäume leben,
Im Vaterland willst du die Meine werden!
Ach, wohl hab' ich es stets geliebt! Ich fühl's,
1700 Es fehlte mir zu jedem Glück der Erden.

Berta

Wo wär' die sel'ge Insel aufzufinden,
Wenn sie nicht hier ist in der Unschuld Land?
Hier, wo die alte Treue heimisch wohnt,
Wo sich die Falschheit noch nicht hingefunden,
1705 Da trübt kein Neid die Quelle unsers Glücks,
Und ewig hell entfliehen uns die Stunden.
— Da seh' ich d i c h im echten Männerwert,
Den Ersten von den Freien und den Gleichen,
Mit reiner, freier Huldigung verehrt,
1710 Groß, wie ein König wirkt in seinen Reichen.

Rudenz

Da seh' ich dich, die Krone aller Frauen,
In weiblich reizender Geschäftigkeit,
In meinem Haus den Himmel mir erbauen

Und, wie der Frühling seine Blumen streut,
1715 Mit schöner Anmut mir das Leben schmücken
Und alles rings beleben und beglücken!

Berta

Sieh, teurer Freund, warum ich trauerte,
Als ich dies höchste Lebensglück dich selbst
Zerstören sah — Weh mir! Wie stünd's um mich,
1720 Wenn ich dem stolzen Ritter müßte folgen,
Dem Landbedrücker, auf sein finstres Schloß!
— Hier ist kein Schloß. Mich scheiden keine Mauern
Von einem Volk, das ich beglücken kann!

Rudenz

Doch wie mich retten — wie die Schlinge lösen,
1725 Die ich mir töricht selbst ums Haupt gelegt?

Berta

Zerreiße sie mit männlichem Entschluß!
Was auch draus werde — steh zu deinem Volk!
Es ist dein angeborner Platz.

(Jagdhörner in der Ferne)

Die Jagd
Kommt näher — Fort, wir müssen scheiden — Kämpfe
1730 Fürs Vaterland, du kämpfst für deine Liebe!
Es ist e i n Feind, vor dem wir alle zittern,
Und e i n e Freiheit macht uns alle frei!

(Gehen ab)

DRITTE SZENE

(Wiese bei Altorf. Im Vordergrund Bäume, in der Tiefe der Hut auf einer Stange. Der Prospekt wird begrenzt durch den Bannberg, über welchem ein Schneegebirg' emporragt. *Frießhard* und *Leuthold* halten Wache.)

Frießhard

Wir passen auf umsonst. Es will sich niemand
Heranbegeben und dem Hut sein' Reverenz
1735 Erzeigen. 's war doch sonst wie Jahrmarkt hier;
Jetzt ist der ganze Anger wie verödet,
Seitdem der Popanz auf der Stange hängt.

Leuthold

Nur schlecht Gesindel läßt sich sehn und schwingt
Uns zum Verdrieße die zerlumpten Mützen.
1740 Was rechte Leute sind, die machen lieber
Den langen Umweg um den halben Flecken,
Eh' sie den Rücken beugten vor dem Hut.

Frießhard

Sie müssen über diesen Platz, wenn sie
Vom Rathaus kommen um die Mittagsstunde.
1745 Da meint' ich schon, 'nen guten Fang zu tun,
Denn keiner dachte dran, den Hut zu grüßen.
Da sieht's der Pfaff, der Rösselmann — kam just
Von einem Kranken her — und stellt sich hin
Mit dem Hochwürdigen, grad' vor die Stange —
1750 Der Sigrist mußte mit dem Glöcklein schellen:
Da fielen all' aufs Knie, ich selber mit,
Und grüßten die Monstranz, doch nicht den Hut. —

Leuthold

Höre, Gesell, es fängt mir an zu deuchten,
Wir stehen hier am Pranger vor dem Hut;

1755 's ist doch ein Schimpf für einen Reitersmann,
Schildwach' zu stehn vor einem leeren Hut —
Und jeder rechte Kerl muß uns verachten.
— Die Reverenz zu machen einem Hut,
Es ist doch, traun, ein närrischer Befehl!

Frießhard

1760 Warum nicht einem leeren, hohlen Hut?
Bückst du dich doch vor manchem hohlen Schädel.

(*Hildegard, Mechthild* und *Elsbet* treten auf mit Kindern und stellen sich um die Stange.)

Leuthold

Und du bist auch so ein dienstfert'ger Schurke
Und brächtest wackre Leute gern ins Unglück.
Mag, wer da will, am Hut vorübergehn,
1765 Ich drück' die Augen zu und seh' nicht hin.

Mechthild

Da hängt der Landvogt! — Habt Respekt, ihr Buben!

Elsbet

Wollt's Gott, er ging' und ließ' uns seinen Hut;
Es sollte drum nicht schlechter stehn ums Land!

Frießhard

(verscheucht sie)

Wollt ihr vom Platz! Verwünschtes Volk der Weiber!
1770 Wer fragt nach euch? Schickt eure Männer her,
Wenn sie der Mut sticht, dem Befehl zu trotzen.

(Weiber gehen. *Tell* mit der Armbrust tritt auf, den Knaben an der Hand führend. Sie gehen an dem Hut vorbei gegen die vordere Szene, ohne darauf zu achten.)

Walter

(zeigt nach dem Bannberg)

Vater, ist's wahr, daß auf dem Berge dort
Die Bäume bluten, wenn man einen Streich
Drauf führte mit der Axt?

Tell

Wer sagt das, Knabe?

Walter

1775 Der Meister Hirt erzählt's — Die Bäume seien
Gebannt, sagt er, und wer sie schädige,
Dem wachse seine Hand heraus zum Grabe.

Tell

Die Bäume sind gebannt, das ist die Wahrheit.
— Siehst du die Firnen dort, die weißen Hörner,
1780 Die hoch bis in den Himmel sich verlieren?

Walter

Das sind die Gletscher, die des Nachts so donnern
Und uns die Schlaglawinen niedersenden.

Tell

So ist's, und die Lawinen hätten längst
Den Flecken Altorf unter ihrer Last
1785 Verschüttet, wenn der Wald dort oben nicht
Als eine Landwehr sich dagegen stellte.

Walter

(nach einigem Besinnen)

Gibt's Länder, Vater, wo n i c h t Berge sind?

Tell

Wenn man hinuntersteigt von unsern Höhen,
Und immer tiefer steigt, den Strömen nach,
1790 Gelangt man in ein großes, ebnes Land,
Wo die Waldwasser nicht mehr brausend schäumen,
Die Flüsse ruhig und gemächlich ziehn;
Da sieht man frei nach allen Himmelsräumen,
Das Korn wächst dort in langen, schönen Auen,
1795 Und wie ein Garten ist das Land zu schauen.

Walter

Ei, Vater, warum steigen wir denn nicht
Geschwind hinab in dieses schöne Land,
Statt daß wir uns hier ängstigen und plagen?

Tell

Das Land ist schön und gütig wie der Himmel;
1800 Doch die's bebauen, s i e genießen nicht
Den Segen, den sie pflanzen.

Walter

Wohnen sie
Nicht frei, wie du, auf ihrem eignen Erbe?

Tell

Das Feld gehört dem Bischof und dem König.

Walter

So dürfen sie doch frei in Wäldern jagen?

Tell

1805 Dem Herrn gehört das Wild und das Gefieder.

Walter

Sie dürfen doch frei fischen in dem Strom?

Tell

Der Strom, das Meer, das Salz gehört dem König.

Walter

Wer ist der König denn, den alle fürchten?

Tell

Es ist der Eine, der sie schützt und nährt.

Walter

1810 Sie können sich nicht mutig selbst beschützen?

Tell

Dort darf der Nachbar nicht dem Nachbar trauen.

Walter

Vater, es wird mir eng im weiten Land;
Da wohn' ich lieber unter den Lawinen.

Tell

Ja, wohl ist's besser, Kind, die Gletscherberge
1815 Im Rücken haben als die bösen Menschen.

(Sie wollen vorübergehen.)

Walter

Ei, Vater, sieh den Hut dort auf der Stange!

Tell

Was kümmert uns der Hut? Komm, laß uns gehen!

(Indem er abgehen will, tritt ihm Frießhard mit vorgehaltener Pike
entgegen.)

Frießhard

In des Kaisers Namen! Haltet an und steht!

Tell

(greift in die Pike)

Was wollt Ihr? Warum haltet Ihr mich auf?

Frießhard

1820 Ihr habt's Mandat verletzt; Ihr müßt uns folgen.

Leuthold

Ihr habt dem Hut nicht Reverenz bewiesen.

Tell

Freund, laß mich gehen!

Frießhard

Fort, fort ins Gefängnis!

Walter

Den Vater ins Gefängnis! Hilfe! Hilfe!

(In die Szene rufend)

Herbei, ihr Männer, gute Leute, helft!
1825 Gewalt! Gewalt! Sie führen ihn gefangen.

(*Rösselmann, der Pfarrer*, und *Petermann, der Sigrist*, kommen herbei
mit drei andern Männern.)

Sigrist

Was gibt's?

Rösselmann

Was legst du Hand an diesen Mann?

Frießhard

Er ist ein Feind des Kaisers, ein Verräter!

Tell

(faßt ihn heftig)

Ein Verräter, ich!

Rösselmann

Du irrst dich, Freund! Das ist
Der Tell, ein Ehrenmann und guter Bürger.

Walter

(erblickt Walter Fürsten und eilt ihm entgegen)

1830 Großvater, hilf! Gewalt geschieht dem Vater.

Frießhard

Ins Gefängnis, fort!

Walter Fürst

(herbeieilend)

Ich leiste Bürgschaft, haltet!
— Um Gottes willen, Tell, was ist geschehen?

(*Melchtal* und *Stauffacher* kommen.)

Frießhard

Des Landvogts oberherrliche Gewalt
Verachtet er und will sie nicht erkennen.

Stauffacher

1835 Das hätt' der Tell getan?

Melchtal

Das lügst du, Bube!

Leuthold

Er hat dem Hut nicht Reverenz bewiesen.

Walter Fürst

Und darum soll er ins Gefängnis?　Freund,
Nimm meine Bürgschaft an und laß ihn ledig!

Frießhard

Bürg' du für dich und deinen eignen Leib!
1840　Wir tun, was unsers Amtes — Fort mit ihm!

Melchtal

(zu den Landleuten)

Nein, das ist schreiende Gewalt!　Ertragen wir's,
Daß man ihn fortführt, frech, vor unsern Augen?

Sigrist

Wir sind die Stärkern.　Freunde, duldet's nicht!
Wir haben einen Rücken an den andern!

Frießhard

1845　Wer widersetzt sich dem Befehl des Vogts?

Noch drei Landleute

(herbeieilend)

Wir helfen euch.　Was gibt's?　Schlagt sie zu Boden!

(*Hildegard*, *Mechthild* und *Elsbet* kommen zurück.)

Tell

Ich helfe mir schon selbst.　Geht, gute Leute!
Meint ihr, wenn ich die Kraft gebrauchen wollte,
Ich würde mich vor ihren Spießen fürchten?

Melchtal

(zu Frießhard)

1850　Wag's, ihn aus unsrer Mitte wegzuführen!

Walter Fürst und Stauffacher

Gelassen! Ruhig!

Frießhard

(schreit)

Aufruhr und Empörung!

(Man hört Jagdhörner.)

Weiber

Da kommt der Landvogt!

Frießhard

(erhebt die Stimme)

Meuterei! Empörung!

Stauffacher

Schrei, bis du berstest, Schurke!

Rösselmann und Melchtal

Willst du schweigen?

Frießhard

(ruft noch lauter)

Zu Hilf', zu Hilf' den Dienern des Gesetzes!

Walter Fürst

1855 Da ist der Vogt! Weh uns, was wird das werden!

(*Geßler* zu Pferd, den Falken auf der Faust, *Rudolf der Harras, Berta* und *Rudenz*, ein großes Gefolge von bewaffneten Knechten, welche einen Kreis von Piken um die ganze Szene schließen.)

Rudolf der Harras

Platz, Platz dem Landvogt!

Geßler

Treibt sie auseinander!
Was läuft das Volk zusammen? Wer ruft Hilfe?

(Allgemeine Stille)

Wer war's? Ich will es wissen.

(Zu Frießhard)

Du tritt vor!
Wer bist du, und was hältst du diesen Mann?

(Er gibt den Falken einem Diener.)

Frießhard

1860 Gestrenger Herr, ich bin dein Waffenknecht
Und wohlbestellter Wächter bei dem Hut.
Diesen Mann ergriff ich über frischer Tat,
Wie er dem Hut den Ehrengruß versagte.
Verhaften wollt' ich ihn, wie du befahlst,
1865 Und mit Gewalt will ihn das Volk entreißen.

Geßler

(nach einer Pause)

Verachtest du so deinen Kaiser, Tell,
Und m i c h , der hier an seiner Statt gebietet,
Daß du die Ehr' versagst dem Hut, den ich
Zur Prüfung des Gehorsams aufgehangen?
1870 Dein böses Trachten hast du mir verraten.

Tell

Verzeiht mir, lieber Herr! Aus Unbedacht,
Nicht aus Verachtung Eurer ist's geschehn.
Wär' ich besonnen, hieß' ich nicht der Tell.
Ich bitt' um Gnad', es soll nicht mehr begegnen.

Geßler

(nach einigem Stillschweigen)

1875 Du bist ein Meister auf der Armbrust, Tell,
Man sagt, du nehmst es auf mit jedem Schützen?

Walter Tell

Und das muß wahr sein, Herr, 'nen Apfel schießt
Der Vater dir vom Baum auf hundert Schritte.

Geßler

Ist das dein Knabe, Tell?

Tell

Ja, lieber Herr.

Geßler

1880 Hast du der Kinder mehr?

Tell

Zwei Knaben, Herr.

Geßler

Und welcher ist's, den du am meisten liebst?

Tell

Herr, beide sind sie mir gleich liebe Kinder.

Geßler

Nun, Tell! Weil du den Apfel triffst vom Baume
Auf hundert Schritt', so wirst du deine Kunst
1885 Vor mir bewähren müssen — Nimm die Armbrust —
Du hast sie gleich zur Hand — und mach' dich fertig,
Einen Apfel von des Knaben Kopf zu schießen —

Doch will ich raten, ziele gut, daß du
Den Apfel treffest auf den ersten Schuß;
1890 Denn fehlst du ihn, so ist dein Kopf verloren.

(Alle geben Zeichen des Schreckens.)

Tell

Herr — Welches Ungeheure sinnet Ihr
Mir an? — Ich soll vom Haupte meines Kindes —
— Nein, nein doch, lieber Herr, das kommt Euch nicht
Zu Sinn — Verhüt's der gnäd'ge Gott! — das könnt Ihr
1895 Im Ernst von einem Vater nicht begehren!

Geßler

Du wirst den Apfel schießen von dem Kopf
Des Knaben — Ich begehr's und will's.

Tell

Ich soll
Mit meiner Armbrust auf das liebe Haupt
Des eignen Kindes zielen? — Eher sterb' ich!

Geßler

1900 Du schießest oder stirbst m i t deinem Knaben.

Tell

Ich soll der Mörder werden meines Kinds!
Herr, Ihr habt keine Kinder — wisset nicht,
Was sich bewegt in eines Vaters Herzen.

Geßler

Ei, Tell, du bist ja plötzlich so besonnen!
1905 Man sagte mir, daß du ein Träumer seist
Und dich entfernst von andrer Menschen Weise.
Du liebst das Seltsame — drum hab' ich jetzt

Ein eigen Wagstück für dich ausgesucht,
Ein andrer wohl bedächte sich — d u drückst
1910 Die Augen zu und greifst es herzhaft an.

Berta

Scherzt nicht, o Herr, mit diesen armen Leuten!
Ihr seht sie bleich und zitternd stehn — So wenig
Sind sie Kurzweils gewohnt aus Eurem Munde.

Geßler

Wer sagt Euch, daß ich scherze?

(Greift nach einem Baumzweige, der über ihn herhängt)

Hier ist der Apfel.
1915 Man mache Raum — Er nehme seine Weite,
Wie's Brauch ist — Achtzig Schritte geb' ich ihm —
Nicht weniger noch mehr — Er rühmte sich,
Auf ihrer hundert seinen Mann zu treffen —
Jetzt, Schütze, triff und fehle nicht das Ziel!

Rudolf der Harras

1920 Gott, das wird ernsthaft — Falle nieder, Knabe,
Es gilt, und fleh' den Landvogt um dein Leben!

Walter Fürst

(beiseite zu Melchtal, der kaum seine Ungeduld bezwingt)

Haltet an Euch, ich fleh' Euch drum, bleibt ruhig!

Berta

(zum Landvogt)

Laßt es genug sein, Herr! Unmenschlich ist's,
Mit eines Vaters Angst also zu spielen.
1925 Wenn dieser arme Mann auch Leib und Leben
Verwirkt durch seine leichte Schuld, bei Gott!

Er hätte jetzt zehnfachen Tod empfunden.
Entlaßt ihn ungekränkt in seine Hütte,
Er hat Euch kennen lernen; dieser Stunde
1930 Wird er und seine Kindeskinder denken.

Geßler

Öffnet die Gasse! — Frisch! Was zauderst du?
Dein Leben ist verwirkt, ich kann dich töten;
Und sieh, ich lege gnädig dein Geschick
In deine eigne kunstgeübte Hand.
1935 Der kann nicht klagen über harten Spruch,
Den man zum Meister seines Schicksals macht.
Du rühmst dich deines sichern Blicks. Wohlan!
Hier gilt es, S c h ü t z e , deine Kunst zu zeigen;
Das Ziel ist würdig, und der Preis ist groß!
1940 Das Schwarze treffen in der Scheibe, d a s
Kann auch ein andrer; d e r ist mir der Meister,
Der seiner Kunst gewiß ist überall,
Dem's Herz nicht in die Hand tritt, noch ins Auge.

Walter Fürst

(wirft sich vor ihm nieder)

Herr Landvogt, wir erkennen Eure Hoheit;
1945 Doch lasset Gnad' vor Recht ergehen! Nehmt
Die Hälfte meiner Habe, nehmt sie ganz!
Nur dieses Gräßliche erlasset einem Vater!

Walter Tell

Großvater, knie nicht vor dem falschen Mann!
Sagt, wo ich hinstehn soll! Ich fürcht' mich nicht.
1950 Der Vater trifft den Vogel ja im Flug,
Er wird nicht fehlen auf das Herz des Kindes.

Stauffacher

Herr Landvogt, rührt Euch nicht des Kindes Unschuld?

Rösselmann

O denket, daß ein Gott im Himmel ist,
Dem Ihr müßt Rede stehn für Eure Taten!

Geßler

(zeigt auf den Knaben)

1955 Man bind' ihn an die Linde dort!

Walter Tell

Mich binden!
Nein, ich will nicht gebunden sein. Ich will
Still halten wie ein Lamm und auch nicht atmen.
Wenn ihr mich bindet, nein, so kann ich's nicht,
So werd' ich toben gegen meine Bande.

Rudolf der Harras

1960 Die Augen nur laß dir verbinden, Knabe!

Walter Tell

Warum die Augen? Denket Ihr, ich fürchte
Den Pfeil von Vaters Hand? — Ich will ihn fest
Erwarten und nicht zucken mit den Wimpern.
— Frisch, Vater, zeig's, daß du ein Schütze bist!
1965 Er glaubt dir's nicht, er denkt uns zu verderben —
Dem Wütrich zum Verdrusse schieß und triff!

(Er geht an die Linde, man legt ihm den Apfel auf.)

Melchtal

(zu den Landleuten)

Was? Soll der Frevel sich vor unsern Augen
Vollenden? Wozu haben wir geschworen?

Stauffacher

Es ist umsonst. Wir haben keine Waffen;
1970 Ihr seht den Wald von Lanzen um uns her.

Melchtal

O, hätten wir's mit frischer Tat vollendet!
Verzeih's Gott denen, die zum Aufschub rieten!

Geßler

(zum Tell)

Ans Werk! Man führt die Waffen nicht vergebens.
Gefährlich ist's, ein Mordgewehr zu tragen,
1975 Und auf den Schützen springt der Pfeil zurück.
Dies stolze Recht, das sich der Bauer nimmt,
Beleidiget den höchsten Herrn des Landes.
Gewaffnet sei niemand, als wer gebietet.
Freut's euch, den Pfeil zu führen und den Bogen,
1980 Wohl, so will ich das Ziel euch dazu geben.

Tell

(spannt die Armbrust und legt den Pfeil auf)

Öffnet die Gasse! Platz!

Stauffacher

Was, Tell? Ihr wolltet — Nimmermehr — Ihr zittert,
Die Hand erbebt Euch, Eure Knie wanken —

Tell

(läßt die Armbrust sinken)

Mir schwimmt es vor den Augen!

Weiber

Gott im Himmel!

Tell

(zum Landvogt)

1985 Erlasset mir den Schuß! Hier ist mein Herz!

(Er reißt die Brust auf.)

Ruft Eure Reisigen und stoßt mich nieder!

Geßler

Ich will dein Leben nicht, ich will den Schuß.
— Du kannst ja alles, Tell! An nichts verzagst du;
Das Steuerruder führst du wie den Bogen,
1990 Dich schreckt kein Sturm, wenn es zu retten gilt.
Jetzt, Retter, hilf dir selbst — du rettest alle!

(Tell steht in fürchterlichem Kampf, mit den Händen zuckend und die
rollenden Augen bald auf den Landvogt, bald zum Himmel gerichtet. — Plötzlich greift er in seinen Köcher, nimmt einen zweiten Pfeil
heraus und steckt ihn in seinen Goller. Der Landvogt bemerkt alle
diese Bewegungen.)

Walter Tell

(unter der Linde)

Vater, schieß zu! Ich fürcht' mich nicht.

Tell

Es muß!

(Er rafft sich zusammen und legt an.)

Rudenz

(der die ganze Zeit über in der heftigsten Spannung gestanden und mit
Gewalt an sich gehalten, tritt hervor)

Herr Landvogt, weiter werdet Ihr's nicht treiben,
Ihr werdet n i c h t — Es war nur eine Prüfung —
1995 Den Zweck habt Ihr erreicht — Zu weit getrieben,
Verfehlt die Strenge ihres weisen Zwecks,
Und allzustraff gespannt, zerspringt der Bogen.

Geßler

Ihr schweigt, bis man Euch aufruft!

Rudenz

                Ich w i l l reden!
Ich darf's! Des Königs Ehre ist mir heilig;
2000 Doch solches Regiment muß Haß erwerben.
Das ist des Königs Wille nicht — Ich darf's
Behaupten — Solche Grausamkeit verdient
Mein Volk nicht; dazu habt Ihr keine Vollmacht.

Geßler

Ha, Ihr erkühnt Euch!

Rudenz

              Ich hab' still geschwiegen
2005 Zu allen schweren Taten, die ich sah;
Mein sehend Auge hab' ich zugeschlossen,
Mein überschwellend und empörtes Herz
Hab' ich hinabgedrückt in meinen Busen.
Doch länger schweigen wär' Verrat zugleich
2010 An meinem Vaterland und an dem Kaiser.

Berta

(wirft sich zwischen ihn und den Landvogt)

O Gott, Ihr reizt den Wütenden noch mehr!

Rudenz

Mein Volk verließ ich, meinen Blutsverwandten
Entsagt' ich, alle Bande der Natur
Zerriß ich, um an Euch mich anzuschließen —
2015 Das Beste aller glaubt' ich zu befördern,
Da ich des Kaisers Macht befestigte —
Die Binde fällt von meinen Augen — Schaudernd

Seh' ich an einen Abgrund mich geführt —
Mein freies Urteil habt Ihr irr' geleitet,
2020 Mein redlich Herz verführt — Ich war daran,
Mein Volk in bester Meinung zu verderben.

Geßler

Verwegner, diese Sprache deinem Herrn?

Rudenz

Der Kaiser ist mein Herr, nicht Ihr — Frei bin ich
Wie Ihr geboren, und ich messe mich
2025 Mit Euch in jeder ritterlichen Tugend.
Und stündet Ihr nicht hier in Kaisers Namen,
Den ich verehre, selbst wo man ihn schändet,
Den Handschuh wärf' ich vor Euch hin, Ihr solltet
Nach ritterlichem Brauch mir Antwort geben.
2030 — Ja, winkt nur Euren Reisigen — Ich stehe
Nicht wehrlos da, wie d i e —

(Auf das Volk zeigend)

Ich hab' ein Schwert,
Und wer mir naht —

Stauffacher

(ruft)

Der Apfel ist gefallen!

(Indem sich alle nach dieser Seite gewendet, und Berta zwischen Rudenz
und den Landvogt sich geworfen, hat Tell den Pfeil abgedrückt.)

Rösselmann

Der Knabe lebt!

Viele Stimmen

Der Apfel ist getroffen!

(Walter Fürst schwankt und droht zu sinken, Berta hält ihn.)

Geßler

(erstaunt)

Er hat geschossen? Wie? Der Rasende!

Berta

2035 Der Knabe lebt! Kommt zu Euch, guter Vater!

Walter Tell

(kommt mit dem Apfel gesprungen)

Vater, hier ist der Apfel — Wußt' ich's ja,
Du würdest deinen Knaben nicht verletzen.

Tell

(stand mit vorgebogenem Leib, als wollt' er dem Pfeil folgen — die
Armbrust entsinkt seiner Hand — wie er den Knaben kommen sieht,
eilt er ihm mit ausgebreiteten Armen entgegen und hebt ihn mit
heftiger Inbrunst zu seinem Herzen hinauf; in dieser Stellung sinkt
er kraftlos zusammen. Alle stehen gerührt.)

Berta

O güt'ger Himmel!

Walter Fürst

(zu Vater und Sohn)

Kinder! meine Kinder!

Stauffacher

Gott sei gelobt.

Leuthold

Das war ein Schuß! Davon
2040 Wird man noch reden in den spätsten Zeiten.

Rudolf der Harras

Erzählen wird man von dem Schützen Tell,
Solang' die Berge stehn auf ihrem Grunde.

(Reicht dem Landvogt den Apfel)

Geßler

Bei Gott! der Apfel mitten durch geschossen!
Es war ein Meisterschuß, ich muß ihn loben.

Rösselmann

2045 Der Schuß war gut, doch wehe dem, der ihn
Dazu getrieben, daß er Gott versuchte!

Stauffacher

Kommt zu Euch, Tell, steht auf, Ihr habt Euch männlich
Gelöst, und frei könnt Ihr nach Hause gehen.

Rösselmann

Kommt, kommt und bringt der Mutter ihren Sohn!

(Sie wollen ihn wegführen.)

Geßler

2050 Tell, höre!

Tell

(kommt zurück)

Was befehlt Ihr, Herr?

Geßler

                              Du stecktest
Noch einen zweiten Pfeil zu dir — Ja, ja,
Ich sah es wohl — Was meintest du damit?

Tell

(verlegen)

Herr, das ist also bräuchlich bei den Schützen.

Geßler

Nein, Tell, die Antwort lass' ich dir nicht gelten;
2055 Es wird was anders wohl bedeutet haben.
Sag' mir die Wahrheit frisch und fröhlich, Tell;
Was es auch sei, dein Leben sichr' ich dir.
Wozu der zweite Pfeil?

Tell

Wohlan, o Herr,
Weil Ihr mich meines Lebens habt gesichert,
2060 So will ich Euch die Wahrheit gründlich sagen.

(Er zieht den Pfeil aus dem Goller und sieht den Landvogt mit einem furchtbaren Blick an.)

Mit diesem zweiten Pfeil durchschoß ich — E u c h ,
Wenn ich mein liebes Kind getroffen hätte,
Und Eurer — wahrlich! hätt' ich nicht gefehlt.

Geßler

Wohl, Tell! Des Lebens hab' ich dich gesichert,
2065 Ich gab mein Ritterwort, das will ich halten —
Doch weil ich deinen bösen Sinn erkannt,
Will ich dich führen lassen und verwahren,
Wo weder Mond noch Sonne dich bescheint,
Damit ich sicher sei vor deinen Pfeilen.
2070 Ergreift ihn, Knechte! Bindet ihn!

(Tell wird gebunden.)

Stauffacher

Wie, Herr!
So könntet Ihr an einem Manne handeln,
An dem sich Gottes Hand sichtbar verkündigt?

Geßler

Laß sehn, ob sie ihn zweimal retten wird.
— Man bring' ihn auf mein Schiff! Ich folge nach
2075 Sogleich, ich selbst will ihn nach Küßnacht führen.

Rösselmann

Das dürft Ihr nicht, das darf der Kaiser nicht,
Das widerstreitet unsern Freiheitsbriefen!

Geßler

Wo sind sie? Hat der Kaiser sie bestätigt?
Er hat sie nicht bestätigt — Diese Gunst
2080 Muß erst erworben werden durch Gehorsam.
Rebellen seid ihr alle gegen Kaisers
Gericht und nährt verwegene Empörung.
Ich kenn' euch alle — ich durchschau' euch ganz —
D e n nehm' ich jetzt heraus aus eurer Mitte,
2085 Doch alle seid ihr teilhaft seiner Schuld.
Wer klug ist, lerne schweigen und gehorchen.

(Er entfernt sich, Berta, Rudenz, Harras und Knechte folgen, Frießhard
und Leuthold bleiben zurück.)

Walter Fürst

(in heftigem Schmerz)

Es ist vorbei; er hat's beschlossen, mich
Mit meinem ganzen Hause zu verderben!

Stauffacher

(zum Tell)

O, warum mußtet Ihr den Wütrich reizen!

Tell

2090 Bezwinge sich, wer meinen Schmerz gefühlt!

Stauffacher

O, nun ist alles, alles hin! Mit Euch
Sind wir gefesselt alle und gebunden!

Landleute

(umringen den Tell)

Mit Euch geht unser letzter Trost dahin!

Leuthold

(nähert sich)

Tell, es erbarmt mich — doch ich muß gehorchen.

Tell

2095 Lebt wohl!

Walter Tell

(sich mit heftigem Schmerz an ihn schmiegend)

O Vater! Vater! Lieber Vater!

Tell

(hebt die Arme zum Himmel)

Dort droben ist dein Vater! Den ruf an!

Stauffacher

Tell, sag' ich Eurem Weibe nichts von Euch?

Tell

(hebt den Knaben mit Inbrunst an seine Brust)

Der Knab' ist unverletzt; mir wird Gott helfen.

(Reißt sich schnell los und folgt den Waffenknechten)

VIERTER AUFZUG

ERSTE SZENE

(Östliches Ufer des Vierwaldstättersees. Die seltsam gestalteten schroffen Felsen im Westen schließen den Prospekt. Der See ist bewegt, heftiges Rauschen und Tosen, dazwischen Blitze und Donnerschläge. *Kunz von Gersau. Fischer* und *Fischerknabe.*)

Kunz

Ich sah's mit Augen an, Ihr könnt mir's glauben;
2100 's ist alles so geschehn, wie ich Euch sagte.

Fischer

Der Tell gefangen abgeführt nach Küßnacht,
Der beste Mann im Land, der bravste Arm,
Wenn's einmal gelten sollte für die Freiheit.

Kunz

Der Landvogt führt ihn selbst den See herauf;
2105 Sie waren eben dran, sich einzuschiffen,
Als ich von Flüelen abfuhr; doch der Sturm,
Der eben jetzt im Anzug ist, und der
Auch mich gezwungen, eilends hier zu landen,
Mag ihre Abfahrt wohl verhindert haben.

Fischer

2110 Der Tell in Fesseln, in des Vogts Gewalt!
O, glaubt, er wird ihn tief genug vergraben,
Daß er des Tages Licht nicht wieder sieht!
Denn fürchten muß er die gerechte Rache
Des freien Mannes, den er schwer gereizt.

Kunz

2115 Der Altlandammann auch, der edle Herr
Von Attinghausen, sagt man, lieg' am Tode.

Fischer

So bricht der letzte Anker unsrer Hoffnung!
Der war es noch allein, der seine Stimme
Erheben durfte für des Volkes Rechte.

Kunz

2120 Der Sturm nimmt überhand. Gehabt Euch wohl!
Ich nehme Herberg' in dem Dorf; denn heut'
Ist doch an keine Abfahrt mehr zu denken.

(Geht ab)

Fischer

Der Tell gefangen, und der Freiherr tot!
Erheb' die freche Stirne, Tyrannei,
2125 Wirf alle Scham hinweg! Der Mund der Wahrheit
Ist stumm, das seh'nde Auge ist geblendet,
Der Arm, der retten sollte, ist gefesselt!

Knabe

Es hagelt schwer. Kommt in die Hütte, Vater,
Es ist nicht kommlich, hier im Freien hausen.

Fischer

2130 Raset, ihr Winde! Flammt herab, ihr Blitze!
Ihr Wolken, berstet! Gießt herunter, Ströme
Des Himmels, und ersäuft das Land! Zerstört
Im Keim die ungeborenen Geschlechter!
Ihr wilden Elemente, werdet Herr!
2135 Ihr Bären, kommt, ihr alten Wölfe wieder
Der großen Wüste, euch gehört das Land!
Wer wird hier leben wollen ohne Freiheit!

Knabe

Hört, wie der Abgrund tost, der Wirbel brüllt!
So hat's noch nie gerast in diesem Schlunde!

Fischer

2140 Zu zielen auf des eignen Kindes Haupt,
Solches ward keinem Vater noch geboten!
Und die Natur soll nicht in wildem Grimm
Sich drob empören? — O, mich soll's nicht wundern,
Wenn sich die Felsen bücken in den See,
2145 Wenn jene Zacken, jene Eisestürme,
Die nie auftauten seit dem Schöpfungstag,
Von ihren hohen Kulmen niederschmelzen,
Wenn die Berge brechen, wenn die alten Klüfte
Einstürzen, eine zweite Sündflut alle
2150 Wohnstätten der Lebendigen verschlingt!

(Man hört läuten.)

Knabe

Hört Ihr, sie läuten droben auf dem Berg.
Gewiß hat man ein Schiff in Not gesehn
Und zieht die Glocke, daß gebetet werde.

(Steigt auf eine Anhöhe)

Fischer

Wehe dem Fahrzeug, das, jetzt unterwegs,
2155 In dieser furchtbarn Wiege wird gewiegt!
Hier ist das Steuer unnütz und der Steurer;
Der Sturm ist Meister, Wind und Welle spielen
Ball mit dem Menschen — Da ist nah und fern
Kein Busen, der ihm freundlich Schutz gewährte.
2160 Handlos und schroff ansteigend starren ihm
Die Felsen, die unwirtlichen, entgegen
Und weisen ihm nur ihre steinern schroffe Brust.

Knabe

(deutet links)

Vater, ein Schiff! Es kommt von Flüelen her.

Fischer

Gott helf' den armen Leuten! Wenn der Sturm
2165 In dieser Wasserkluft sich erst verfangen,
Dann rast er um sich mit des Raubtiers Angst,
Das an des Gitters Eisenstäbe schlägt;
Die Pforte sucht er heulend sich vergebens,
Denn ringsum schränken ihn die Felsen ein,
2170 Die himmelhoch den engen Paß vermauern.

(Er steigt auf die Anhöhe.)

Knabe

Es ist das Herrenschiff von Uri, Vater,
Ich kenn's am roten Dach und an der Fahne.

Fischer

Gerichte Gottes! Ja, er ist es selbst,
Der Landvogt, der da fährt — Dort schifft er hin
2175 Und führt im Schiffe sein Verbrechen mit!
Schnell hat der Arm des Rächers ihn gefunden;
Jetzt kennt er über sich den stärkern Herrn.
Diese Wellen geben nicht auf seine Stimme,
Diese Felsen bücken ihre Häupter nicht
2180 Vor seinem Hute — Knabe, bete nicht!
Greif nicht dem Richter in den Arm!

Knabe

Ich bete für den Landvogt nicht — Ich bete
Für den Tell, der auf dem Schiff sich mit befindet.

Fischer

O Unvernunft des blinden Elements!
2185 Mußt du, um e i n e n Schuldigen zu treffen,
Das Schiff mitsamt dem Steuermann verderben!

Knabe

Sieh, sieh, sie waren glücklich schon vorbei
Am B u g g i s g r a t ; doch die Gewalt des Sturms,
Der von dem T e u f e l s m ü n s t e r widerprallt,
2190 Wirft sie zum großen A x e n b e r g zurück.
— Ich seh' sie nicht mehr.

Fischer

       Dort ist das H a c k m e s s e r ,
Wo schon der Schiffe mehrere gebrochen.
Wenn sie nicht weislich dort vorüberlenken,
So wird das Schiff zerschmettert an der Fluh,
2195 Die sich gähstotzig absenkt in die Tiefe.
— Sie haben einen guten Steuermann
An Bord: könnt' einer retten, wär's der Tell;
Doch dem sind Arm' und Hände ja gefesselt.

(*Wilhelm Tell* mit der Armbrust. Er kommt mit raschen Schritten,
blickt erstaunt umher und zeigt die heftigste Bewegung. Wenn er
mitten auf der Szene ist, wirft er sich nieder, die Hände zu der Erde
und dann zum Himmel ausbreitend.)

Knabe

(bemerkt ihn)

Sieh, Vater, wer der Mann ist, der dort kniet!

Fischer

2200 Er faßt die Erde an mit seinen Händen
Und scheint wie außer sich zu sein.

Knabe

(kommt vorwärts)

Was seh' ich! Vater! Vater, kommt und seht!

Fischer

(nähert sich)

Wer ist es? — Gott im Himmel! Was! der Tell?
Wie kommt Ihr hieher? Redet!

Knabe

Wart Ihr nicht

2205 Dort auf dem Schiff gefangen und gebunden?

Fischer

Ihr wurdet nicht nach Küßnacht abgeführt?

Tell

(steht auf)

Ich bin befreit.

Fischer und Knabe

Befreit! O Wunder Gottes!

Knabe

Wo kommt Ihr her?

Tell

Dort aus dem Schiffe.

Fischer

Was?

Knabe

(zugleich)

Wo ist der Landvogt?

Tell

Auf den Wellen treibt er.

Fischer

2210 Ist's möglich? Aber I h r ? wie seid Ihr hier?
Seid Euren Banden und dem Sturm entkommen?

Tell

Durch Gottes gnäd'ge Fürsehung — Hört an!

Fischer und Knabe

O redet, redet!

Tell

Was in Altorf sich
Begeben, wißt Ihr's?

Fischer

Alles weiß ich, redet!

Tell

2215 Daß mich der Landvogt fahen ließ und binden,
Nach seiner Burg zu Küßnacht wollte führen?

Fischer

Und sich mit Euch zu Flüelen eingeschifft!
Wir wissen alles. Sprecht, wie Ihr entkommen!

Tell

Ich lag im Schiff, mit Stricken fest gebunden,
2220 Wehrlos, ein aufgegebner Mann — Nicht hofft' ich,
Das frohe Licht der Sonne mehr zu sehn,
Der Gattin und der Kinder liebes Antlitz,
Und trostlos blickt' ich in die Wasserwüste —

Fischer

O armer Mann!

Tell

So fuhren wir dahin,
2225 Der Vogt, Rudolf der Harras und die Knechte.
Mein Köcher aber mit der Armbrust lag
Am hintern Gransen bei dem Steuerruder.
Und als wir an die Ecke jetzt gelangt
Beim kleinen Axen, da verhängt' es Gott,
2230 Daß solch ein grausam mördrisch Ungewitter
Gählings herfürbrach aus des Gotthards Schlünden,
Daß allen Ruderern das Herz entsank,
Und meinten alle, elend zu ertrinken.
Da hört' ich's, wie der Diener einer sich
2235 Zum Landvogt wendet' und die Worte sprach:
„Ihr sehet Eure Not und unsre, Herr,
Und daß wir all' am Rand des Todes schweben —
Die Steuerleute aber wissen sich
Für großer Furcht nicht Rat und sind des Fahrens
2240 Nicht wohl berichtet — Nun aber ist der Tell
Ein starker Mann und weiß ein Schiff zu steuern.
Wie, wenn wir sein jetzt brauchten in der Not?"
Da sprach der Vogt zu mir: „Tell, wenn du dir's
Getrautest, uns zu helfen aus dem Sturm,
2245 So möcht' ich dich der Bande wohl entled'gen."
Ich aber sprach: „Ja, Herr, mit Gottes Hilfe
Getrau' ich mir's und helf' uns wohl hiedannen."
So ward ich meiner Bande los und stand
Am Steuerruder und fuhr redlich hin;
2250 Doch schielt' ich seitwärts, wo mein Schießzeug lag,
Und an dem Ufer merkt' ich scharf umher,
Wo sich ein Vorteil auftät' zum Entspringen.
Und wie ich eines Felsenriffs gewahre,
Das abgeplattet vorsprang in den See —

Fischer

2255 Ich kenn's, es ist am Fuß des großen Axen,
Doch nicht für möglich acht' ich's — so gar steil
Geht's an — vom Schiff es springend abzureichen —

Tell

Schrie ich den Knechten, handlich zuzugehn,
Bis daß wir vor die Felsenplatte kämen,
2260 Dort, rief ich, sei das Ärgste überstanden —
Und als wir sie frisch rudernd bald erreicht,
Fleh' ich die Gnade Gottes an und drücke,
Mit allen Leibeskräften angestemmt,
Den hintern Gransen an die Felswand hin.
2265 Jetzt, schnell mein Schießzeug fassend, schwing' ich selbst
Hochspringend auf die Platte mich hinauf,
Und mit gewalt'gem Fußstoß hinter mich
Schleudr' ich das Schifflein in den Schlund der Wasser —
Dort mag's, wie Gott will, auf den Wellen treiben!
2270 So bin ich hier, gerettet aus des Sturms
Gewalt und aus der schlimmeren der Menschen.

Fischer

Tell, Tell! ein sichtbar Wunder hat der Herr
An Euch getan; kaum glaub' ich's meinen Sinnen —
Doch saget! Wo gedenket Ihr jetzt hin?
2275 Denn Sicherheit ist nicht für Euch, wofern
Der Landvogt lebend diesem Sturm entkommt.

Tell

Ich hört' ihn sagen, da ich noch im Schiff
Gebunden lag, er woll' bei Brunnen landen,
Und über Schwyz nach seiner Burg mich führen.

Fischer

2280 Will er den Weg dahin zu Lande nehmen?

Tell

Er denkt's.

Fischer

O, so verbergt Euch ohne Säumen!
Nicht zweimal hilft Euch Gott aus seiner Hand.

Tell

Nennt mir den nächsten Weg nach Arth und Küßnacht.

Fischer

Die offne Straße zieht sich über Steinen;
2285 Doch einen kürzern Weg und heimlichern
Kann Euch mein Knabe über Lowerz führen.

Tell

(gibt ihm die Hand)

Gott lohn' Euch Eure Guttat! Lebet wohl!

(Geht und kehrt wieder um)

— Habt Ihr nicht auch im Rütli mitgeschworen?
Mir deucht, man nannt' Euch mir —

Fischer

Ich war dabei
2290 Und hab' den Eid des Bundes mit beschworen.

Tell

So eilt nach Bürglen, tut die Lieb' mir an!
Mein Weib verzagt um mich; verkündet ihr,
Daß ich gerettet sei und wohl geborgen.

Fischer

Doch wohin, sag' ich ihr, daß Ihr geflohn?

Tell

2295 Ihr werdet meinen Schwäher bei ihr finden
Und andre, die im Rütli mitgeschworen —
Sie sollen wacker sein und gutes Muts:
Der Tell sei frei und seines Armes mächtig;
Bald werden sie ein Weitres von mir hören.

Fischer

2300 Was habt Ihr im Gemüt? Endeckt mir's frei!

Tell

Ist es g e t a n , wird's auch zur Rede kommen.

(Geht ab)

Fischer

Zeig' ihm den Weg, Jenni — Gott steh' ihm bei!
Er führt's zum Ziel, was er auch unternommen.

(Geht ab)

ZWEITE SZENE

(Edelhof zu Attinghausen. *Der Freiherr*, in einem Armsessel, sterbend.
Walter Fürst, Stauffacher, Melchtal und *Baumgarten* um ihn beschäftigt.
Walter Tell, kniend vor dem Sterbenden.)

Walter Fürst

Es ist vorbei mit ihm, er ist hinüber.

Stauffacher

2305 Er liegt nicht wie ein Toter — Seht, die Feder
Auf seinen Lippen regt sich! Ruhig ist
Sein Schlaf, und friedlich lächeln seine Züge.

(Baumgarten geht an die Türe und spricht mit jemand.)

Walter Fürst
(zu Baumgarten)

Wer ist's?

Baumgarten
(kommt zurück)

Es ist Frau Hedwig, Eure Tochter;
Sie will Euch sprechen, will den Knaben sehn.

(Walter Tell richtet sich auf.)

Walter Fürst

2310 Kann ich sie trösten? Hab' ich selber Trost?
Häuft alles Leiden sich auf meinem Haupt?

Hedwig
(hereindringend)

Wo ist mein Kind? Laßt mich, ich muß es sehn —

Stauffacher

Faßt Euch! Bedenkt, daß Ihr im Haus des Todes —

Hedwig
(stürzt auf den Knaben)

Mein Wälti! O, er lebt mir!

Walter Tell
(hängt an ihr)

Arme Mutter!

Hedwig

2315 Ist's auch gewiß? Bist du mir unverletzt?
(Betrachtet ihn mit ängstlicher Sorgfalt)

Und ist es möglich? Konnt' er auf dich zielen?
W i e konnt' er's? O, er hat kein Herz — Er konnte
Den Pfeil abdrücken auf sein eignes Kind!

Walter Fürst

Er tat's mit Angst, mit schmerzzerrißner Seele;
2320 Gezwungen tat er's, denn es galt das Leben.

Hedwig

O, hätt' er eines Vaters Herz, eh' er's
Getan, er wäre tausendmal gestorben!

Stauffacher

Ihr solltet Gottes gnäd'ge Schickung preisen,
Die es so gut gelenkt —

Hedwig

Kann ich vergessen,
2325 Wie's hätte kommen k ö n n e n ? — Gott des Himmels!
Und lebt' ich achtzig Jahr' — Ich seh' den Knaben ewig
Gebunden stehn, den Vater auf ihn zielen,
Und ewig fliegt der Pfeil mir in das Herz.

Melchtal

Frau, wüßtet Ihr, wie ihn der Vogt gereizt!

Hedwig

2330 O rohes Herz der Männer! Wenn ihr Stolz
Beleidigt wird, dann achten sie nichts mehr;
Sie setzen in der blinden Wut des Spiels
Das Haupt des Kindes und das Herz der Mutter!

Baumgarten

Ist Eures Mannes Los nicht hart genug,
2335 Daß Ihr mit schwerem Tadel ihn noch kränkt?
Für s e i n e Leiden habt Ihr kein Gefühl?

Hedwig

(kehrt sich nach ihm um und sieht ihn mit einem großen Blicke an)

Hast du nur Tränen für des Freundes Unglück?
— Wo waret ihr, da man den Trefflichen
In Bande schlug? Wo war d a eure Hilfe?
2340 Ihr sahet zu, ihr ließt das Gräßliche geschehn;
Geduldig littet ihr's, daß man den Freund
Aus eurer Mitte führte — Hat der Tell
Auch so an euch gehandelt? Stand er auch
Bedauernd da, als hinter dir die Reiter
2345 Des Landvogts drangen, als der wüt'ge See
Vor dir erbrauste? Nicht mit müß'gen Tränen
Beklagt' er dich: in den Nachen sprang er, Weib
Und Kind vergaß er und befreite dich —

Walter Fürst

Was konnten wir zu seiner Rettung wagen,
2350 Die kleine Zahl, die unbewaffnet war!

Hedwig

(wirft sich an seine Brust)

O Vater! Und auch du hast ihn verloren!
Das Land, wir alle haben ihn verloren!
Uns allen fehlt er, ach, wir fehlen ihm!
Gott rette seine Seele vor Verzweiflung.
2355 Zu ihm hinab ins öde Burgverließ
Dringt keines Freundes Trost — Wenn er erkrankte!
Ach, in des Kerkers feuchter Finsternis
Muß er erkranken — Wie die Alpenrose
Bleicht und verkümmert in der Sumpfesluft,
2360 So ist für ihn kein Leben als im Licht
Der Sonne, in dem Balsamstrom der Lüfte.
Gefangen! Er! Sein Atem ist die Freiheit;
Er kann nicht leben in dem Hauch der Grüfte.

Stauffacher

Beruhigt Euch! Wir alle wollen handeln,
2365 Um seinen Kerker aufzutun.

Hedwig

Was könnt i h r schaffen ohne ihn? — Solang'
Der Tell noch frei war, ja, d a war noch Hoffnung,
Da hatte noch die Unschuld einen Freund,
Da hatte einen Helfer der Verfolgte;
2370 Euch alle rettete der Tell — Ihr alle
Zusammen könnt nicht s e i n e Fesseln lösen!

(Der Freiherr erwacht.)

Baumgarten

Er regt sich, still!

Attinghausen

(sich aufrichtend)

Wo ist er?

Stauffacher

Wer?

Attinghausen

Er fehlt mir,
Verläßt mich in dem letzten Augenblick!

Stauffacher

Er meint den Junker — Schickte man nach ihm?

Walter Fürst

2375 Es ist nach ihm gesendet — Tröstet Euch!
Er hat sein Herz gefunden, er ist unser.

Attinghausen

Hat er gesprochen für sein Vaterland?

Stauffacher

Mit Heldenkühnheit.

Attinghausen

Warum kommt er nicht,
Um meinen letzten Segen zu empfangen?
2380 Ich fühle, daß es schleunig mit mir endet.

Stauffacher

Nicht also, edler Herr! Der kurze Schlaf
Hat Euch erquickt, und hell ist Euer Blick.

Attinghausen

Der Schmerz ist Leben, er verließ mich auch;
Das Leiden ist, so wie die Hoffnung, aus.

(Er bemerkt den Knaben.)

2385 Wer ist der Knabe?

Walter Fürst

Segnet ihn, o Herr!
Er ist mein Enkel und ist vaterlos.

(Hedwig sinkt mit dem Knaben vor dem Sterbenden nieder.)

Attinghausen

Und vaterlos lass' ich euch alle, alle
Zurück — Weh mir, daß meine letzten Blicke
Den Untergang des Vaterlands gesehn!
2390 Mußt' ich des Lebens höchstes Maß erreichen,
Um ganz mit allen Hoffnungen zu sterben!

Stauffacher

(zu Walter Fürst)

Soll er in diesem finstern Kummer scheiden?
Erhellen wir ihm nicht die letzte Stunde
Mit schönem Strahl der Hoffnung? — Edler Freiherr!
2395 Erhebet Euren Geist! Wir sind nicht ganz
Verlassen, sind nicht rettungslos verloren.

Attinghausen

Wer soll euch retten?

Walter Fürst

Wir uns selbst. Vernehmt!
Es haben die drei Lande sich das Wort
Gegeben, die Tyrannen zu verjagen.
2400 Geschlossen ist der Bund; ein heil'ger Schwur
Verbindet uns. Es wird gehandelt werden,
Eh' noch das Jahr den neuen Kreis beginnt.
Euer Staub wird ruhn in einem freien Lande.

Attinghausen

O, saget mir! Geschlossen ist der Bund?

Melchtal

2405 Am gleichen Tage werden alle drei
Waldstätte sich erheben. Alles ist
Bereit, und das Geheimnis wohlbewahrt
Bis jetzt, obgleich viel' Hunderte es teilen.
Hohl ist der Boden unter den Tyrannen,
2410 Die Tage ihrer Herrschaft sind gezählt,
Und bald ist ihre Spur nicht mehr zu finden.

Attinghausen

Die festen Burgen aber in den Landen?

Melchtal

Sie fallen alle an dem gleichen Tag.

Attinghausen

Und sind die Edeln dieses Bunds teilhaftig?

Stauffacher

2415 Wir harren ihres Beistands, wenn es gilt;
Jetzt aber hat der Landmann nur geschworen.

Attinghausen

(richtet sich langsam in die Höhe, mit großem Erstaunen)

Hat sich der Landmann solcher Tat verwogen,
Aus eignem Mittel, ohne Hilf' der Edeln,
Hat er der eignen Kraft so viel vertraut —
2420 Ja, dann bedarf es unserer nicht mehr,
Getröstet können wir zu Grabe steigen,
Es lebt n a c h uns — durch andre Kräfte will
Das Herrliche der Menschheit sich erhalten.

(Er legt seine Hand auf das Haupt des Kindes, das vor ihm auf den Knien liegt.)

Aus diesem Haupte, wo der Apfel lag,
2425 Wird euch die neue, beßre Freiheit grünen;
Das Alte stürzt, es ändert sich die Zeit,
Und neues Leben blüht aus den Ruinen.

Stauffacher

(zu Walter Fürst)

Seht, welcher Glanz sich um sein Aug' ergießt!
Das ist nicht das Erlöschen der Natur,
2430 Das ist der Strahl schon eines neuen Lebens.

Attinghausen

Der Adel steigt von seinen alten Burgen
Und schwört den Städten seinen Bürgereid;

Im Ü c h t l a n d schon, im T h u r g a u hat's begonnen,
Die edle B e r n erhebt ihr herrschend Haupt,
2435 F r e i b u r g ist eine sichre Burg der Freien,
Die rege Z ü r i c h waffnet ihre Zünfte
Zum kriegerischen Heer — Es bricht die Macht
Der Könige sich an ihren ew'gen Wällen —

(Er spricht das Folgende mit dem Ton eines Sehers — seine Rede steigt
bis zur Begeisterung.)

Die Fürsten seh' ich und die edeln Herrn
2440 In Harnischen herangezogen kommen,
Ein harmlos Volk von Hirten zu bekriegen.
Auf Tod und Leben wird gekämpft, und herrlich
Wird mancher Paß durch blutige Entscheidung.
Der Landmann stürzt sich mit der nackten Brust,
2445 Ein freies Opfer, in die Schar der Lanzen!
Er bricht sie, und des Adels Blüte fällt,
Es hebt die Freiheit siegend ihre Fahne.

(Walter Fürsts und Stauffachers Hände fassend)

Drum haltet fest zusammen — fest und ewig —
Kein Ort der Freiheit sei dem andern fremd —
2450 Hochwachten stellet aus auf euren Bergen,
Daß sich der Bund zum Bunde rasch versammle —
Seid einig — einig — einig —

(Er fällt in das Kissen zurück — seine Hände halten entseelt noch die
andern gefaßt. Fürst und Stauffacher betrachten ihn noch eine
Zeitlang schweigend; dann treten sie hinweg, jeder seinem Schmerz
überlassen. Unterdessen sind die Knechte still hereingedrungen, sie
nähern sich mit Zeichen eines stillern oder heftigern Schmerzens, einige
knien bei ihm nieder und weinen auf seine Hand; während dieser
stummen Szene wird die Burgglocke geläutet. *Rudenz* zu den *Vorigen*.)

Rudenz

(rasch eintretend)

Lebt er? O saget, kann er mich noch hören?

Walter Fürst

(deutet hin mit weggewandtem Gesicht)

I h r seid jetzt unser Lehensherr und Schirmer,
2455 Und dieses Schloß hat einen andern Namen.

Rudenz

(erblickt den Leichnam und steht von heftigem Schmerz ergriffen)

O güt'ger Gott! — Kommt meine Reu' zu spät?
Konnt' er nicht wen'ge Pulse länger leben,
Um mein geändert Herz zu sehn?
Verachtet hab' ich seine treue Stimme,
2460 Da er noch wandelte im Licht — Er ist
Dahin, ist fort auf immerdar und läßt mir
Die schwere, unbezahlte Schuld! — O saget!
Schied er dahin im Unmut gegen mich?

Stauffacher

Er hörte sterbend noch, was Ihr getan,
2465 Und segnete den Mut, mit dem Ihr spracht!

Rudenz

(kniet an dem Toten nieder)

Ja, heil'ge Reste eines teuren Mannes!
Entseelter Leichnam! Hier gelob' ich dir's
In deine kalte Totenhand — Zerrissen
Hab' ich auf ewig alle fremden Bande;
2470 Zurückgegeben bin ich meinem Volk;
Ein Schweizer bin ich, und ich will es sein
Von ganzer Seele — —

(Aufstehend)

Trauert um den Freund,
Den Vater aller, doch verzaget nicht!
Nicht bloß sein Erbe ist mir zugefallen,

2475 Es steigt sein Herz, sein Geist auf mich herab,
Und leisten soll euch meine frische Jugend,
Was euch sein greises Alter schuldig blieb.
— Ehrwürd'ger Vater, gebt mir Eure Hand!
Gebt mir die Eurige! Melchtal, auch Ihr!
2480 Bedenkt Euch nicht! O, wendet Euch nicht weg!
Empfanget meinen Schwur und mein Gelübde!

Walter Fürst

Gebt ihm die Hand! Sein wiederkehrend Herz
Verdient Vertraun.

Melchtal

Ihr habt den Landmann nichts geachtet.
Sprecht, wessen soll man sich zu Euch versehn?

Rudenz

2485 O, denket nicht des Irrtums meiner Jugend!

Stauffacher

(zu Melchtal)

„Seid einig!" war das letzte Wort des Vaters.
Gedenket dessen!

Melchtal

Hier ist meine Hand!
Des Bauern Handschlag, edler Herr, ist auch
Ein Manneswort! Was ist der Ritter ohne uns?
2490 Und unser Stand ist älter als der Eure.

Rudenz

Ich ehr' ihn, und mein Schwert soll ihn beschützen.

Melchtal

D e r Arm, Herr Freiherr, der die harte Erde
Sich unterwirft und ihren Schoß befruchtet,
Kann auch des Mannes Brust beschützen.

Rudenz

                                          Ihr
2495 Sollt m e i n e Brust, ich will die E u r e schützen,
So sind wir einer durch den andern stark.
— Doch wozu reden, da das Vaterland
Ein Raub noch ist der fremden Tyrannei?
Wenn erst der Boden rein ist von dem Feind,
2500 Dann wollen wir's in Frieden schon vergleichen.

(Nachdem er einen Augenblick innegehalten)

Ihr schweigt? Ihr habt mir nichts zu sagen? Wie?
Verdien' ich's noch nicht, daß ihr mir vertraut?
So muß ich wider euren Willen mich
In das Geheimnis eures Bundes drängen.
2505 Ihr habt getagt — geschworen auf dem Rütli —
Ich weiß — weiß alles, was ihr dort verhandelt,
Und was mir nicht von euch vertrauet ward,
Ich hab's bewahrt gleichwie ein heilig Pfand.
Nie war ich meines Landes Feind, glaubt mir,
2510 Und niemals hätt' ich gegen euch gehandelt.
— Doch übel tatet ihr, es zu verschieben;
Die Stunde dringt, und rascher Tat bedarf's —
Der Tell ward schon das Opfer eures Säumens —

Stauffacher

Das Christfest abzuwarten, schwuren wir.

Rudenz

2515 Ich war nicht dort, ich hab' nicht mitgeschworen.
Wartet ihr ab, ich handle.

Melchtal

Was? Ihr wolltet —

Rudenz

Des Landes Vätern zähl' ich mich jetzt bei,
Und meine erste Pflicht ist, euch zu schützen.

Walter Fürst

Der Erde diesen teuren Staub zu geben,
2520 Ist Eure nächste Pflicht und heiligste.

Rudenz

Wenn wir das Land befreit, dann legen wir
Den frischen Kranz des Siegs ihm auf die Bahre.
— O Freunde! Eure Sache nicht allein,
Ich habe meine eigne auszufechten
2525 Mit dem Tyrannen — Hört und wißt! Verschwunden
Ist meine Berta, heimlich weggeraubt,
Mit kecker Freveltat aus unsrer Mitte!

Stauffacher

Solcher Gewalttat hätte der Tyrann
Wider die freie Edle sich verwogen?

Rudenz

2530 O meine Freunde! Euch versprach ich Hilfe,
Und ich zuerst muß sie von euch erflehn.
Geraubt, entrissen ist mir die Geliebte.
Wer weiß, wo sie der Wütende verbirgt,
Welcher Gewalt sie frevelnd sich erkühnen,
2535 Ihr Herz zu zwingen zum verhaßten Band!
Verlaßt mich nicht, o helft mir sie erretten —
Sie liebt euch, o sie hat's verdient um's Land,
Daß alle Arme sich für sie bewaffnen —

Walter Fürst

Was wollt Ihr unternehmen?

Rudenz

Weiß ich's? Ach!
2540 In dieser Nacht, die ihr Geschick umhüllt,
In dieses Zweifels ungeheurer Angst,
Wo ich nichts Festes zu erfassen weiß,
Ist mir nur dieses in der Seele klar:
Unter den Trümmern der Tyrannenmacht
2545 Allein kann sie hervorgegraben werden;
Die Festen alle müssen wir bezwingen,
Ob wir vielleicht in ihren Kerker dringen.

Melchtal

Kommt, führt uns an! Wir folgen Euch. Warum
Bis morgen sparen, was wir heut' vermögen?
2550 Frei war der Tell, als wir im Rütli schwuren;
Das Ungeheure war noch nicht geschehen.
Es bringt die Zeit ein anderes Gesetz;
Wer ist so feig, der jetzt noch könnte zagen!

Rudenz

(zu Stauffacher und Walter Fürst)

Indes bewaffnet und zum Werk bereit,
2555 Erwartet ihr der Berge Feuerzeichen;
Denn schneller, als ein Botensegel fliegt,
Soll euch die Botschaft unsers Siegs erreichen,
Und seht ihr leuchten die willkommnen Flammen,
Dann auf die Feinde stürzt wie Wetters Strahl
2560 Und brecht den Bau der Tyrannei zusammen!

(Gehen ab)

DRITTE SZENE

(Die hohle Gasse bei Küßnacht. Man steigt von hinten zwischen Felsen herunter, und die Wanderer werden, ehe sie auf der Szene erscheinen, schon von der Höhe gesehen. Felsen umschließen die ganze Szene; auf einem der vordersten ist ein Vorsprung, mit Gesträuch bewachsen.)

Tell

(tritt auf mit der Armbrust)

Durch diese hohle Gasse muß er kommen;
Es führt kein andrer Weg nach Küßnacht — Hier
Vollend' ich's — Die Gelegenheit ist günstig.
Dort der Holunderstrauch verbirgt mich ihm,
2565 Von dort herab kann ihn mein Pfeil erlangen;
Des Weges Enge wehret den Verfolgern.
Mach' deine Rechnung mit dem Himmel, Vogt!
Fort mußt du, deine Uhr ist abgelaufen.

Ich lebte still und harmlos — das Geschoß
2570 War auf des Waldes Tiere nur gerichtet,
Meine Gedanken waren rein von Mord —
D u hast aus meinem Frieden mich heraus-
Geschreckt; in gärend Drachengift hast du
Die Milch der frommen Denkart mir verwandelt;
2575 Zum Ungeheuren hast du mich gewöhnt —
Wer sich des Kindes Haupt zum Ziele setzte,
Der kann auch treffen in das Herz des Feinds.

Die armen Kindlein, die unschuldigen,
Das treue Weib muß ich vor deiner Wut
2580 Beschützen, Landvogt! — Da, als ich den Bogenstrang
Anzog — als mir die Hand erzitterte —
Als du mit grausam teuflischer Lust
Mich zwangst, aufs Haupt des Kindes anzulegen —
Als ich ohnmächtig flehend rang vor dir,

2585 Damals gelobt' ich mir in meinem Innern
Mit furchtbarm Eidschwur, den nur Gott gehört,
Daß meines n ä c h s t e n Schusses e r s t e s Ziel
Dein Herz sein sollte — Was ich mir gelobt
In jenes Augenblickes Höllenqualen,
2590 Ist eine heil'ge Schuld, ich will sie zahlen.

Du bist mein Herr und meines Kaisers Vogt;
Doch nicht der Kaiser hätte sich erlaubt,
Was d u — Er sandte dich in diese Lande,
Um Recht zu sprechen — strenges, denn er zürnet —
2595 Doch nicht, um mit der mörderischen Lust
Dich jedes Greuels straflos zu erfrechen;
Es lebt ein Gott, zu strafen und zu rächen.

Komm du hervor, du Bringer bittrer Schmerzen,
Mein teures Kleinod jetzt, mein höchster Schatz!
2600 Ein Ziel will ich dir geben, das bis jetzt
Der frommen Bitte undurchdringlich war —
Doch dir soll es nicht widerstehn — Und du,
Vertraute Bogensehne, die so oft
Mir treu gedient hat in der Freude Spielen,
2605 Verlaß mich nicht im fürchterlichen Ernst!
Nur jetzt noch halte fest, du treuer Strang,
Der mir so oft den herben Pfeil beflügelt —
Entränn' er jetzo kraftlos meinen Händen,
Ich habe keinen zweiten zu versenden.

(Wanderer gehen über die Szene.)

2610 Auf dieser Bank von Stein will ich mich setzen,
Dem Wanderer zur kurzen Ruh' bereitet —
Denn hier ist keine Heimat — Jeder treibt
Sich an dem andern rasch und fremd vorüber
Und fraget nicht nach seinem Schmerz — Hier geht
2615 Der sorgenvolle Kaufmann und der leicht
Geschürzte Pilger — der andächt'ge Mönch,

Der düstre Räuber und der heitre Spielmann,
Der Säumer mit dem schwer beladnen Roß,
Der ferne herkommt von der Menschen Ländern.
2620 Denn jede Straße führt ans End' der Welt.
Sie alle ziehen ihres Weges fort
An ihr Geschäft — und meines ist der Mord!

(Setzt sich)

Sonst, wenn der Vater auszog, liebe Kinder,
Da war ein Freuen, wenn er wiederkam;
2625 Denn niemals kehrt' er heim, er bracht' euch etwas,
War's eine schöne Alpenblume, war's
Ein seltner Vogel oder Ammonshorn,
Wie es der Wandrer findet auf den Bergen —
Jetzt geht er einem andern Weidwerk nach,
2630 Am wilden Weg sitzt er mit Mordgedanken;
Des Feindes Leben ist's, worauf er lauert.
— Und doch an e u c h nur denkt er, lieben Kinder,
Auch jetzt — euch zu verteid'gen, eure holde Unschuld
Zu schützen vor der Rache des Tyrannen,
2635 Will er zum Morde jetzt den Bogen spannen.

(Steht auf)

Ich laure auf ein edles Wild — Läßt sich's
Der Jäger nicht verdrießen, tagelang
Umherzustreifen in des Winters Strenge,
Von Fels zu Fels den Wagesprung zu tun,
2640 Hinanzuklimmen an den glatten Wänden,
Wo er sich anleimt mit dem eignen Blut,
— Um ein armselig Grattier zu erjagen.
Hier gilt es einen köstlicheren Preis,
Das Herz des Todfeinds, der mich will verderben.

(Man hört von ferne eine heitere Musik, welche sich nähert.)

2645 Mein ganzes Leben lang hab' ich den Bogen
Gehandhabt, mich geübt nach Schützenregel;

Ich habe oft geschossen in das Schwarze
Und manchen schönen Preis mir heimgebracht
Vom Freudenschießen — Aber heute will ich
2650 Den M e i s t e r s c h u ß tun und das Beste mir
Im ganzen Umkreis des Gebirgs gewinnen.

(Eine Hochzeit zieht über die Szene und durch den Hohlweg hinauf.
Tell betrachtet sie, auf seinen Bogen gelehnt; *Stüssi, der Flurschütz,*
gesellt sich zu ihm.)

Stüssi

Das ist der Klostermei'r von Mörlischachen,
Der hier den Brautlauf hält — ein reicher Mann,
Er hat wohl zehen Senten auf den Alpen.
2655 Die Braut holt er jetzt ab zu Imisee,
Und diese Nacht wird hoch geschwelgt zu Küßnacht.
Kommt mit! 's ist jeder Biedermann geladen.

Tell

Ein ernster Gast stimmt nicht zum Hochzeitshaus.

Stüssi

Drückt Euch ein Kummer, werft ihn frisch vom Herzen!
2660 Nehmt mit, was kommt; die Zeiten sind jetzt schwer;
Drum muß der Mensch die Freude leicht ergreifen.
Hier wird gefreit und anderswo begraben.

Tell

Und oft kommt gar das eine zu dem andern.

Stüssi

So geht die Welt nun. Es gibt allerwegen
2665 Unglücks genug — Ein Ruffi ist gegangen
Im Glarner Land, und eine ganze Seite
Vom Glärnisch eingesunken.

Tell

Wanken auch
Die Berge selbst? Es steht nichts fest auf Erden.

Stüssi

Auch anderswo vernimmt man Wunderdinge.
2670 Da sprach ich einen, der von Baden kam.
Ein Ritter wollte zu dem König reiten,
Und unterwegs begegnet ihm ein Schwarm
Von Hornissen; die fallen auf sein Roß,
Daß es vor Marter tot zu Boden sinkt,
2675 Und er zu Fuße ankommt bei dem König.

Tell

Dem Schwachen ist sein Stachel auch gegeben.

(*Armgard* kommt mit mehreren Kindern und stellt sich an den Eingang des Hohlwegs.)

Stüssi

Man deutet's auf ein großes Landesunglück,
Auf schwere Taten wider die Natur.

Tell

Dergleichen Taten bringet jeder Tag;
2680 Kein Wunderzeichen braucht sie zu verkünden.

Stüssi

Ja, wohl dem, der sein Feld bestellt in Ruh'
Und ungekränkt daheim sitzt bei den Seinen.

Tell

Es kann der Frömmste nicht im Frieden bleiben,
Wenn es dem bösen Nachbar nicht gefällt.

(Tell sieht oft mit unruhiger Erwartung nach der Höhe des Weges.)

Stüssi

2685 Gehabt Euch wohl — Ihr wartet hier auf jemand?

Tell

Das tu' ich.

Stüssi

Frohe Heimkehr zu den Euren!

— Ihr seid aus Uri?   Unser gnäd'ger Herr,
Der Landvogt, wird noch heut' von dort erwartet.

Wandrer

(kommt)

Den Vogt erwartet heut' nicht mehr.   Die Wasser
2690 Sind ausgetreten von dem großen Regen,
Und alle Brücken hat der Strom zerrissen.

(Tell steht auf.)

Armgard

(kommt vorwärts)

Der Landvogt kommt nicht!

Stüssi

Sucht Ihr was an ihm?

Armgard

Ach freilich!

Stüssi

Warum stellet Ihr Euch denn

In dieser hohlen Gass' ihm in den Weg?

Armgard

2695 Hier weicht er mir nicht aus, er muß mich hören.

Frießhard

(kommt eilfertig den Hohlweg herab und ruft in die Szene)

Man fahre aus dem Weg — Mein gnäd'ger Herr,
Der Landvogt, kommt dicht hinter mir geritten.

(Tell geht ab.)

Armgard

(lebhaft)

Der Landvogt kommt!

(Sie geht mit ihren Kindern nach der vordern Szene. *Geßler* und
Rudolf der Harras zeigen sich zu Pferd auf der Höhe des Wegs.)

Stüssi

(zu Frießhard)

Wie kamt Ihr durch das Wasser,
Da doch der Strom die Brücken fortgeführt?

Frießhard

2700 Wir haben mit dem See gefochten, Freund,
Und fürchten uns vor keinem Alpenwasser.

Stüssi

Ihr wart zu Schiff in dem gewalt'gen Sturm?

Frießhard

Das waren wir. Mein Lebtag denk' ich dran —

Stüssi

O bleibt, erzählt!

Frießhard

Laßt mich, ich muß voraus,
2705 Den Landvogt muß ich in der Burg verkünden.

(Ab)

Stüssi

Wär'n gute Leute auf dem Schiff gewesen,
In Grund gesunken wär's mit Mann und Maus;
D e m Volk kann weder Wasser bei noch Feuer.

(Er sieht sich um.)

Wo kam der Weidmann hin, mit dem ich sprach?

(Geht ab; *Geßler* und *Rudolf der Harras* zu Pferd)

Geßler

2710 Sagt, was Ihr wollt, ich bin des Kaisers Diener
Und muß drauf denken, wie ich ihm gefalle,
Er hat mich nicht ins Land geschickt, dem Volk
Zu schmeicheln und ihm sanft zu tun — Gehorsam
Erwartet er; der Streit ist, ob der Bauer
2715 Soll Herr sein in dem Lande oder der Kaiser.

Armgard

Jetzt ist der Augenblick! Jetzt bring' ich's an!

(Nähert sich furchtsam)

Geßler

Ich hab' den Hut nicht aufgesteckt zu Altorf
Des Scherzes wegen, oder um die Herzen
Des Volks zu prüfen; diese kenn' ich längst.
2720 Ich hab' ihn aufgesteckt, daß sie den Nacken
Mir lernen beugen, den sie aufrecht tragen —
Das U n b e q u e m e hab' ich hingepflanzt
Auf ihren Weg, wo sie vorbeigehn müssen,
Daß sie drauf stoßen mit dem Aug' und sich
2725 Erinnern ihres Herrn, den sie vergessen.

Rudolf

Das Volk hat aber doch gewisse Rechte —

Geßler

Die abzuwägen, ist jetzt keine Zeit!
— Weitschicht'ge Dinge sind im Werk und Werden;
Das Kaiserhaus will wachsen; was der Vater
2730 Glorreich begonnen, will der Sohn vollenden.
Dies kleine Volk ist uns ein Stein im Weg —
So oder so — es muß sich unterwerfen.

(Sie wollen vorüber. Die Frau wirft sich vor dem Landvogt nieder.)

Armgard

Barmherzigkeit, Herr Landvogt! Gnade! Gnade!

Geßler

Was dringt Ihr Euch auf offner Straße mir
2735 In Weg? — Zurück!

Armgard

                    Mein Mann liegt im Gefängnis;
Die armen Waisen schrei'n nach Brot — Habt Mitleid,
Gestrenger Herr, mit unserm großen Elend!

Rudolf

Wer seid Ihr? Wer ist Euer Mann?

Armgard

                            Ein armer
Wildheuer, guter Herr, vom Rigiberge,
2740 Der überm Abgrund weg das freie Gras
Abmähet von den schroffen Felsenwänden,
Wohin das Vieh sich nicht getraut zu steigen —

Rudolf

(zum Landvogt)

Bei Gott, ein elend und erbärmlich Leben!
Ich bitt' Euch, gebt ihn los, den armen Mann!

2745 Was er auch Schweres mag verschuldet haben,
Strafe genug ist sein entsetzlich Handwerk.

(Zu der Frau)

Euch soll Recht werden — Drinnen auf der Burg
Nennt Eure Bitte — Hier ist nicht der Ort.

Armgard

Nein, nein, ich weiche nicht von diesem Platz,
2750 Bis mir der Vogt den Mann zurückgegeben!
Schon in den sechsten Mond liegt er im Turm
Und harret auf den Richterspruch vergebens.

Geßler

Weib, wollt Ihr mir Gewalt antun? Hinweg!

Armgard

Gerechtigkeit, Landvogt! Du bist der Richter
2755 Im Lande an des Kaisers Statt und Gottes.
Tu deine Pflicht! So du Gerechtigkeit
Vom Himmel hoffest, so erzeig' sie uns!

Geßler

Fort! Schafft das freche Volk mir aus den Augen!

Armgard

(greift in die Zügel des Pferdes)

Nein, nein, ich habe nichts mehr zu verlieren.
2760 — Du kommst nicht von der Stelle, Vogt, bis du
Mir Recht gesprochen — Falte deine Stirne,
Rolle die Augen, wie du willst — Wir sind
So grenzenlos unglücklich, daß wir nichts
Nach deinem Zorn mehr fragen —

Geßler

Weib, mach' Platz,
2765 Oder mein Roß geht über dich hinweg.

Armgard

Laß es über mich dahingehn — Da —

(Sie reißt ihre Kinder zu Boden und wirft sich mit ihnen ihm in den Weg.)

Hier lieg' ich
Mit meinen Kindern — Laß die armen Waisen
Von deines Pferdes Huf zertreten werden!
Es ist das Ärgste nicht, was du getan —

Rudolf

2770 Weib, seid Ihr rasend?

Armgard

(heftiger fortfahrend)

Tratest du doch längst
Das Land des Kaisers unter deine Füße!
— O, ich bin nur ein Weib! Wär' ich ein Mann,
Ich wüßte wohl was Besseres, als hier
Im Staub zu liegen —

(Man hört die vorige Musik wieder auf der Höhe des Wegs, aber gedämpft.)

Geßler

Wo sind meine Knechte?
2775 Man reiße sie von hinnen, oder ich
Vergesse mich und tue, was mich reuet.

Rudolf

Die Knechte können nicht hindurch, o Herr!
Der Hohlweg ist gesperrt durch eine Hochzeit.

Geßler

Ein allzu milder Herrscher bin ich noch
2780 Gegen dies Volk — die Zungen sind noch frei,
Es ist noch nicht ganz, wie es soll, gebändigt —
Doch es soll anders werden, ich gelob' es:
Ich will ihn brechen, diesen starren Sinn,
Den kecken Geist der Freiheit will ich beugen,
2785 Ein neu Gesetz will ich in diesen Landen
Verkündigen — ich will —

(Ein Pfeil durchbohrt ihn; er fährt mit der Hand ans Herz und will
sinken. Mit matter Stimme:)

Gott sei mir gnädig!

Rudolf

Herr Landvogt — Gott! Was ist das? Woher kam das?

Armgard

(auffahrend)

Mord! Mord! Er taumelt, sinkt! Er ist getroffen!
Mitten ins Herz hat ihn der Pfeil getroffen!

Rudolf

(springt vom Pferde)

2790 Welch gräßliches Ereignis — Gott — Herr Ritter —
Ruft die Erbarmung Gottes an! — Ihr seid
Ein Mann des Todes!

Geßler

Das ist Tells Geschoß!

(Ist vom Pferde herab dem Rudolf Harras in den Arm gegleitet und
wird auf der Bank niedergelassen)

Tell

(erscheint oben auf der Höhe des Felsens)

Du kennst den Schützen, suche keinen andern!
Frei sind die Hütten, sicher ist die Unschuld
2795 Vor dir, du wirst dem Lande nicht mehr schaden.

(Verschwindet von der Höhe. Volk stürzt herein.)

Stüssi

(voran)

Was gibt es hier? Was hat sich zugetragen?

Armgard

Der Landvogt ist von einem Pfeil durchschossen.

Volk

(im Hereinstürzen)

Wer ist erschossen?

(Indem die Vordersten von dem Brautzug auf die Szene kommen, sind
die Hintersten noch auf der Höhe, und die Musik geht fort.)

Rudolf der Harras

Er verblutet sich.
Fort, schaffet Hilfe! Setzt dem Mörder nach!
2800 — Verlorner Mann, so muß es mit dir enden;
Doch meine Warnung wolltest du nicht hören!

Stüssi

Bei Gott! Da liegt er bleich und ohne Leben!

Viele Stimmen

Wer hat die Tat getan?

Rudolf der Harras

Rast dieses Volk,
Daß es dem Mord Musik macht? Laßt sie schweigen!

(Musik bricht plötzlich ab, es kommt noch mehr Volk nach.)

2805 Herr Landvogt, redet, wenn Ihr könnt — Habt Ihr
Mir nichts mehr zu vertrauen?

(Geßler gibt Zeichen mit der Hand, die er mit Heftigkeit wiederholt, da
sie nicht gleich verstanden werden.)

Wo soll ich hin?
— Nach Küßnacht? — Ich versteh' Euch nicht — O werdet
Nicht ungeduldig — Laßt das Irdische,
Denkt jetzt Euch mit dem Himmel zu versöhnen!

(Die ganze Hochzeitgesellschaft umsteht den Sterbenden mit einem
fühllosen Grausen.)

Stüssi

2810 Sieh, wie er bleich wird — Jetzt, jetzt tritt der Tod
Ihm an das Herz — die Augen sind gebrochen.

Armgard

(hebt ein Kind empor)

Seht, Kinder, wie ein Wüterich verscheidet!

Rudolf der Harras

Wahnsinn'ge Weiber, habt ihr kein Gefühl,
Daß ihr den Blick an diesem Schrecknis weidet?
2815 Helft — Leget Hand an — Steht mir niemand bei,
Den Schmerzenspfeil ihm aus der Brust zu ziehn?

Weiber

(treten zurück)

Wir ihn berühren, welchen Gott geschlagen!

Rudolf der Harras

Fluch treff' euch und Verdammnis!

(Zieht das Schwert)

Stüssi

(fällt ihm in den Arm)

Wagt es, Herr!
Eu'r Walten hat ein Ende. Der Tyrann
2820 Des Landes ist gefallen. Wir erdulden
Keine Gewalt mehr. Wir sind freie Menschen.

Alle

(tumultuarisch)

Das Land ist frei!

Rudolf der Harras

Ist es dahin gekommen?
Endet die Furcht so schnell und der Gehorsam?

(Zu den Waffenknechten, die hereindringen)

Ihr seht die grausenvolle Tat des Mords,
2825 Die hier geschehen — Hilfe ist umsonst —
Vergeblich ist's, dem Mörder nachzusetzen.
Uns drängen andre Sorgen — Auf, nach Küßnacht,
Daß wir dem Kaiser seine Feste retten!
Denn aufgelöst in diesem Augenblick
2830 Sind aller Ordnung, aller Pflichten Bande,
Und keines Mannes Treu' ist zu vertrauen.

(Indem er mit den Waffenknechten abgeht, erscheinen *sechs barmherzige Brüder*.)

Armgard

Platz! Platz! da kommen die barmherz'gen Brüder.

Stüssi

Das Opfer liegt — Die Raben steigen nieder.

Barmherzige Brüder

(schließen einen Halbkreis um den Toten und singen in tiefem Ton)

Rasch tritt der Tod den Menschen an,

2835   Es ist ihm keine Frist gegeben;

Es stürzt ihn mitten in der Bahn,

Es reißt ihn fort vom vollen Leben.

Bereitet oder nicht, zu gehen,

Er muß vor seinen Richter stehen!

(Indem die letzten Zeilen wiederholt werden, fällt der Vorhang.)

FÜNFTER AUFZUG

ERSTE SZENE

(Öffentlicher Platz bei Altorf. Im Hintergrunde rechts die Feste Zwing Uri mit dem noch stehenden Baugerüste, wie in der dritten Szene des ersten Aufzugs; links eine Aussicht in viele Berge hinein, auf welchen allen Signalfeuer brennen. Es ist eben Tagesanbruch, Glocken ertönen aus verschiedenen Fernen. *Ruodi, Kuoni, Werni, Meister Steinmetz* und viele andere *Landleute,* auch *Weiber* und *Kinder.*)

Ruodi

2840 Seht ihr die Feuersignale auf den Bergen?

Steinmetz

Hört ihr die Glocken drüben überm Wald?

Ruodi

Die Feinde sind verjagt.

Steinmetz

Die Burgen sind erobert.

Ruodi

Und wir im Lande Uri dulden noch
Auf unserm Boden das Tyrannenschloß?
2845 Sind wir die Letzten, die sich frei erklären?

Steinmetz

Das J o c h soll stehen, das uns zwingen wollte?
Auf, reißt es nieder!

Alle

Nieder! nieder! nieder!

Ruodi

Wo ist der Stier von Uri?

Stier von Uri

Hier. Was soll ich?

Ruodi

Steigt auf die Hochwacht, blast in Euer Horn,
2850 Daß es weitschmetternd in die Berge schalle
Und, jedes Echo in den Felsenklüften
Aufweckend, schnell die Männer des Gebirgs
Zusammenrufe!

(Stier von Uri geht ab. *Walter Fürst* kommt.)

Walter Fürst

Haltet, Freunde! Haltet!
Noch fehlt uns Kunde, was in Unterwalden
2855 Und Schwyz geschehen. Laßt uns Boten erst
Erwarten!

Ruodi

Was erwarten? Der Tyrann
Ist tot, der Tag der Freiheit ist erschienen.

Steinmetz

Ist's nicht genug an diesen flammenden Boten,
Die rings herum auf allen Bergen leuchten?

Ruodi

2860 Kommt alle, kommt, legt Hand an, Männer und Weiber!
Brecht das Gerüste! Sprengt die Bogen! Reißt
Die Mauern ein! Kein Stein bleib' auf dem andern!

Steinmetz

Gesellen, kommt! Wir haben's aufgebaut,
Wir wissen's zu zerstören.

Alle

Kommt, reißt nieder!

(Sie stürzen sich von allen Seiten auf den Bau.)

Walter Fürst

2865 Es ist im Lauf. Ich kann sie nicht mehr halten.

(*Melchtal* und *Baumgarten* kommen.)

Melchtal

Was? Steht die Burg noch, und Schloß Sarnen liegt
In Asche, und der Roßberg ist gebrochen?

Walter Fürst

Seid Ihr es, Melchtal? Bringt Ihr uns die Freiheit?
Sagt! Sind die Lande alle rein vom Feind?

Melchtal

(umarmt ihn)

2870 Rein ist der Boden. Freut Euch, alter Vater!
In diesem Augenblick, da wir reden,
Ist kein Tyrann mehr in der Schweizer Land.

Walter Fürst

O sprecht, wie wurdet Ihr der Burgen mächtig?

Melchtal

Der Rudenz war es, der das Sarner Schloß
2875 Mit mannlich kühner Wagetat gewann.
Den Roßberg hatt' ich nachts zuvor erstiegen.

— Doch höret, was geschah. Als wir das Schloß,
Vom Feind geleert, nun freudig angezündet,
Die Flamme prasselnd schon zum Himmel schlug,
2880 Da stürzt der Diethelm, Geßlers Bub, hervor
Und ruft, daß die Bruneckerin verbrenne.

Walter Fürst

Gerechter Gott!

(Man hört die Balken des Gerüstes stürzen.)

Melchtal

　　　　　Sie war es selbst, war heimlich
Hier eingeschlossen auf des Vogts Geheiß.
Rasend erhub sich Rudenz — denn wir hörten
2885 Die Balken schon, die festen Pfosten stürzen,
Und aus dem Rauch hervor den Jammerruf
Der Unglückseligen.

Walter Fürst

　　　　　Sie ist gerettet?

Melchtal

Da galt Geschwindsein und Entschlossenheit!
— Wär' er n u r unser Edelmann gewesen,
2890 Wir hätten unser Leben wohl geliebt;
Doch er war unser Eidgenoß, und Berta
Ehrte das Volk — So setzten wir getrost
Das Leben dran und stürzten in das Feuer.

Walter Fürst

Sie ist gerettet?

Melchtal

　　　　　Sie ist's. Rudenz und ich,
2895 Wir trugen sie selbander aus den Flammen,

Und hinter uns fiel krachend das Gebälk.
— Und jetzt, als sie gerettet sich erkannte,
Die Augen aufschlug zu dem Himmelslicht,
Jetzt stürzte mir der Freiherr an das Herz,
2900 Und schweigend ward ein Bündnis jetzt beschworen,
Das, fest gehärtet in des Feuers Glut,
Bestehen wird in allen Schicksalsproben —

Walter Fürst

Wo ist der Landenberg?

Melchtal

Über den Brünig.
Nicht lag's an mir, daß er das Licht der Augen
2905 Davontrug, der den Vater mir geblendet.
Nach jagt' ich ihm, erreicht' ihn auf der Flucht
Und riß ihn zu den Füßen meines Vaters.
Geschwungen über ihn war schon das Schwert;
Von der Barmherzigkeit des blinden Greises
2910 Erhielt er flehend das Geschenk des Lebens.
U r f e h d e schwur er, nie zurückzukehren;
Er wird sie halten; unsern Arm hat er
Gefühlt.

Walter Fürst

Wohl Euch, daß Ihr den reinen Sieg
Mit Blute nicht geschändet!

Kinder

(eilen mit Trümmern des Gerüstes über die Szene)
Freiheit! Freiheit!

(Das Horn von Uri wird mit Macht geblasen.)

Walter Fürst

2915 Seht, welch ein Fest! Des Tages werden sich
Die Kinder spät als Greise noch erinnern.

(Mädchen bringen den Hut auf einer Stange getragen; die ganze Szene füllt sich mit Volk an.)

Ruodi

Hier ist der Hut, dem wir uns beugen mußten.

Baumgarten

Gebt uns Bescheid, was damit werden soll.

Walter Fürst

Gott! Unter diesem Hute stand mein Enkel!

Mehrere Stimmen

2920 Zerstört das Denkmal der Tyrannenmacht!
Ins Feuer mit ihm!

Walter Fürst

Nein, laßt ihn aufbewahren!
Der Tyrannei mußt' er zum Werkzeug dienen,
Er soll der Freiheit ewig Zeichen sein!

(Die Landleute, Männer, Weiber und Kinder stehen und sitzen auf den Balken des zerbrochenen Gerüstes malerisch gruppiert in einem großen Halbkreis umher.)

Melchtal

So stehen wir nun fröhlich auf den Trümmern
2925 Der Tyrannei, und herrlich ist's erfüllt,
Was wir im Rütli schwuren, Eidgenossen.

Walter Fürst

Das Werk ist angefangen, nicht vollendet.
Jetzt ist uns Mut und feste Eintracht not;
Denn, seid gewiß, nicht säumen wird der König,
2930 Den Tod zu rächen seines Vogts und den
Vertriebnen mit Gewalt zurückzuführen.

Melchtal

Er zieh' heran mit seiner Heeresmacht!
Ist aus dem Innern doch der Feind verjagt;
Dem Feind von außen wollen wir begegnen.

Ruodi

2935 Nur wen'ge Pässe öffnen ihm das Land,
Die wollen wir mit unsern Leibern decken.

Baumgarten

Wir sind vereinigt durch ein ewig Band,
Und seine Heere sollen uns nicht schrecken!

(*Rösselmann* und *Stauffacher* kommen.)

Rösselmann

(im Eintreten)

Das sind des Himmels furchtbare Gerichte.

Landleute

2940 Was gibt's?

Rösselmann

In welchen Zeiten leben wir!

Walter Fürst

Sagt an, was ist es? — Ha, seid Ihr's, Herr Werner?
Was bringt Ihr uns?

Landleute

Was gibt's?

Rösselmann

Hört und erstaunet!

Stauffacher

Von einer großen Furcht sind wir befreit —

Rösselmann

Der Kaiser ist ermordet.

Walter Fürst

Gnäd'ger Gott!

(Landleute machen einen Aufstand und umdrängen den Stauffacher.)

Alle

2945 Ermordet! Was? Der Kaiser! Hört! Der Kaiser!

Melchtal

Nicht möglich! Woher kam Euch diese Kunde?

Stauffacher

Es ist gewiß. Bei Bruck fiel König Albrecht
Durch Mörders Hand — ein glaubenswerter Mann,
J o h a n n e s M ü l l e r, bracht' es von Schaffhausen.

Walter Fürst

2950 Wer wagte solche grauenvolle Tat?

Stauffacher

Sie wird noch grauenvoller durch den Täter.
Es war sein Neffe, seines Bruders Kind,
Herzog Johann von Schwaben, der's vollbrachte.

Melchtal

Was trieb ihn zu der Tat des Vatermords?

Stauffacher

2955 Der Kaiser hielt das väterliche Erbe
Dem ungeduldig Mahnenden zurück;

Es hieß, er denk' ihn ganz darum zu kürzen,
Mit einem Bischofshut ihn abzufinden.
Wie dem auch sei — der Jüngling öffnete
2960 Der Waffenfreunde bösem Rat sein Ohr,
Und mit den edeln Herrn von E s c h e n b a c h ,
Von T e g e r f e l d e n , von der W a r t und P a l m
Beschloß er, da er Recht nicht konnte finden,
Sich Rach' zu holen mit der eignen Hand.

Walter Fürst

2965 O sprecht, wie ward das Gräßliche vollendet?

Stauffacher

Der König ritt herab vom Stein zu Baden,
Gen Rheinfeld, wo die Hofstatt war, zu ziehn,
Mit ihm die Fürsten H a n s und L e o p o l d
Und ein Gefolge hochgeborner Herren.
2970 Und als sie kamen an die R e u ß , wo man
Auf einer Fähre sich läßt übersetzen,
Da drängten sich die Mörder in das Schiff,
Daß sie den Kaiser vom Gefolge trennten.
Drauf, als der Fürst durch ein geackert Feld
2975 Hinreitet, — eine alte große Stadt
Soll drunter liegen aus der Heiden Zeit —
Die alte Feste Habsburg im Gesicht,
Wo seines Stammes Hoheit ausgegangen —
Stößt Herzog Hans den Dolch ihm in die Kehle,
2980 Rudolf von Palm durchrennt ihn mit dem Speer,
Und Eschenbach zerspaltet ihm das Haupt,
Daß er heruntersinkt in seinem Blut,
Gemordet von den Seinen, a u f dem Seinen.
Am andern Ufer sahen sie die Tat;
2985 Doch durch den Strom geschieden, konnten sie
Nur ein ohnmächtig Wehgeschrei erheben;

Am Wege aber saß ein armes Weib,
In ihrem Schoß verblutete der Kaiser.

Melchtal

So hat er nur sein frühes Grab gegraben,
2990 Der unersättlich alles wollte haben!

Stauffacher

Ein ungeheurer Schrecken ist im Land umher;
Gesperrt sind alle Pässe des Gebirgs,
Jedweder Stand verwahret seine Grenzen;
Die alte Zürich selbst schloß ihre Tore,
2995 Die dreißig Jahr' lang offen standen, zu,
Die Mörder fürchtend und noch mehr — die Rächer.
Denn, mit des Bannes Fluch bewaffnet, kommt
Der Ungarn Königin, die strenge Agnes,
Die nicht die Milde kennet ihres zarten
3000 Geschlechts, des Vaters königliches Blut
Zu rächen an der Mörder ganzem Stamm,
An ihren Knechten, Kindern, Kindeskindern,
Ja an den Steinen ihrer Schlösser selbst.
Geschworen hat sie, ganze Zeugungen
3005 Hinabzusenden in des Vaters Grab,
In Blut sich wie in Maientau zu baden.

Melchtal

Weiß man, wo sich die Mörder hingeflüchtet?

Stauffacher

Sie flohen alsbald nach vollbrachter Tat
Auf fünf verschiednen Straßen auseinander
3010 Und trennten sich, um nie sich mehr zu sehn —
Herzog Johann soll irren im Gebirge.

Walter Fürst

So trägt die Untat ihnen keine Frucht!
Rache trägt keine Frucht! Sich selbst ist sie
Die fürchterliche Nahrung, ihr Genuß
3015 Ist Mord, und ihre Sättigung das Grausen.

Stauffacher

Den Mördern bringt die Untat nicht Gewinn;
W i r aber brechen mit der reinen Hand
Des blut'gen Frevels segenvolle Frucht.
Denn einer großen Furcht sind wir entledigt;
3020 Gefallen ist der Freiheit größter Feind,
Und wie verlautet, wird das Zepter gehn
Aus Habsburgs Haus zu einem andern Stamm,
Das Reich will seine Wahlfreiheit behaupten.

Walter Fürst und mehrere

Vernahmt Ihr was?

Stauffacher

Der Graf von Luxemburg
3025 Ist von den mehrsten Stimmen schon bezeichnet.

Walter Fürst

Wohl uns, daß wir beim Reiche treu gehalten;
Jetzt ist zu hoffen auf Gerechtigkeit!

Stauffacher

Dem neuen Herrn tun tapfre Freunde not;
Er wird uns schirmen gegen Östreichs Rache.

(Die Landleute umarmen einander. *Sigrist* mit einem *Reichsboten*)

Sigrist

3030 Hier sind des Landes würd'ge Oberhäupter.

Rösselmann und mehrere

Sigrist, was gibt's?

Sigrist

Ein Reichsbot' bringt dies Schreiben.

Alle

(zu Walter Fürst)

Erbrecht und leset!

Walter Fürst

(liest)

„Den bescheidnen Männern
Von Uri, Schwyz und Unterwalden bietet
Die Königin Elsbet Gnad' und alles Gutes."

Viele Stimmen

3035 Was will die Königin? Ihr Reich ist aus.

Walter Fürst

(liest)

„In ihrem großen Schmerz und Witwenleid,
Worein der blut'ge Hinscheid ihres Herrn
Die Königin versetzt, gedenkt sie noch
Der alten Treu' und Lieb' der Schwyzerlande."

Melchtal

3040 In ihrem Glück hat sie das nie getan.

Rösselmann

Still! Lasset hören!

Walter Fürst

(liest)

„Und sie versieht sich zu dem treuen Volk,
Daß es gerechten Abscheu werde tragen
Vor den verfluchten Tätern dieser Tat.
3045 Darum erwartet sie von den drei Landen,
Daß sie den Mördern nimmer Vorschub tun,
Vielmehr getreulich dazu helfen werden,
Sie auszuliefern in des Rächers Hand,
Der Lieb' gedenkend und der alten Gunst,
3050 Die sie von Rudolfs Fürstenhaus empfangen."

(Zeichen des Unwillens unter den Landleuten)

Viele Stimmen

Der Lieb' und Gunst!

Stauffacher

Wir haben Gunst empfangen von dem Vater;
Doch wessen rühmen wir uns von dem Sohn?
Hat er den Brief der Freiheit uns bestätigt,
3055 Wie v o r ihm alle Kaiser doch getan?
Hat er gerichtet nach gerechtem Spruch
Und der bedrängten Unschuld Schutz verliehn?
Hat er auch nur die Boten wollen hören,
Die wir in unsrer Angst zu ihm gesendet?
3060 Nicht eins von diesem allen hat der König
An uns getan, und hätten wir nicht selbst
Uns Recht verschafft mit eigner mut'ger Hand,
Ihn rührte unsre Not nicht an — Ihm Dank?
Nicht Dank hat er gesät in diesen Tälern.
3065 Er stand auf einem hohen Platz, er konnte
Ein Vater seiner Völker sein; doch ihm
Gefiel es, nur zu sorgen für die Seinen;
Die er gemehrt hat, mögen um ihn meinen!

Walter Fürst

Wir wollen nicht frohlocken seines Falls,
3070 Nicht des empfangnen Bösen j e t z t gedenken,
Fern sei's von uns! Doch daß wir r ä c h e n sollten
Des Königs Tod, der nie uns Gutes tat,
Und die verfolgen, die uns nie betrübten,
Das ziemt uns nicht und will uns nicht gebühren.
3075 Die Liebe will ein freies Opfer sein;
Der Tod entbindet von erzwungnen Pflichten,
— Ihm haben wir nichts weiter zu entrichten.

Melchtal

Und weint die Königin in ihrer Kammer,
Und klagt ihr wilder Schmerz den Himmel an,
3080 So seht Ihr hier ein angstbefreites Volk
Zu eben diesem Himmel dankend flehen —
Wer Tränen ernten will, muß Liebe säen.

(Reichsbote geht ab.)

Stauffacher

(zu dem Volk)

Wo ist der Tell? Soll er allein uns fehlen,
Der unsrer Freiheit Stifter ist? Das Größte
3085 Hat e r getan, das Härteste erduldet,
Kommt alle, kommt, nach seinem Haus zu wallen,
Und rufet Heil dem Retter von uns allen!

(Alle gehen ab.)

ZWEITE SZENE

(Tells Hausflur. Ein Feuer brennt auf dem Herd. Die offenstehende Türe zeigt ins Freie. *Hedwig. Walter* und *Wilhelm*.)

Hedwig

Heut' kommt der Vater. Kinder, liebe Kinder!
Er lebt, ist frei, und wir sind frei und alles!
3090 Und euer Vater ist's, der's Land gerettet.

Walter

Und ich bin auch dabei gewesen, Mutter!
Mich muß man auch mit nennen. Vaters Pfeil
Ging mir am Leben hart vorbei, und ich
Hab' nicht gezittert.

Hedwig

(umarmt ihn)

Ja, du bist mir wieder
3095 Gegeben! Zweimal hab' ich dich geboren!
Zweimal litt ich den Mutterschmerz um dich!
Es ist vorbei — Ich hab' euch beide, beide!
Und heute kommt der liebe Vater wieder!

(Ein *Mönch* erscheint an der Haustüre.)

Wilhelm

Sieh, Mutter, sieh — dort steht ein frommer Bruder;
3100 Gewiß wird er um eine Gabe flehn.

Hedwig

Führ' ihn herein, damit wir ihn erquicken;
Er fühl's, daß er ins Freudenhaus gekommen.

(Geht hinein und kommt bald mit einem Becher wieder)

Wilhelm

(zum Mönch)

Kommt, guter Mann! Die Mutter will Euch laben.

Walter

Kommt, ruht Euch aus und geht gestärkt von dannen!

Mönch

(scheu umherblickend, mit zerstörten Zügen)

3105 Wo bin ich? Saget an, in welchem Lande?

Walter

Seid Ihr verirret, daß Ihr das nicht wißt?
Ihr seid zu Bürglen, Herr, im Lande Uri,
Wo man hineingeht in das Schächental.

Mönch

(zur Hedwig, welche zurückkommt)

Seid Ihr allein? Ist Euer Herr zu Hause?

Hedwig

3110 Ich erwart' ihn eben — doch was ist Euch, Mann?
Ihr seht nicht aus, als ob Ihr Gutes brächtet.
— Wer Ihr auch seid, Ihr seid bedürftig, nehmt!

(Reicht ihm den Becher)

Mönch

Wie auch mein lechzend Herz nach Labung schmachtet,
Nichts rühr' ich an, bis Ihr mir zugesagt —

Hedwig

3115 Berührt mein Kleid nicht, tretet mir nicht nah,
Bleibt ferne stehn, wenn ich Euch hören soll.

Mönch

Bei diesem Feuer, das hier gastlich lodert,
Bei Eurer Kinder teurem Haupt, das ich
Umfasse —

(Ergreift die Knaben)

Hedwig

Mann, was sinnet Ihr? Zurück
3120 Von meinen Kindern! — Ihr seid kein Mönch! Ihr seid
Es nicht! Der Friede wohnt in diesem Kleide;
In Euren Zügen wohnt der Friede nicht.

Mönch

Ich bin der unglückseligste der Menschen.

Hedwig

Das Unglück spricht gewaltig zu dem Herzen,
3125 Doch Euer Blick schnürt mir das Innre zu.

Walter

(aufspringend)

Mutter, der Vater!

(Eilt hinaus)

Hedwig

O mein Gott!

(Will nach, zittert und hält sich an)

Wilhelm

(eilt nach)

Der Vater!

Walter

(draußen)

Da bist du wieder!

Wilhelm

(draußen)

Vater, lieber Vater!

Tell

(draußen)

Da bin ich wieder — Wo ist eure Mutter?

(Treten herein)

Walter

Da steht sie an der Tür' und kann nicht weiter;
3130 So zittert sie vor Schrecken und vor Freude.

Tell

O Hedwig! Hedwig! Mutter meiner Kinder!
Gott hat geholfen — Uns trennt kein Tyrann mehr.

Hedwig

(an seinem Halse)

O Tell! Tell! Welche Angst litt ich um dich!

(Mönch wird aufmerksam.)

Tell

Vergiß sie jetzt und lebe nur der Freude!
3135 Da bin ich wieder! Das ist meine Hütte!
Ich stehe wieder auf dem Meinigen!

Wilhelm

Wo aber hast du deine Armbrust, Vater?
Ich seh' sie nicht.

Tell

Du wirst sie nie mehr sehn.
An heil'ger Stätte ist sie aufbewahrt;
3140 Sie wird hinfort zu keiner Jagd mehr dienen.

Hedwig

O Tell! Tell!

(Tritt zurück, läßt seine Hand los)

Tell

Was erschreckt dich, liebes Weib?

Hedwig

Wie — w i e kommst du mir wieder? — Diese Hand
— Darf ich sie fassen? — Diese Hand — O Gott!

Tell

(herzlich und mutig)

Hat euch verteidigt und das Land gerettet;
3145 Ich darf sie frei hinauf zum Himmel heben.

(Mönch macht eine rasche Bewegung, er erblickt ihn.)

Wer ist der Bruder hier?

Hedwig

Ach, ich vergaß ihn!
Sprich d u mit ihm, mir graut in seiner Nähe.

Mönch

(tritt näher)

Seid Ihr der Tell, durch den der Landvogt fiel?

Tell

Der bin ich, ich verberg' es keinem Menschen.

Mönch

3150 Ihr seid der Tell! Ach, es ist Gottes Hand,
Die unter Euer Dach mich hat geführt.

Tell

(mißt ihn mit den Augen)

Ihr seid kein Mönch! Wer seid Ihr?

Mönch

Ihr erschlugt
Den Landvogt, der Euch Böses tat — Auch ich
Hab' einen Feind erschlagen, der mir Recht
3155 Versagte — Er war Euer Feind wie meiner —
Ich hab' das Land von ihm befreit.

Tell

(zurückfahrend)

Ihr seid —
Entsetzen! — Kinder! Kinder, geht hinein!
Geh, liebes Weib! Geh, geh! — Unglücklicher,
Ihr wäret —

Hedwig

Gott, wer ist es?

Tell

Frage nicht!
3160 Fort! fort! Die Kinder dürfen es nicht hören.
Geh aus dem Hause — weit hinweg — Du darfst
Nicht unter e i n e m Dach mit diesem wohnen.

Hedwig

Weh mir, was ist das? Kommt!

(Geht mit den Kindern)

Tell

(zu dem Mönch)

Ihr seid der Herzog
Von Österreich — Ihr seid's! Ihr habt den Kaiser
3165 Erschlagen, Euren Ohm und Herrn.

Johannes Parricida

Er war
Der Räuber meines Erbes.

Tell

Euren Ohm
Erschlagen, Euern Kaiser! Und Euch trägt
Die Erde noch! Euch leuchtet noch die Sonne!

Parricida

Tell, hört mich, eh' Ihr —

Tell

Von dem Blute triefend
3170 Des Vatermordes und des Kaisermords,
Wagst du zu treten in mein reines Haus?
Du wagst's, dein Antlitz einem guten Menschen
Zu zeigen und das Gastrecht zu begehren?

Parricida

Bei Euch hofft' ich Barmherzigkeit zu finden;
3175 Auch I h r nahmt Rach' an Eurem Feind.

Tell

Unglücklicher!
Darfst du der Ehrsucht blut'ge Schuld vermengen
Mit der gerechten Notwehr eines Vaters?
Hast du der Kinder liebes Haupt verteidigt?
Des Herdes Heiligtum beschützt? das Schrecklichste,
3180 Das Letzte von den Deinen abgewehrt?
— Zum Himmel heb' ich meine reinen Hände,
Verfluche dich und deine Tat — Gerächt
Hab' ich die heilige Natur, die d u
Geschändet — Nichts teil' ich mit dir — Gemordet
3185 Hast d u , i c h hab' mein Teuerstes verteidigt.

Parricida

Ihr stoßt mich von Euch, trostlos, in Verzweiflung?

Tell

Mich faßt ein Grausen, da ich mit dir rede.
Fort! Wandle deine fürchterliche Straße!
Laß rein die Hütte, wo die Unschuld wohnt!

Parricida
(wendet sich, zu gehen)

3190 S o k a n n ich, und s o w i l l ich nicht mehr leben!

Tell

Und doch erbarmt mich deiner — Gott des Himmels!
So jung, von solchem adeligen Stamm,
Der Enkel Rudolfs, meines Herrn und Kaisers,

Als Mörder flüchtig, hier an meiner Schwelle,
3195 Des armen Mannes, flehend und verzweifelnd —

(Verhüllt sich das Gesicht)

Parricida

O, wenn Ihr weinen könnt, laßt mein Geschick
Euch jammern; es ist fürchterlich — Ich bin
Ein Fürst — ich w a r ' s — ich konnte glücklich werden,
Wenn ich der Wünsche Ungeduld bezwang.
3200 Der Neid zernagte mir das Herz — Ich sah
Die Jugend meines Vetters Leopold
Gekrönt mit Ehre und mit Land belohnt,
Und mich, der gleiches Alters mit ihm war,
In sklavischer Unmündigkeit gehalten —

Tell

3205 Unglücklicher, wohl kannte dich dein Ohm,
Da er dir Land und Leute weigerte!
Du selbst mit rascher, wilder Wahnsinnstat
Rechtfertigst furchtbar seinen weisen Schluß.
— Wo sind die blut'gen Helfer deines Mords?

Parricida

3210 Wohin die Rachegeister sie geführt;
Ich sah sie seit der Unglückstat nicht wieder.

Tell

Weißt du, daß dich die Acht verfolgt, daß du
Dem Freund verboten und dem Feind erlaubt?

Parricida

Darum vermeid' ich alle offne Straßen;
3215 An keine Hütte wag' ich anzupochen —
Der Wüste kehr' ich meine Schritte zu;

Mein eignes Schrecknis irr' ich durch die Berge
Und fahre schaudernd vor mir selbst zurück,
Zeigt mir ein Bach mein unglückselig Bild.
3220 O, wenn Ihr Mitleid fühlt und Menschlichkeit —

(Fällt vor ihm nieder)

Tell

(abgewendet)

Steht auf! Steht auf!

Parricida

Nicht bis Ihr mir die Hand gereicht zur Hilfe.

Tell

Kann ich Euch helfen? Kann's ein Mensch der Sünde?
Doch stehet auf — Was Ihr auch Gräßliches
3225 Verübt — Ihr seid ein Mensch — Ich bin es auch;
Vom Tell soll keiner ungetröstet scheiden —
Was ich vermag, das will ich tun.

Parricida

(aufspringend und seine Hand mit Heftigkeit ergreifend)

O Tell!
Ihr rettet meine Seele von Verzweiflung.

Tell

Laßt meine Hand los — Ihr müßt fort. Hier könnt
3230 Ihr unentdeckt nicht bleiben, könnt entdeckt
Auf Schutz nicht rechnen — Wo gedenkt Ihr hin?
Wo hofft Ihr Ruh' zu finden?

Parricida

Weiß ich's? Ach!

Tell

Hört, was mir Gott ins Herz gibt — Ihr müßt fort
Ins Land Italien, nach Sankt Peters Stadt!
3235 Dort werft Ihr Euch dem Papst zu Füßen, beichtet
Ihm Eure Schuld und löset Eure Seele.

Parricida

Wird er mich nicht dem Rächer überliefern?

Tell

Was er Euch tut, das nehmet an von Gott!

Parricida

Wie komm' ich in das unbekannte Land?
3240 Ich bin des Wegs nicht kundig, wage nicht,
Zu Wanderern die Schritte zu gesellen.

Tell

Den Weg will ich Euch nennen, merket wohl!
Ihr steigt hinauf, dem Strom der Reuß entgegen,
Die wildes Laufes von dem Berge stürzt —

Parricida

(erschrickt)

3245 Seh' ich die Reuß? Sie floß bei meiner Tat.

Tell

Am Abgrund geht der Weg, und viele Kreuze
Bezeichnen ihn, errichtet zum Gedächtnis
Der Wanderer, die die Lawine begraben.

Parricida

Ich fürchte nicht die Schrecken der Natur,
3250 Wenn ich des Herzens wilde Qualen zähme.

Tell

Vor jedem Kreuze fallet hin und büßet
Mit heißen Reuetränen Eure Schuld —
Und seid Ihr glücklich durch die Schreckensstraße,
Sendet der Berg nicht seine Windeswehen
3255 Auf Euch herab von dem beeisten Joch,
So kommt Ihr auf die B r ü c k e , welche s t ä u b e t .
Wenn sie nicht einbricht unter Eurer Schuld,
Wenn Ihr sie glücklich hinter Euch gelassen,
So reißt ein schwarzes F e l s e n t o r sich auf —
3260 Kein Tag hat's noch erhellt — da geht Ihr durch,
Es führt Euch in ein heitres T a l der Freude —
Doch schnellen Schritts müßt Ihr vorüber eilen;
Ihr dürft nicht weilen, wo die Ruhe wohnt.

Parricida

O Rudolf! Rudolf! Königlicher Ahn!
3265 So zieht dein Enkel ein auf deines Reiches Boden!

Tell

So immer steigend kommt Ihr auf die Höhen
Des G o t t h a r d s , wo die ew'gen Seen sind,
Die von des Himmels Strömen selbst sich füllen.
Dort nehmt Ihr Abschied von der deutschen Erde,
3270 Und muntern Laufs führt Euch ein andrer Strom
Ins Land Italien hinab, Euch das gelobte —

(Man hört den Kuhreihen von vielen Alphörnern geblasen.)

Ich höre Stimmen. Fort!

Hedwig

(eilt herein)

Wo bist du, Tell?
Der Vater kommt! Es nahn in frohem Zug
Die Eidgenossen alle —

Parricida

(verhüllt sich)

Wehe mir!
3275 Ich darf nicht weilen bei den Glücklichen.

Tell

Geh, liebes Weib! Erfrische diesen Mann,
Belad' ihn reich mit Gaben; denn sein Weg
Ist weit, und keine Herberg' findet er.
Eile! Sie nahn.

Hedwig

Wer ist es?

Tell

Forsche nicht!
3280 Und wenn er geht, so wende deine Augen,
Daß sie nicht sehen, welchen Weg er wandelt!

(Parricida geht auf den Tell zu mit einer raschen Bewegung; dieser aber
bedeutet ihn mit der Hand und geht. Wenn beide zu verschiedenen
Seiten abgegangen, verändert sich der Schauplatz, und man sieht in der

LETZTEN SZENE

den ganzen Talgrund vor Tells Wohnung, nebst den Anhöhen, welche
ihn einschließen, mit Landleuten besetzt, welche sich zu einem ma-
lerischen Ganzen gruppieren. Andere kommen über einen hohen Steg,
der über den Schächen führt, gezogen. *Walter Fürst* mit den beiden
Knaben, *Melchtal* und *Stauffacher* kommen vorwärts; andere drängen
nach; wie *Tell* heraustritt, empfangen ihn alle mit lautem Frohlocken.)

Alle

Es lebe Tell, der Schütz und der Erretter!

(Indem sich die Vordersten um den Tell drängen und ihn umarmen, erscheinen noch *Rudenz* und *Berta*, jener die Landleute, diese die Hedwig umarmend. Die Musik vom Berge begleitet diese stumme Szene. Wenn sie geendigt, tritt Berta in die Mitte des Volks.)

Berta

Landleute! Eidgenossen! Nehmt mich auf
In euern Bund, die erste Glückliche,
3285 Die Schutz gefunden in der Freiheit Land.
In eure tapfre Hand leg' ich mein Recht,
Wollt ihr als eure Bürgerin mich schützen?

Landleute

Das wollen wir mit Gut und Blut.

Berta

Wohlan!
So reich' ich diesem Jüngling meine Rechte,
3290 Die freie Schweizerin dem freien Mann!

Rudenz

Und frei erklär' ich alle meine Knechte.

(Indem die Musik von neuem rasch einfällt, fällt der Vorhang.)

FAMILIAR QUOTATIONS

1. Das Tier hat auch Vernunft. (Werni, 57.)
2. Dem nächsten muß man helfen. (Kuoni, 107.)
3. Wo's not tut, läßt sich alles wagen. (Tell, 136.)
4. Der brave Mann denkt an sich selbst zuletzt. (Tell, 139.)
5. Vom sichern Port läßt sich's gemächlich raten. (Ruodi, 141.)
6. Mit eitler Rede wird hier nichts geschafft. (Tell, 148.)
7. Ich hab' getan, was ich nicht lassen konnte. (Tell, 160.)
8. Der kluge Mann baut vor. (Gertrud, 274.)
9. Dem Mutigen hilft Gott. (Gertrud, 313.)
10. Unbilliges erträgt kein edles Herz. (Gertrud, 317.)
11. Die Unschuld hat im Himmel einen Freund. (Gertrud, 324.)
12. Die letzte Wahl steht auch dem Schwächsten offen.
    (Gertrud, 328.)
13. Was Hände bauten, können Hände stürzen. (Tell, 388.)
14. Das schwere Herz wird nicht durch Worte leicht. (Tell, 419.)
15. Die schnellen Herrscher sind's, die kurz regieren. (Tell, 423.)
16. Dem Friedlichen gewährt man gern den Frieden. (Tell, 429.)
17. Die Schlange sticht nicht ungereizt. (Tell, 430.)
18. Beim Schiffbruch hilft der Einzelne sich leichter. (Tell, 434.)
19. Ein jeder zählt nur sicher auf sich selbst. (Tell, 436.)
20. Verbunden werden auch die Schwachen mächtig.
    (Stauffacher, 437.)
21. Der Starke ist am mächtigsten allein. (Tell, 438.)
22. Wie soll die rasche Jugend sich bezähmen! (Fürst, 485.)
23. Die Gerichte Gottes sind gerecht! (Fürst, 553.)
24. O, mächtig ist der Trieb des Vaterlands. (Attinghausen, 849.)
25. Ans Vaterland, ans teure, schließ' dich an. (Attinghausen, 923.)
26. Doch Redlichkeit gedeiht in jedem Stande. (Stauffacher, 1086.)
27. Gott ist überall, wo man das Recht verwaltet,
    Und unter seinem Himmel stehen wir. (Rösselmann, 1115 f.)
28. Herrenlos ist auch der Freiste nicht. (Stauffacher, 1217.)

29.   Schrecklich immer,
Auch in gerechter Sache, ist Gewalt.
Gott hilft nur dann, wenn Menschen nicht mehr helfen.
                                        (Reding, 1321 ff.)

30.   Bill'ge Furcht erwecket sich ein Volk,
Das mit dem Schwerte in der Faust sich mäßigt. (Fürst, 1375 f.)

31. Der Eifer auch, der gute, kann verraten. (Rösselmann, 1391.)

32. Die Zeit bringt Rat. (Reding, 1438.)

33. Man muß dem Augenblick auch was vertrauen. (Reding, 1439.)

34. Wir wollen sein ein einzig Volk von Brüdern. (Rösselmann, 1449.)

35. Wir wollen trauen auf den höchsten Gott
Und uns nicht fürchten vor der Macht der Menschen.
                                        (Reding, 1453 f.)

36. Raub begeht am allgemeinen Gut,
Wer selbst sich hilft in seiner eignen Sache. (Stauffacher, 1465 f.)

37. Ein rechter Schütze hilft sich selbst. (Tell, 1480.)

38. Früh übt sich, was ein Meister werden will. (Tell, 1482.)

39. Den schreckt der Berg nicht, der darauf geboren. (Tell, 1513.)

40. Die Axt im Haus erspart den Zimmermann. (Tell, 1515.)

41. Ein jeder wird besteuert nach Vermögen. (Tell, 1525.)

42. Wer gar zu viel bedenkt, wird wenig leisten. (Tell, 1533.)

43. Tue recht und scheue keinen Feind. (Tell, 1545.)

44. Der kann nicht klagen über harten Spruch,
Den man zum Meister seines Schicksals macht. (Geßler, 1935 f.)

45.   Der ist mir der Meister,
Der seiner Kunst gewiß ist überall. (Geßler, 1941 f.)

46.   Zu weit getrieben,
Verfehlt die Strenge ihres weisen Zwecks,
Und allzustraff gespannt, zerspringt der Bogen. (Rudenz, 1995 ff.)

47.   Man führt die Waffen nicht vergebens.
Gefährlich ist's, ein Mordgewehr zu tragen,
Und auf den Schützen springt der Pfeil zurück. (Geßler, 1973 ff.)

48. Seid einig — einig — einig. (Attinghausen, 2452.)

49. Des Bauern Handschlag ist auch ein Manneswort.
                                        (Melchtal, 2488.)

50. Es bringt die Zeit ein anderes Gesetz. (Melchtal, 2552.)

51. Es lebt ein Gott, zu strafen und zu rächen. (Tell, 2597.)

52. Dem Schwachen ist sein Stachel auch gegeben. (Tell, 2676.)

53. Es kann der Frömmste nicht im Frieden bleiben,
    Wenn es dem bösen Nachbar nicht gefällt. (Tell, 2683 f.)
54. Rache trägt keine Frucht. (Fürst, 3013.)
55. Dem neuen Herrn tun tapfre Freunde not. (Stauffacher, 3028.)
56. Die Liebe will ein freies Opfer sein. (Fürst, 3075.)
57. Wer Tränen ernten will, muß Liebe säen. (Melchtal, 3082.)
58. Das Unglück spricht gewaltig zu dem Herzen. (Hedwig, 3124.)

FRAGEN

ERSTER AUFZUG

ERSTE SZENE

1. Wo spielt diese Szene?
2. Wie heißt der See? Warum?
3. Was sieht man auf der Bühne?
4. Was hört man, als der Vorhang aufgeht?
5. Wo ist der Fischerknabe und was tut er?
6. Warum fängt er nicht gleich an zu singen?
7. Was ist der Kuhreihen? Woher der Name?
8. Was erzählt das Lied des Fischerknaben?
9. Wo ist der Hirte und was macht er?
10. Was sind Matten? Was ein Senn?
11. Warum muß er scheiden? Wohin geht er?
12. Wann will er wiederkommen? Warum?
13. Welche Jahreszeit haben wir hier?
14. Wo steht der Alpenjäger und was sieht er?
15. Warum ist kein Frühling da?
16. Welches Meer ist hier gemeint?
17. Warum haben die drei Sänger bis jetzt keine Namen?
18. Welche Namen bekommen sie?
19. Beschreiben Sie das Kommen des Sturmes.
20. Warum läßt Schiller den Sturm heranziehen?
21. Wie weiß Ruodi, daß einer kommt?
22. Was ist der graue Talvogt? Der Firn?
23. Wo ist der Mythenstein?
24. Was für eine Haube zieht er an?
25. Warum glaubt Kuoni, daß es Regen gibt?
26. Warum braucht Seppi nicht nach dem Vieh zu sehen?
27. Was ist ein Geläute?
28. Woher weiß Kuoni, daß das Vieh sich nicht verlaufen?
29. Warum trägt Lisel ein Band um den Hals?
30. Wie beweist Werni, daß Tiere auch Vernunft haben?
31. Wo gehen die Gemsen zur Weide?
32. Was ist eine Vorhut? Wozu dient sie?

33. Warum kehrt der Jäger nicht immer wieder?
34. Wer erscheint jetzt und wie kommt er?
35. Warum hat er solche Eile?
36. Wie soll Ruodi ihm helfen?
37. Warum tut er es nicht gleich?
38. Was fragt ihn Ruodi und warum antwortet er nicht?
39. Warum fürchtet er sich so sehr?
40. Was hat er getan?
41. Was denken die anderen darüber?
42. Warum schafft ihn Ruodi denn nicht hinüber?
43. Wie breit ist hier der See?
44. Warum kann Baumgarten nicht warten?
45. Warum glauben die anderen, daß Ruodi doch helfen sollte?
46. Was antwortet Ruodi darauf?
47. Wie kommt es, daß Werni den Tell gleich erkennt?
48. Wie antwortet Kuoni auf Tells Frage?
49. Wie sucht Tell, den Ruodi zur Hilfe zu bewegen?
50. Warum will Ruodi es trotzdem nicht?
51. An welchem Tage spielt diese Szene?
52. Warum rettet Tell dann selber den Baumgarten?
53. Welch Andrer soll aus Sturmes Nöten helfen?
54. Was soll Kuoni Tells Frau sagen?
55. Welchen Vorwurf macht Kuoni dem Fischer?
56. Wie entschuldigt sich dieser?
57. Wie sehen wir noch das Schifflein, nachdem Tell abgestoßen?
58. Wie war das Hilfe in der Not?
59. Welche Reiter kommen jetzt?
60. Was verlangen sie?
61. Welche Antwort bekommen sie?
62. Wie rächen sie sich dafür, daß Baumgarten entkommen?
63. Wozu dient die Frage am Schluß der Szene?
64. Welches sind die besten Zeilen und Stellen in der Szene?

Aufsätze: 1. Die Geschichte Baumgartens. 2. Tells erstes Auftreten. 3. Der Druck der Vögte. 4. Anfang und Ende der Szene als Kontraste. 5. Bilder für die Szene.*

* Suppose you were making the pictures for an illustrated edition of the play, what pictures would you draw, so as best to help tell the story and show characters, costumes, scenery, etc.?

ZWEITE SZENE

1. Was und wo ist Steinen?
2. An welchem Tage spielt die Szene?
3. Wo steht Stauffachers Haus?
4. Wer ist Pfeifer und warum ist er hier?
5. Worüber sprechen die beiden Freunde?
6. Welchen Rat gibt Pfeifer und was wünscht er?
7. Wie ist hier „Reich" zu verstehen? „Östreich"?
8. Wer ist Stauffachers Wirtin und warum nennt er sie so?
9. Warum kann Pfeifer nicht bleiben?
10. Warum soll man den Druck der Vögte geduldig tragen?
11. Warum soll man nicht zu Östreich schwören?
12. Was tut Stauffacher, nachdem Pfeifer gegangen ist?
13. Wer findet ihn und was fragt sie ihn?
14. Woher weiß sie, daß ein Kummer ihn drückt?
15. Welches Recht hat sie, sein Vertrauen zu fordern?
16. Woher wissen wir, daß er ein reicher Mann ist?
17. Beschreiben Sie sein Haus.
18. Warum ist er so traurig?
19. Erzählen Sie seine Begegnung mit Geßler.
20. Warum darf Gertrud auch über solche Dinge mitsprechen?
21. Warum grollt Geßler dem Stauffacher?
22. Warum ist er neidisch?
23. Warum ist er nicht so reich?
24. Welchen Herrn erkennt Stauffacher über sich?
25. Wer ist der Höchste in der Christenheit und warum?
26. Wer ist Herr über Geßler?
27. Warum leiden auch die Unterwaldner und Urner?
28. Was wissen wir schon von Landenberg?
29. Welchen Rat gibt Gertrud ihrem Mann?
30. Was für Freunde hat er in Uri?
31. Warum will er Gertruds Rat nicht folgen?
32. Was würde der Krieg für Land und Leute bedeuten?
33. Wie denkt Gertrud darüber?
34. Welche letzte Wahl steht ihr offen?
35. Glauben Sie, daß eine Mutter so sprechen könnte?
36. Woher wissen wir, daß sie keine Kinder hat?

37. Warum will Stauffacher jetzt doch nach Uri gehen?
38. Worüber will er mit seinen Freunden sprechen?
39. Was soll Gertrud tun, während er fort ist?
40. Warum erwartet er solches von ihr?
41. Warum führt Tell den Baumgarten zu Stauffacher?
42. Wo sind die beiden hergekommen?
43. Wie spät ist es jetzt am Tage?
44. Wie wird diese Szene mit der ersten verbunden?
45. Welches sind die schönsten Stellen in der Szene?

Aufsätze: 1. Gertrud, die Schweizer Portia. 2. Vogt und Bürger.
3. Stauffacher als Mann und Freund. 4. Das Reich und Östreich.
5. Bilder für die Szene.

DRITTE SZENE

1. Wo führt uns Schiller jetzt hin?
2. Warum nach diesem dritten Kanton?
3. An welchem Tage spielt die Szene?
4. Was geht auf der Bühne vor?
5. Wie weit ist die Feste schon fertig?
6. Was machen die Werkleute jetzt?
7. Was ist das Amt des Fronvogts?
8. Welche Befehle gibt er?
9. Warum treibt er die Leute so zur Arbeit?
10. Woran sehen wir, daß er böse ist?
11. Was denkt er von dem Volk?
12. Warum murrt das Volk?
13. Wie soll die Feste genannt werden und warum?
14. Warum lachen die Arbeiter?
15. Warum will der Steinmetz den Hammer wegwerfen?
16. Wo kommen Tell und Stauffacher her? Warum?
17. Warum führt uns Schiller schon vorher nach Altorf?
18. Was denkt Stauffacher über Zwing Uri?
19. Was beweist uns, daß es ein festes Schloß ist?
20. Was will die Trommel, die wir jetzt hören?
21. Wer führt den Zug und wer folgt?

22. Warum wird der Hut aufgesteckt?
23. Was sollen die Leute dann tun?
24. Was soll dem geschehen, der nicht gehorcht?
25. Was denkt das Volk über den Befehl?
26. Wie weiß der Gesell, daß es der Hut von Östreich ist?
27. Wie könnte der Hut das Volk verraten?
28. Wohin will Tell jetzt gehen? Warum?
29. Warum soll er länger bleiben?
30. Warum glaubt er, daß die Gefahr nicht groß ist?
31. Warum vergleicht er sie mit dem Föhn?
32. Wie sollen sich die Leute davor schützen?
33. Was will Stauffacher, daß Tell tue?
34. Warum will Tell nicht mit den andern zusammenstehen?
35. Was beweist, daß er das Vaterland doch nicht verläßt?
36. Warum will er dem Rat fernbleiben?
37. Wie will er seinen Freunden helfen?
38. Was hat ihn zum Mann der Tat gemacht?
39. Warum läßt ihn Schiller so allein stehen?
40. Warum der Auflauf um das Gerüste?
41. Wer ist Berta und warum ist sie hier?
42. Warum und wie will sie helfen?
43. Was denkt der Steinmetz von ihr?
44. Wie tut er ihr Unrecht?
45. Welches sind die besten Zeilen in der Szene?

Aufsätze: 1. Der Bau von Zwing Uri. 2. Der Mann des Rats und der Mann der Tat. 3. Der Hut und das Volk. 4. Des Schieferdeckers Tod. 5. Bilder für die Szene.

VIERTE SZENE

1. Wer ist Walter Fürst und wo wohnt er?
2. Wer ist Melchtal und wo ist er zu Hause?
3. Warum weilt er hier bei Fürst?
4. Warum soll er nicht herauskommen?
5. Was will er von Fürst wissen?
6. Warum muß er sich jetzt verbergen?

7. Warum hat der Bube ihm die Ochsen weggetrieben?
8. Warum sollte er den Buben nicht schlagen?
9. Worüber war er so zornig geworden?
10. Warum hat er jetzt Angst?
11. Warum haßt der Vogt seinen Vater?
12. Was glaubt Melchtal, jetzt tun zu müssen?
13. Welchen Rat gibt ihm Fürst?
14. Warum ist er auch nicht in Uri sicher?
15. Warum will Fürst die Tür nicht aufmachen?
16. Warum fühlte man sich in der alten Schweiz so sicher?
17. Warum ist das hier anders geworden?
18. Warum ist Fürst so erstaunt, als er die Tür öffnet?
19. Wie zeigt er, daß er sich freut, Stauffacher zu sehen?
20. Was fragt er Stauffacher?
21. Wie antwortet ihm dieser?
22. Was hat ihn nach Altorf geführt?
23. Was sagt er über die Sorgen der Schweizer?
24. Wie denkt Attinghausen darüber?
25. Welche Nachricht aus Unterwalden bringt Stauffacher?
26. Was will Fürst besonders über Baumgarten wissen?
27. Was hatte ihm dieser aus dem Melchtal berichtet?
28. Was für ein Mann ist Heinrich von der Halden?
29. Wer ist sein Sohn und warum wurde er flüchtig?
30. Wo befindet er sich jetzt?
31. Warum bestrafte Landenberg seinen Vater?
32. Welche Strafe mußte dieser erleiden?
33. Wie wird Stauffachers Bericht unterbrochen?
34. Was macht Melchtals Erscheinen so ergreifend?
35. Was tut er, da er hört, daß sein Vater wirklich blind ist?
36. Wie wird sein Schmerz noch vergrößert?
37. Was hat der Vogt seinem Vater noch getan?
38. Wie ändert sich jetzt Melchtals bitterer Schmerz?
39. Was denkt er von sich selbst?
40. Was will er jetzt tun?
41. Wie will er sich an dem Landvogt rächen?
42. Warum will ihn Fürst nicht gehen lassen?
43. Was will er tun, wenn die andern nicht helfen?
44. Warum denkt er, daß sie ihm nicht helfen wollen?

45. Warum glaubt er, daß die Hirten ihm beistehen werden?
46. Warum will er nicht länger warten?
47. Wie verteidigt sich der Hirsch? die Gemse? der Stier?
48. Was hören wir von Melchtals Verwandten?
49. Warum muß er in der Gemeinde schweigen?
50. Warum sollen die beiden anderen helfen?
51. Warum soll ihnen seine Not nicht fremd sein?
52. Warum ist für sie die Gefahr ebenso groß?
53. Was haben auch sie getan?
54. Wie zeigt Stauffacher, daß er tief gerührt ist?
55. Warum will Fürst erst mit den Edelleuten reden?
56. Wie zeigt sich der Charakter der drei in ihren Reden?
57. Wie alt denken Sie sich diese drei?
58. Warum will Melchtal die Edeln nicht um Hilfe bitten?
59. Warum haben sich diese nicht gegen die Vögte erhoben?
60. Was werden sie aber tun, wenn es not tut?
61. Warum müssen die Schweizer sich selbst helfen?
62. Warum soll Melchtal nicht nach Unterwalden gehen?
63. Warum will er dennoch gehen?
64. Was meint Stauffacher darüber?
65. Wer ist der Alzeller und was soll er tun?
66. Wo ist er jetzt? Warum ist er dort?
67. Warum dürfen sie sich nicht in Brunnen versammeln?
68. Was ist das Rütli und wo liegt es?
69. Warum will Fürst, daß sie sich dort beraten?
70. Was für Männer soll jeder mitbringen?
71. Wie wird der Bund der drei Männer geschlossen?
72. Wie verbindet das die drei Länder?
73. Wie wird dadurch diese Szene mit I, 2 verbunden?
74. Warum das Schweigen einige Pausen lang?
75. Was hofft Melchtal für seinen Vater?
76. Wie soll das geschehen?
77. Welches sind die besten Stellen in der Szene?

Aufsätze: 1. Zweck dieser Szene. 2. Geschichte Heinrichs von der Halden. 3. Bedeutung des Dreimännerbundes. 4. Charakter des jungen Melchtal. 5. Jüngling, Mann und Greis in Szene. 6. Bilder für die Szene.

ZWEITER AUFZUG
ERSTE SZENE

1. Wie lange nach dem ersten Aufzug spielt der zweite?
2. Wo ist der Schauplatz der Szene?
3. Welche Personen treten auf und wie sehen sie aus?
4. Wer ist Rudenz und warum kommt er?
5. Warum will Attinghausen nicht gleich mit ihm reden?
6. Warum trinkt jener mit den Knechten?
7. Wie spät ist es am Tage?
8. An welche Arbeit wollen die Knechte gehen?
9. Warum geht der Freiherr nicht mehr mit?
10. Wie alt ist er? Warum hier so alt?
11. Was sagt er darüber?
12. Wo haben wir Kuoni schon gesehen?
13. Warum ist er hier?
14. Warum will Rudenz nicht mit ihm trinken?
15. Was ist Feierabend?
16. Wie ist Rudenz gekleidet? Warum so?
17. Warum hat er es so eilig?
18. Welchen Vorwurf macht ihm sein Onkel?
19. Wie entschuldigt er sich?
20. Warum trägt er Pfauenfeder und Purpurmantel?
21. Was denkt er vom Landmann?
22. Wie denkt er über die Not der Seinen?
23. Wie könnten diese des Dranges los werden?
24. Warum haben sie nicht zu Östreich geschworen?
25. Warum ist der Freiherr erstaunt, das von ihm zu hören?
26. Welchen höheren Stolz, sagt Rudenz, sollte sein Onkel haben?
27. Was wäre besser, als hier zu Hause zu bleiben?
28. Was kann Rudenz nicht ertragen?
29. Was hofft er am Hof zu finden?
30. Was hat Rudenz verführt?
31. Wie wird er wohl später denken?
32. Wie wird es ihm am Kaiserhof ergehen?
33. Denkt Attinghausen besser von ihm, als er verdient?
34. Wie wird man ein Fürstenknecht?
35. Was ist ein Selbstherr?

36. Wie zeigt Attinghausen hier sein tiefes Gefühl?
37. Warum sollen Helm und Schild mit ihm begraben werden?
38. Was will er nicht beim Tode denken?
39. Warum sollen die Schweizer dem König nicht widerstehen?
40. Beschreiben Sie seine Macht.
41. Was bedeutet „sich untern Schirm des Adlers flüchten"?
42. Warum darf man den Kaisern nicht trauen?
43. Warum sich lieber an ein mächtig Haupt anschließen?
44. Welchen Erbherrn hat Rudenz im Sinne?
45. Warum soll er nach Luzern fahren?
46. Was wird er dort hören?
47. Was sagte schon Pfeifer darüber?
48. Was wird Habsburg tun, wenn Uri sich unterwirft?
49. Wie kennt Attinghausen sein Volk so gut?
50. Welches Adels sollte Rudenz sich rühmen?
51. Warum sollte er sich ans Vaterland anschließen?
52. Warum will Rudenz des Onkels Bitte nicht erfüllen?
53. Was zieht ihn auf die Seite Östreichs?
54. Wo haben wir Berta schon gesehen?
55. Warum ist sie jetzt in der Herrenburg?
56. Warum darf Rudenz nicht hoffen, sie zu besitzen?
57. Was ist eine Braut?
58. Warum nimmt Rudenz so plötzlich Abschied?
59. Warum hält ihn Attinghausen für wahnsinnig?
60. Warum ist dem Freiherrn das Herz so schwer?
61. Welches sind die schönsten Stellen in der Szene?

Aufsätze: 1. Die gute alte Zeit. 2. Der fremde Zauber. 3. Liebe und Vaterland im Kampfe. 4. Der Charakter Attinghausens. 5. Die Macht Östreichs. 6. Bilder für die Szene.

ZWEITE SZENE

1. Wo und wann spielt diese Szene?
2. Wo und was haben wir schon vom Rütli gehört?
3. Was ist auf der Bühne zu sehen?
4. Warum sind die Unterwaldner die ersten auf dem Platz?
5. Woher weiß man, wie spät es ist?

6. Welches Läuten hört man?
7. Warum klingt es so hell?
8. Warum läßt Melchtal Feuer anzünden?
9. Beschreiben Sie den See und den Regenbogen.
10. Was bedeutet dieser?
11. Warum kommen die Urner so spät?
12. Wieviel Männer bringt Stauffacher mit? Warum?
13. Was beginnt jetzt Melchtal zu erzählen?
14. Warum sagt er so wenig von seinem Vater?
15. Was will Stauffacher lieber von ihm hören?
16. Wie ging er nach Hause zurück?
17. Warum wählte er solche Wege?
18. Was ist eine Alpentrift?
19. Wie bekam er Essen und Trinken?
20. Warum waren die Sennhütten leer?
21. Von welchem neuen Greuel hatten die Leute gehört?
22. Was dachten sie darüber?
23. Wie wurde Melchtal empfangen?
24. Wie zeigten sich die Leute bereit, Melchtal zu folgen?
25. Wie fand dieser seinen Vater?
26. Warum weinte er da nicht?
27. Was tat er dann weiter?
28. Wie weit kam er hin?
29. Was fand er dort?
30. Wie gewann er die Leute für die gute Sache?
31. Wie konnte er in Schloß Sarnen kommen?
32. Was machte der Landvogt, als er ihn sah?
33. Warum erschlug er ihn nicht?
34. Warum ist Stauffacher so wohl bekannt?
35. Was hat er von Winkelried gehört?
36. Was ist ein Strauß?
37. Was sind eigne Leute?
38. Warum sind sie nicht zu verachten?
39. Welchen Streit haben Meier und Reding gehabt?
40. Warum legen sie ihn hier beiseite?
41. Wie weiß man, daß die Urner jetzt kommen?
42. Warum kommt der Pfarrer mit?
43. Warum sucht Baumgarten den Tell in der Menge?

44. Warum ist dieser nicht da?
45. Warum kommen sie bei Nacht und heimlich zusammen?
46. Was ist in der Versammlung ungesetzlich?
47. Wie wird das alles entschuldigt?
48. Welche Frage muß zuerst entschieden werden?
49. Wie entscheidet sie Rösselmann?
50. Warum will Stauffacher nicht Haupt des Tages sein?
51. Warum darf es nicht der Schmied?
52. Warum und wie wird Reding gewählt?
53. Welchen Eid schwört er?
54. Was ist der Zweck der Versammlung?
55. Warum sollen die drei Völker zusammenstehen?
56. Wo war, nach Stauffacher, die alte Heimat?
57. Warum mußten sie diese verlassen?
58. Wohin zogen sie aus?
59. Wie fanden sie das neue Land?
60. Warum beschlossen sie, dort zu bleiben?
61. Was machten sie im neuen Land?
62. Was haben sie nie vergessen?
63. Von welchen andern Zungen spricht Stauffacher?
64. Was hat er in dieser Rede bewiesen?
65. Was beweist er in der nächsten?
66. Warum wählten die Schweizer den Schutz der Kaiser?
67. Was ist die welsche Erde?
68. Was hat der Kaiser damit zu tun?
69. Warum zogen die Schweizer mit nach Rom?
70. Wie wurden die drei Lande regiert?
71. Warum wollte man dem Kaiser nicht gehorchen?
72. Erzählen Sie den Streit mit Einsiedeln.
73. Welches neue Joch will man nicht erdulden?
74. Warum gehört das Land nur den Schweizern?
75. Wer ist der fremde Herrenknecht?
76. Wann darf man sich selbst helfen?
77. Was ist der alte Zustand der Natur?
78. Was ist der Güter höchstes?
79. Welchen Vorschlag macht Rösselmann?
80. Wie wird er aufgenommen?
81. Was beweist, daß er nicht ernst gemeint?

82. Was wird dagegen vorgeschlagen?
83. Welchen Vorschlag macht nun Reding?
84. Warum ging Hunn nach Rheinfelden?
85. Welche anderen fand er dort und welches Glück hatten sie?
86. Wie wurde er behandelt?
87. Wer ist Herzog Hans und warum weinte er?
88. Wie beraubte ihn der König?
89. Welche große Frage stellt jetzt Reding?
90. Wie macht Fürst die Absicht der Schweizer klar?
91. Durch welche Mittel will er sie erreichen?
92. Warum soll das ohne Blut geschehen?
93. Was hofft Stauffacher?
94. Was muß zuerst getan werden?
95. Warum darf man nicht lange säumen?
96. Welcher Streit entsteht jetzt unter den Männern?
97. Wie schlichtet ihn Reding?
98. Was ist das Fest des Herrn? An welchem Tage?
99. Warum wollen sie so lange warten?
100. Wie soll Sarnen erobert werden? Wie Roßberg?
101. Was soll geschehen, nachdem die Burgen gefallen?
102. Was ist der Landsturm?
103. Warum fürchten sie Geßler so sehr?
104. Warum wird nichts über ihn beschlossen?
105. Was will Baumgarten gern tun?
106. Warum wird Tell hier genannt?
107. Woran sieht man, daß der Morgen kommt?
108. Wie zeigt uns Schiller die Schönheit der Morgenröte?
109. Was ist der Eid des neuen Bundes?
110. Warum werden drei Finger erhoben?
111. Was macht den Eid besonders heilig?
112. Was soll jeder nun tun?
113. Warum darf keiner sich selbst helfen?
114. Was bedeutet die Musik am Schluß?
115. Was sagt uns die aufgehende Sonne?
116. Welche Stellen sind die besten in der Szene? Warum?

Aufsätze: 1. Melchtals Heimkehr. 2. Stauffacher als Redner. 3. Kontrast mit II, 1. 4. Hauptinhalt dieser Szene. 5. Der Zauber der Natur in der Szene. 6. Bilder für die Szene.

DRITTER AUFZUG
ERSTE SZENE

1. Wo ist Tells Haus?
2. Was macht er jetzt?
3. Wo haben wir ihn zuletzt gesehen?
4. Warum spielen die Knaben mit einer Armbrust?
5. Um welche Hilfe bittet Walter?
6. Warum wird sie ihm versagt?
7. Worüber klagt die Mutter?
8. Warum sollen die Knaben alles lernen?
9. Was bedeutet „das Leben jeden Tag aufs neu' erbeuten"?
10. Was haben die Knechte von Tell erzählt?
11. Warum fürchtet sich dieser nicht?
12. Wie weit ist Altorf von Bürglen?
13. Warum soll Tell nicht dahin gehen?
14. Wie hat Hedwig vom Rütlibund gehört?
15. Welchen Unterwaldner rettete Tell und warum?
16. Was denkt Hedwig darüber?
17. Warum hat ihr Tell nicht davon erzählt?
18. Warum soll er von Altorf wegbleiben?
19. Warum soll er die Armbrust nicht mitnehmen?
20. Warum fürchtet Hedwig den Geßler? Tell nicht?
21. Wo war Tell einmal dem Geßler begegnet?
22. Was tat und sagte er damals?
23. Warum fürchtete sich Geßler?
24. Warum hat Hedwig solche Angst?
25. Warum soll Tell doch nach Altorf gehen?
26. Warum geht Walter mit?
27. Wie zeigt Hedwig am Schluß ihre Angst und Liebe?
28. Welche Stellen sind die besten in der Szene?

> *Aufsätze:* 1. Tell als Mann und Vater. 2. Hedwig als Frau und Mutter. 3. Kontrast zwischen Hedwig und Gertrud. 4. Bilder für die Szene.

ZWEITE SZENE

1. Wo und wann spielt diese Szene?
2. Woher weiß man das?
3. Was will Berta dem Rudenz erklären?
4. Was hat er ihr zu sagen?
5. Warum ist der Augenblick so teuer?
6. Warum sieht ihn Berta so streng an?
7. Warum darf er ihr nicht von Treue sprechen?
8. Was sind des Menschen nächste Pflichten?
9. Warum glaubt Berta, daß Rudenz schlimmer als Geßler ist?
10. Warum liebt sie das Volk?
11. Was hat Rudenz getan, das sie kränkt?
12. Was sagt sie ihm, das ihn doch freut?
13. Wie beweist sie ihm, daß sie noch an ihn glaubt?
14. Was soll er tun, um sie zu verdienen?
15. Was will der Kaiser mit ihrem Erbe machen?
16. Welches Schicksal droht ihr am Hofe?
17. Warum ist es ihr leicht, Rudenz für sein Volk zu gewinnen?
18. Welches Lebensglück hat er fast zerstört?
19. Wie soll er sich von Östreich losmachen?
20. Warum müssen die beiden jetzt scheiden?
21. Welche Stellen finden Sie besonders gut?

Aufsätze: 1. Glück und Pflicht wieder vereint. 2. Bedeutung der Szene für die Sache der Schweizer. 3. Bilder für die Szene.

DRITTE SZENE

1. Wie lange nach Szene 1 spielt diese Szene?
2. Woher weiß man das?
3. Beschreiben Sie was man auf der Bühne sieht.
4. Warum vermeiden es die Leute, über den Platz zu gehen?
5. Wo haben wir den Hut schon gesehen?
6. Welchen Befehl hatte Geßler gegeben?
7. Wie ist „das Gesindel" zu verstehen?
8. Warum fürchten sich solche Leute nicht?

9. Warum machen die andern den langen Umweg?
10. Warum dachte Frießhard, viele zu fangen?
11. Wie hat Rösselmann das verhindert?
12. Warum fiel Frießhard mit aufs Knie?
13. Warum erzählt er dem Leuthold dieses?
14. Was denkt dieser über sein Amt?
15. Was für ein Mann ist er? Frießhard?
16. Was denken die Weiber über den Hut?
17. Warum achten Tell und Walter nicht darauf?
18. Wo kommen sie her und was wollen sie in Altorf tun?
19. Was hat Walter vom Meister Hirt gehört?
20. Was sind Firnen und weiße Hörner? Schlaglawinen?
21. Warum fallen diese nicht auf Altorf?
22. Was ist ein Flecken?
23. Von welchem großen Land spricht Tell?
24. Wie sieht es dort aus?
25. Warum will Walter doch nicht dort leben?
26. Warum kümmert sich Tell nicht um den Hut?
27. Warum wird er erst jetzt verhaftet?
28. Beschreiben Sie den Streit, welcher jetzt entsteht.
29. Wie wollen Tells Freunde ihm helfen?
30. Warum will er diese Hilfe nicht annehmen?
31. Wie wird ein Kampf verhindert?
32. Wie weiß man, daß Geßler jetzt kommt?
33. Wie erscheint er, und wer kommt mit?
34. Warum hat er den Falken auf der Faust?
35. Was zeigen seine ersten Worte?
36. Warum die allgemeine Stille?
37. Was berichtet Frießhard?
38. Was bedeutet „über frischer Tat"?
39. Wie kommt es, daß Geßler den Tell gleich erkennt?
40. Wie entschuldigt sich jetzt Tell?
41. Warum schweigt Geßler eine Weile?
42. Auf welchen Gedanken wird Geßler durch Walter gebracht?
43. Was soll dem Tell geschehen, wenn er den Apfel nicht trifft?
44. Was denkt Tell über diese Strafe?
45. Was droht ihm Geßler, wenn er nicht schießt?
46. Wie denkt sich Berta den grausamen Befehl?

47. Wodurch zeigt Geßler, daß er ihn ernst meint?
48. Wie suchen Berta und Harras zu helfen?
49. Wie will Geßler zeigen, daß er nicht grausam sei?
50. Warum könne Tell nicht klagen?
51. Wie könne er zeigen, daß er wirklich ein Meister ist?
52. Wie versucht Fürst den Tell zu retten?
53. Warum fürchtet sich der Knabe nicht?
54. Welchen letzten Versuch machen andere?
55. Warum will Walter nicht gebunden sein?
56. Warum sollen ihm die Augen nicht verbunden werden?
57. Warum bittet er den Vater zu schießen?
58. Warum können die Landleute nichts tun?
59. Was wünscht Melchtal?
60. Warum sollen die Bauern nicht Waffen tragen?
61. Was fühlt Tell, da er sich zum Schuß fertig macht?
62. Welche letzte Bitte richtet er an Geßler?
63. Wodurch zeigt sich Geßler unmenschlich grausam?
64. Beschreiben Sie Tells fürchterlichen Kampf.
65. Was bedeutet dieser Kampf für das ganze Drama?
66. Warum tritt jetzt Rudenz so kühn hervor?
67. Warum will er nicht länger schweigen?
68. Wie ist er jetzt anders geworden?
69. Welches Recht hat er, sich mit Geßler zu messen?
70. Was hindert ihn, Geßler zum Kampf aufzufordern?
71. Was war der ritterliche Brauch bei solchem Kampfe?
72. Welche Bedeutung hat dieser Streit für den Charakter des Rudenz?
73. Wann hat Tell geschossen?
74. Warum sehen wir den Schuß nicht?
75. Warum ist Fürst so ergriffen?
76. Welches Bild haben wir vom Tell nach dem Schuß?
77. Welchen Charakter zeigen die andern durch ihre Worte?
78. Warum ruft Geßler den Tell zurück?
79. Warum wird dieser verlegen?
80. Warum spricht er nachher so kühn?
81. Was wollte er mit dem zweiten Pfeil?
82. Was will Geßler mit ihm jetzt tun?
83. Warum darf er ihn nicht nach Küßnacht führen?
84. Warum glaubt er, es doch tun zu dürfen?

85. Warum nennt er die Schweizer Rebellen?
86. Welche Warnung gibt er ihnen?
87. Warum folgen ihm Berta und Rudenz?
88. Warum mußte Tell den Geßler reizen?
89. Warum haben Tells Freunde allen Mut verloren?
90. Warum erbarmt es Leuthold, den Tell wegzuführen?
91. Wie scheidet Tell von seinem Knaben?
92. Wen soll Walter jetzt Vater nennen?
93. Was läßt Tell seiner Frau sagen?
94. Warum reißt er sich schnell los?
95. Welche Stellen finden Sie besonders schön?

Aufsätze: 1. Vater und Sohn. 2. Rudenz spricht für sein Volk. 3. Geßlers Grausamkeit. 4. Inhalt der Szene. 5. Kontraste in der Szene. 6. Die Meisterszene des Dramas. 7. Der Wendepunkt des Ganzen. 8. Bilder für die Szene.

VIERTER AUFZUG
ERSTE SZENE

1. Beschreiben Sie den Schauplatz der Szene.
2. Wo und wann spielt sie? Wie weiß man das?
3. Was ist Gersau und wo liegt es?
4. Wer sind hier der Fischer und der Knabe? Warum?
5. Wo haben wir sie schon gesehen?
6. Warum sind sie jetzt hier?
7. Was hat Kunz gesehen?
8. Wie läßt Schiller auch uns das sehen?
9. Was denkt Ruodi vom Tell?
10. Was hat er früher einmal von ihm gesagt?
11. Warum ist Kunz hier gelandet?
12. Warum hat der Sturm Geßlers Abfahrt nicht verhindert?
13. Was erzählt Kunz weiter?
14. Warum will er nicht nach Hause fahren?
15. Warum klagt Ruodi über das, was er gehört?
16. Wie denkt er sich hier den Sturm (2142 ff.)?
17. Beschreiben Sie den Sturm.
18. Welches Läuten hört der Knabe?

19. Wer soll beten und für wen?
20. Warum ist die Gefahr hier so groß?
21. Womit wird der Sturm verglichen?
22. Wie weiß der Knabe, daß Geßler kommt?
23. Welcher Rächer hat ihn gefunden?
24. Warum ist er in so großer Gefahr?
25. Warum sieht der Knabe das Schiff nicht mehr?
26. Beschreiben Sie Tells Erscheinen.
27. Warum ist er „erstaunt"?
28. Warum wirft er sich nieder?
29. Warum hebt er die Hände zum Himmel?
30. Warum sind die Fischer so erstaunt, ihn zu sehen?
31. Was wollen sie wissen?
32. Erzählen Sie, wie Tell entkommen: seine Gedanken am Anfang; das Hervorbrechen des Sturmes; die Furcht der Knechte; wie er der Bande los wurde; was er dann tat und suchte; wo und wie er aus dem Schiff entsprungen; was er mit diesem gemacht.
33. Hat er Geßler treulos verlassen? Warum?
34. Wie kommt es, daß Ruodi die Platte schon kennt?
35. Was denkt Ruodi über Tells Rettung?
36. Warum fürchtet er noch für ihn?
37. Welchen Rat gibt er ihm?
38. Was beweist Tells Antwort?
39. Welchen Weg will Geßler nach Küßnacht nehmen?
40. Warum nimmt Tell einen kürzeren?
41. Um welchen Dienst bittet er?
42. Was ist ein Schwäher? Wer ist gemeint?
43. Warum sagt Tell nicht, was er tun will?
44. Wie viel sagen uns Ruodis Worte am Schluß?
45. Was gefällt Ihnen am besten in der Szene?

Aufsätze: 1. Die Natur in wildem Grimm. 2. Die Rettung Tells. 3. Bilder für die Szene.

ZWEITE SZENE

1. Wann spielt die Szene? Woher wissen wir das?
2. Woher weiß man schon, daß der Freiherr stirbt?

3. Warum sind die andern hier?
4. Wie weiß man, daß der Freiherr nicht tot ist?
5. Was führt Hedwig hierher?
6. Warum kann sie sich nicht fassen?
7. Warum tadelt sie ihren Mann?
8. Wie sucht ihn Fürst zu entschuldigen?
9. Wie denkt sich Hedwig den Apfelschuß?
10. Warum ist sie gegen Tell so ungerecht?
11. Warum sieht sie Baumgarten mit großem Blick an?
12. Warum tadelt sie ihn und die andern Freunde?
13. Warum konnten diese dem Tell nicht helfen?
14. Wo denkt sie, daß dieser jetzt ist? Warum?
15. Warum glaubt sie, daß er dort krank werden muß?
16. Wodurch zeigt sie ihren Stolz auf ihren Mann?
17. Warum will Attinghausen den Rudenz sehen?
18. Was hört er über ihn?
19. Warum fühlt er keinen Schmerz mehr?
20. Welcher Kummer trübt ihm die letzte Stunde?
21. Durch welche Hoffnung soll diese erhellt werden?
22. Warum hält er das kaum für möglich?
23. Warum kann er getrost zu Grabe steigen?
24. Welche Zukunft sieht er im Geiste für die Schweiz?
25. Was werden Adel und Bürger tun?
26. Was ist Bern? Zürich? Üchtland? Thurgau?
27. Beschreiben Sie Winkelrieds Heldentod.
28. Was ist des Adels Blüte?
29. Wie nimmt der Freiherr Abschied von seinem Volk?
30. Wie zeigt jeder seinen Schmerz?
31. Warum erscheinen die Knechte noch ein letztes Mal?
32. Warum die stumme Szene? Warum die Burgglocke?
33. Warum tritt Rudenz rasch ein?
34. Warum ist er nicht früher gekommen?
35. Warum hat das Schloß einen andern Namen?
36. Was bedauert Rudenz so ganz besonders?
37. Von welcher unbezahlten Schuld spricht er?
38. Was gelobt er in die Hand des Toten?
39. Was verspricht er den Schweizern?
40. Warum will ihm Melchtal die Hand nicht geben?

41. Warum tut er's am Ende aoch?
42. Wodurch zeigt er seinen Stolz?
43. Worauf wartet Rudenz in der kleinen Pause?
44. Warum verdient er, daß man ihm vertraut?
45. Warum hat er das Rütligeheimnis treu bewahrt?
46. Warum will und darf er rasch handeln?
47. Warum will er den Onkel noch nicht begraben?
48. Welch' eigne Sache hat er auszufechten?
49. Was ist der Berta geschehen?
50. Warum erwartet Rudenz, daß man ihm hilft?
51. Was hat den Melchtal gewonnen?
52. Warum bricht er seinen Rütlieid?
53. Was sollen die andern indessen tun?
54. Was soll die Botschaft des Sieges bringen?
55. Welche Stellen finden Sie besonders gut?

Aufsätze: 1. Frauenliebe und Mutterherz. 2. Die neue Zeit.
3. Attinghausens Tod. 4. Rudenz, durch Erfahrung gereift.
5. Bauer und Baron im Bund. 6. Bilder für die Szene.

DRITTE SZENE

1. Wo und wann spielt diese Szene?
2. Was sehen wir auf der Bühne?
3. Wo haben wir den Tell zuletzt gesehen?
4. Warum ist er jetzt hier?
5. Warum wählt er diesen Platz für seine Tat?
6. Warum haben wir hier einen langen Monolog?
7. Was hat Tell so verwandelt?
8. Warum glaubt er, den Vogt töten zu müssen und zu dürfen?
9. Wann hat er sich dazu entschlossen?
10. Was hat ihn dazu getrieben?
11. Welche heilige Schuld will er jetzt bezahlen?
12. Warum will er seinen Herrn und Vogt töten?
13. Von welchem Kleinod spricht er?
14. Welches Ziel meint er?
15. Warum hat er keinen zweiten Pfeil zu versenden?

16. Was für Leute ziehen diesen Weg, an dem er sitzt?
17. Was ist ein Kaufmann? ein Mönch? ein Pilger? ein Säumer?
18. Warum nennt er sein Geschäft „Mord"?
19. Warum denkt er immer wieder an seine Kinder?
20. Wodurch zeigt er seine Liebe zu ihnen?
21. Warum wird wieder der Grund zu dem „Mord" gegeben?
22. Warum zieht der Hochzeitszug über die Szene?
23. Warum will Tell nicht mit zur Hochzeit?
24. Von welchen Wunderdingen erzählt Stüssi? Warum?
25. Erzählen Sie von dem Ritter und den Hornissen.
26. Was bedeutet Tells Antwort?
27. Warum sieht er oft nach der Höhe des Weges?
28. Woher weiß Stüssi, daß Tell aus Uri ist?
29. Warum hören wir, daß der Vogt kommt, nicht kommt, doch kommt?
30. Warum stellt sich Armgard ihm in den Weg?
31. Wie verbindet Frießhard diese Szene mit IV, 1?
32. Warum kann er nicht bleiben und erzählen?
33. Warum sind Geßlers Knechte nicht da?
34. Warum geht Tell ab? Warum fragt Stüssi nach ihm?
35. Worüber spricht Geßler mit Harras?
36. Was erwartet der Kaiser von ihm?
37. Wie erklärt er den Hut zu Altorf?
38. Wie denkt Harras über diese Dinge?
39. Wie entschuldigt Geßler sein Tun?
40. Von welchem Kaiser, Vater, Sohn spricht er?
41. Erzählen Sie die Geschichte von Armgard und ihrem Mann.
42. Wie handelt Geßler an der armen Frau?
43. Was täte sie, wenn sie ein Mann wäre?
44. Warum hört man die Musik wieder und gedämpft?
45. Warum glaubt Geßler, ein milder Herrscher zu sein?
46. Was gelobt er jetzt? Warum viermal „will" in vier Zeilen?
47. Warum wählt Tell diesen Augenblick für seinen Schuß?
48. Woher weiß Geßler, daß das Tells Geschoß ist?
49. Warum sagt Tell so offen, daß er der Schütze ist?
50. Was hat er durch diese Tat erreicht?
51. Warum kommt der Brautzug wieder?
52. Welche Kontraste haben wir noch hier?

53. Warum will niemand helfen?
54. Was bedeutet Geßlers Tod für das Volk?
55. Was will Harras jetzt tun? Warum?
56. Welchem Zweck dient das Lied der Barmherzigen Brüder?
57. Welche Stellen gefallen Ihnen besonders?

Aufsätze: 1. Tell mit seinen Gedanken allein. 2. Zweck der Armgard Episode. 3. Geßlers Tod. 4. Kraft und Schönheit dieser Szene. 5. Bilder für die Szene.

FÜNFTER AUFZUG
ERSTE SZENE

1. Wo haben wir diesen Schauplatz schon gehabt?
2. Wie ist er jetzt anders geworden?
3. Warum brennen Signalfeuer? Was sagen die Glocken?
4. Warum ist Ruodi so tapfer geworden?
5. Warum will Fürst noch warten? Das Volk nicht?
6. Welche Nachricht bringt Melchtal?
7. Warum soll Fürst sich freuen?
8. Was erzählt Melchtal? Wie wurde Berta gerettet?
9. Warum haben die Schweizer gern geholfen?
10. Welches Bündnis wurde geschlossen?
11. Wie wurde Landenberg gefangen?
12. Warum tötete ihn Melchtal nicht?
13. Welchen Eid mußte er schwören?
14. Warum wird der Hut nicht verbrannt?
15. Was fürchtet noch Fürst?
16. Warum ist die Gefahr nicht groß?
17. Welche Nachricht wird gebracht?
18. Warum wurde der Kaiser ermordet?
19. Wo, wie, und von wem wurde er getötet?
20. Warum konnte ihm niemand helfen?
21. Warum sind die Pässe gesperrt, die Tore geschlossen?
22. Welche Rache will Agnes nehmen?
23. Was bedeutet „sich im Maientau baden"?

24. Was ist aus den Mördern geworden?
25. Warum ist den Schweizern des Kaisers Tod ein Segen?
26. Was erwartet man vom neuen Kaiser?
27. Was hofft die Königin von den Schweizern?
28. Warum wollen diese ihren Wunsch nicht erfüllen?
29. Was schlägt Stauffacher jetzt vor? Warum?
30. Welchen Zwecken dient diese Szene?
31. Welche Zeilen sind besonders gut?

Aufsätze: 1. Der Fall der Schlösser. 2. Die Rettung Bertas. 3. Melchtal, durch Leiden gereift. 4. Der Tod des Kaisers. 5. Der Brief der Königin. 6. Bilder für die Szene.

ZWEITE SZENE

1. Wann und wo spielt diese Szene?
2. Wo haben wir diesen Schauplatz schon gehabt?
3. Vergleichen Sie Hedwigs Glück mit ihrer Angst damals.
4. Wer ist der Mönch und was will er?
5. Warum will ihn Hedwig erquicken?
6. Warum weiß er nicht, wo er ist?
7. Warum glaubt Hedwig, daß er kein Mönch ist?
8. Warum geht sie nicht, um Tell zu grüßen?
9. Was beweist uns Tells erste Frage?
10. Was hat er mit seiner Armbrust getan?
11. Was erschreckt Hedwig?
12. Wie weiß Tell, wer der Mönch ist?
13. Warum schickt er Frau und Kinder hinaus?
14. Warum erwartet der Mönch Tells Hilfe?
15. Vergleichen Sie Tells Tat mit der Parricidas.
16. Warum hat dieser den Kaiser getötet?
17. Was ist die Acht? Warum will Tell doch helfen?
18. Warum muß Parricida fort? Wohin?
19. Warum zum Papst?
20. Beschreiben Sie den Weg, den er nehmen soll.
21. Was bedeuten die vielen Kreuze?
22. Warum stäubt die Brücke? Was ist das Tal der Freude?

23. Warum soll Hedwig nicht fragen, wer Parricida ist?
24. Welche Stellen gefallen Ihnen?

Aufsätze: 1. Zweck der Szene. 2. Tells Urteil über Parricida.
3. Die Frucht der Rache. 4. Bilder für die Szene.

LETZTE SZENE

1. Beschreiben Sie den veränderten Schauplatz.
2. Warum sind die vielen Leute hier?
3. Was verdanken sie dem Tell?
4. Wie begrüßen sie ihn?
5. Worum bittet Berta?
6. Warum will sie als Bürgerin geschützt werden?
7. Was denken die Leute von ihr?
8. Was erklärt sie dem Volk durch ihre letzten Worte?
9. Welchen Schluß hat dieses Drama der Freiheit?

Aufsätze: 1. Tell als Hauptperson des Dramas. 2. Schlußbild.

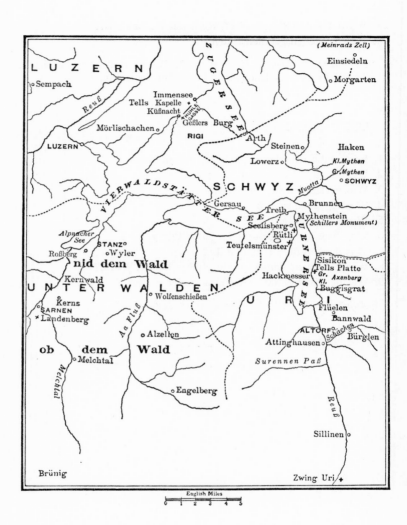

English Miles
0 1 2 3 4 5

ACT I SCENE 1

The asterisk (*) means that the note is on a word in the stage-direction before or after the line indicated. Translations are offered in single quotation marks, literal meanings in double quotation marks.

*Aufzug (from *aufziehen,* 'to draw up'), the raising of the curtain at the beginning of an act, then 'act.' Schiller uses *Akt* only in his earlier plays.

*Szene (pronounce *stsay'nuh*), German has two words for 'scene,' *Szene* and *Auftritt,* with a difference now often forgotten. *Auftritt* is strictly the "stepping up" on the stage of some important new character, so that we might have several *Auftritte* with one stage setting. A new *Szene* comes only with a new setting, no matter how many characters have entered. The scenes in *Tell* change only with the setting, so *Szene* is properly used.

*Vierwaldstättersee, lit. "Four-wood-steads (districts) lake," i.e. 'Lake of the Four Forest Cantons,' so named from the four cantons Uri, Schwyz, Unterwalden, and Luzern, lying around it; in English, Lake Lucerne.

*Schwyz (pronounce *y* as *ie*), dat. with **gegenüber;** the 'canton' just across the lake. Do not confuse *Schwyz* with *Schweiz* = Switzerland. The scene is laid then on the west shore of Lake Lucerne, in canton Uri, near Treib and directly opposite Brunnen. See map.

*unweit, now generally with genitive.

*Matten, Swiss for *Wiesen;* gives local color.

*sieht . . . liegen, 'sees lying.' Such an infinitive is also common with *finden, fühlen, heißen, hören, helfen* and is best translated by the present participle.

*Haken, a single peak east of Steinen, wrongly identified here with the two peaks **(Spitzen),** *der große Mythen* and *der kleine Mythen,* near by. The **Eisgebirge** (really not visible) are those of canton Glarus, directly east.

*noch ehe, emphatic, 'even before.'

*Kuhreihen, 'the (*or* a) Kuhreihen.' It is the Swiss herdsman's call to his cows, especially as he drives them in for the milking. Sometimes merely a call, it is usually a simple, plaintive melody, a "yodel" of long-drawn-out notes without words, though the names of the cows are also used. It is generally sung, but is also blown on the *Alphorn* (3271*) and has many variations, of which three are given in the songs below, skillfully provided with an accompaniment in the **Geläut'** of the herd-bells.

*Zeitlang, purposely continues the melody after the curtain goes up, delays the spoken word, and gives the spectator time to realize that he is looking upon a scene of rare beauty right in the heart of Swiss nature.

1. Es lächelt der See = *der See lächelt;* the very common *es* which anticipates the real subject. — **ladet,** old and poetic for *ladet . . . ein.* The poetic personification is striking.

9. es ruft, 'there's a call'; this impersonal *es,* different from the *es* in 1, is often used to lend an air of mystery.

10. Lieb, for *lieber.* The nom. or acc. of a neuter adj. often loses its ending in poetry and familiar style, but in masc. and fem. such omission is rare and poetic. — **bist,** poetry and familiar speech often omit the subject, as here; omit in English for the same effect.

12. Such superstitions about the attracting charm and power of the water are old and widespread. Swiss tradition gives Lake Calandari, near Chur, the mysterious power of drawing into its waters all who fall asleep near it. Goethe's famous ballad *Der Fischer* illustrates the same idea.

17. The cattle are driven by degrees up to the high mountain pastures (*zu Berg fahren*) in May or June, spend the summer grazing, and are then in September gradually driven down to the valleys (*zu Tal fahren* or *heimtreiben,* 62) for the winter in the barns (203–206). — **kommen** (present for future) **wieder,** repeats and explains the first half of the line. Line 16 dates the scene in a general way; 146 shows that it is Oct. 28, much too late for the home-coming of the herds. Note the highly poetic word-order in 17–20.

20. Brünnlein, intermittent springs, fed by melting snow, hence active only in summer; also called *Maibrunnen.*

25. Es donnern (cf. 1, note), i.e. with the noise of avalanches or the cracking ice of the glaciers. — **Steg,** 'path,' or possibly footbridge of tree trunks.

26. For prose (*Es*) *grauet dem Schützen nicht,* 'the hunter is not afraid'; lit. "there is no dread for," etc. Note the lengthened forms *grauet, pranget, grünet* required by the meter.

31. neblichtes Meer, 'sea of fog'; out of it, to an observer from a mountain peak above, the other peaks seem to rise like rocky islands; the hunter, standing on a peak, catches a glimpse of the lowlands through occasional rifts in the clouds below him.

35. Wassern, figuratively the 'waters' of the sea of cloud.

As yet the three singers are not named, because, so far, they are merely types of three classes of Swiss people. This people is the real hero of the play, so that we have thus three phases of his character, because each song is characteristic of the class the singer belongs to. It is a quiet, peaceable, even dreamy people, gentle, but brave and daring; they love their lakes and mountains and fear neither man nor Nature. This lyric introduction is used to put us at once in the midst of the idyllic scenes and characters among which the play is to be laid. The opening scenes in *Macbeth* have a similar purpose.

*A storm darkens the sunny landscape, forebodes the fast-coming conflict between people and rulers, and symbolizes the threatening tyranny so soon to blight the lives of these happy people.

***Ruodi** (pronounce *Rúⁿdi*), **Werni, Kuoni** (*Kúⁿni*), **Seppi,** Swiss diminutives from *Rudolf* (older *Ruodolf*), *Werner, Konrad* (older *Kuonrat*), and *Jo-seph;* *-i* and *-li* correspond to North German *-chen* and *-lein.*

37. Jenni (pronounce *Yénnee*), dim. of *Johann;* cf. Engl. 'Johnny.' — **Naue,** here Jenni's *Kahn,* usually a freight boat of some size.

38. Talvogt, "dale king," the driving fog masses personified. — **Firn,** the glaciers, formed by the condensed snows of many years; the reference is to the dull rumbling of the cracking ice.

39. Mythenstein, a rock rising eighty-five feet out of the lake close to shore near Treib; it was made into a monument to Schiller on his one hundredth birthday, Nov. 10, 1859. Ruodi means here the *Mythenstock,* one of the peaks mentioned in the opening stage-direction as covered by clouds, the 'hood' in question here. Schiller was never in the Alps, and such a mistake is very natural.

40. Wetterloch, some mountain gorge through which the wind blows fresher just before a storm; at first it is warmer, then colder as the storm breaks. In 38–40 we have the fisherman's weather signs, in 42–45 those of herdsman and hunter; Werni's would fit Ruodi better.

42. 's (=*es*) **kommt,** pron. "*skommt*". — **Wächter,** lit. "watcher"; 'Watch' is his dog.

46. Lug'...ob, South German and Swiss for *sehen, nachsehen.* Cf. Engl. 'look and see if.' — **verlaufen** (*hat*), note once for all this very common omission of the tense auxiliary after a past participle in a dependent clause.

47. Lisel, dim. of *Lise,* from *Elisabet;* the cow's name. — **am Geläut**(*e*), 'by (the sound of) her bell.'

48. keine mehr, 'no other' cow. — **die,** emphatic demonstrative for personal pronoun, 'she'; very common construction.

49. Ihr, the usual older word for modern *Sie,* with capital when one person is meant, small letter for several; so also *Euer,* 'your,' refers to one, *euer* to several. — **schön**(*es*) **Geläute** (cf. 10, note), 'fine set of bells'; each herdsman has a number of different-toned bells, blending with each other into a chime. — **Meister Hirt,** term of respect; he is head herdsman.

50. Landsmann, "fellow countryman" and very different from *Landmann,* "peasant"; a common familiar address.

51. meines...Herrn, des Attinghäusers, 'my master's, Baron Attinghausen's'; predicate genitives. — **mir zugezählt,** lit. "counted out to me," 'put in my charge.'

53. der Kuh (possess. dat.) **...zu Halse steht,** 'looks on that cow's neck.' — **Band,** the broad strap carries the bell which marks the leader of the herd.

55. nähm' ich, condensed condition = *wenn ich nehmen sollte.* — **ihr,** 'from her.'

56. nicht klug, 'foolish'; 'you don't know what you are talking about.'

57. das Tier, 'animals'; Engl. "the horse" = horses as a class.

59. Die, emphatic *sie,* 48, note. — **wo,** just like Engl. "where," often used for 'when.'

60. 'ne = *Eine.* This is said to be really true, as 55 is also true of the cows.

61. heller Pfeife = *hellem Pfeifen,* 'a sharp, hoarse call'; danger signal.

62. Cf. 17, note. — **Die Alp,** not "Alps," but mountain 'pasture.'

63. Glücksel'ge, poetic for *glückliche.* — **Die,** 'that,' 'the same.'

64. kehrt sich's = *kehrt man.* Hunting chamois is dangerous.

65. gelaufen, note once for all that in German such a verb of motion takes the past, in Engl. the present participle to express the mode of motion. The passage marks the beginning of the real action of the play.

66. Der Baumgart, familiar for *Baumgarten*. This use of the definite article implies that the person is well known; it sometimes adds contempt. Cf. Engl. "the Smith woman." — **Alzellen,** see map.

68. was gibt's ("what is there") **so eilig,** 'what's your hurry?' — **Bindet** *(den Kahn)* **los.**

70. was habt Ihr, 'what's the matter with you?' — **denn,** conveys the force of: 'I'd like to know.'

72. Landvogts, Beringer von Landenberg (the *Landenberger* of 282), imperial bailiff in Unterwalden, is meant; he lived in castle Sarnen. *Vogt,* generic term for governor, representing the Emperor and ruling in his stead, occurs in several compounds: Gessler is *Reichsvogt,* Wolfenschiessen is *Burgvogt* (77), a subordinate in charge of Rossberg. Cf. also *Talvogt* (38) and *Fronvogt* (* 353).

75. steh' (= *werde stehen*) . . . **Rede,** 'I'll answer (talk to) you.'

78. Wolfenschießen, one of the younger Swiss nobles induced by the Austrian court to take sides against his own country. Cf. Act II, sc. 1, especially 946. The village of Wolfenschiessen was the family home. See map. — **Läßt . . . verfolgen,** 'is he having you pursued.' — **der** is strongly emphatic.

81. Add *getan hätte.*

82. Hausrecht, it was his legal '(household) right' to kill the invader of his home.

83. und *(der Ehre)* **meines Weibes,** i.e. against him who attacked the honor of them both.

86. Hat; Gott and **Axt,** each in turn, is subject; a common construction, especially when the verb stands first.

89. er, Ruodi.

92. lieg', hab', sei depend upon an omitted *sie sagte;* this shows Baumgarten's excitement and increases the dramatic tension.

94. Ungebührliches . . . verlangt, 'made insulting demands.'

96. lief frisch (here, as often = *schnell*) **hinzu,** 'ran up quickly.'

97. hab' . . . gesegnet, 'I blessed his bath for him'; bitter irony. The fatal blow here takes the place of the pious wish: "God bless your bath" spoken by the attendant of the mediaeval bather. Cf. Engl. "he got a blessing" = threshing.

100. ums, 'from, at the hands of.' His tyranny is no new thing.

101. mir wird nachgesetzt, 'I am pursued.' The active form *man setzt mir nach* becomes in the passive *es wird mir nachgesetzt,* and *es* is then omitted, as in 26.

103. Note change from *Ihr* to *du;* due to strong feeling here, as often.

104. *(Es)* **geht nicht,** "it's no go"; 'can't do it.' After a look at the water Ruodi returns.

105. Heiliger Gott, 'Great God!' or 'Good Lord!' By no means irreverent.

106. tötet, 'means death.'

108. ja, 'Why!' at beginning, or 'you know' at the end of the sentence.

109. Der Föhn ist los (lit. "loose"), 'The Föhn is up.' It is a violent south wind, very dangerous to boats and apt to start fires in the villages unless precautions are taken.

111. mein, frequent in poetry for *meiner* (gen. of *ich*). A passionate appeal for help.

115. Kind, in poetry often as plural; so in Engl. Ruodi isn't a coward, he merely shrinks from what seems impossible.

121. Rettungsufer, acc. absolute (31, note), 'with the . . . in sight.' The other shore is less than a mile away.

124. hinübertrüge, 'might (would) carry me across.'

125. muß = *ich muß;* we wonder why he doesn't escape by land.

126. der Tell, cf. 66, note. — **Bürglen,** Tell's home and traditional birthplace, a hamlet a mile or so from Altorf. Tell's first word at once shows his character.

130. Königs, Albrecht von Habsburg, called both *Kaiser* and *König* without distinction in the play. His title was really only *Deutscher König,* because (though duly elected) he was never actually crowned emperor. — **saß,** 'had his seat' (castle).

135. zeugen = *bezeugen.* — **zu wagen** *(ist).*

136. läßt . . . wagen, 'anything may be risked.' Schiller often uses these very short speeches to gain vivid dramatic action, to emphasize character, and to drive home a truth; many such lines in *Tell* are almost proverbs now.

139. brave, 'real, true'; *brav* is more than 'brave.'

141. läßt ... raten, 'it's easy to advise.'

143. 'The lake may have pity, the governor cannot.'

144. *Hirten, Kuoni and Seppi; **Jäger,** Werni.

145. und (emphatic) **wär's,** 'even if it were.' — **und,** 'or.' — **leiblich**(*es*) = *eigenes.*

146. kann, emphatic change to indicative instead of *könnte.* — **Simons und Judä** (*Tag*), 'St. Simon's and St. Jude's day'; *Judä* is Latin genitive of *Judas.* Simon the Canaanite (not Simon Peter) and Jude, son of James (not Iscariot), are meant. While the season is indicated by 16, 61, this fixes the date of the scene exactly, Oct. 28. As Albrecht of Habsburg was murdered May 1, 1308, this must be Oct. 28, 1307. It is about noon — which would give Baumgarten time to get here from his home.

149. dem ... Hilfe (prose adds *zuteil*) **werden,** 'the man must be helped'; *werden* with dat. of recipient means "to be given to." Cf. 646.

152. Characteristic of Tell, the modest man of action (127, 148 ff.); his ready sympathy is touched, with quick decision and daring heroism, all the more splendid because it is unconscious, he helps his fellow man, whose name even he does not know, while Ruodi in the grip of his superstition is overawed by the danger. Schiller often uses such contrasts to paint character and add dramatic tension.

155. Wohl, 'True! (To be sure!).'

158. in (*die Hand*) **der Menschen.**

159. was (for *etwas*) **Menschliches** ("any human fate"), 'if anything should happen to me.'

160. lassen, "let alone," 'leave undone'; helpfulness is second nature to him. Schiller purposely allows only a glance (125–160) at Tell, but it is enough to show his essential character in bold relief and to begin the "Tell plot," for this rescue of Baumgarten hints at what he may do for the whole people, whose distress is typified by the wrong Baumgarten suffers.

161. Meister (cf. Engl. 'master' workman), different from 49; has here the accent and a reproachful sense.

163. Wohl, 'even.' — **beßre,** i.e. than I am.

166. d(*a*)**rüber weg,** 'over it.' The passage shows us Tell through the eyes of others and vivid action off the stage.

171. weiß Gott, sie sind's, 'Good Heavens! there they are.'

173. Des = *dieses*, as indicated by spaced type and strong accent; this adverbial gen. is very common, especially with *kommen, gehen, fahren.*

175. Reit (= *Reit't* = *Reitet;* cf. *fürcht't*, 133) **zu,** 'ride on.'

176. Wenn . . . beilegt, 'if you hurry'; *beilegen*, lit. "lay to," seems to be a nautical word mistaken by Schiller for 'lay on' (spurs?) and does not occur elsewhere in this sense. Werni's speech is natural — from a safe place.

178. Ihr . . . uns (ethical dat.) **büßen,** 'you shall pay for it.' — **in,** 'upon.'

182. The bright opening of the scene is in strong contrast with this cry of despair. Yet in this despair is the vague hope that help may soon come.

This scene is often praised for its skillful dramatic exposition. In 182 lines we are made acquainted with Swiss scenery in all its romantic beauty and wild grandeur (the scenery is almost one of the players in this drama) and with the character and daily lives of several types of the people; we learn at once the theme of the play, just resistance by an outraged people to ruthless oppression; the cause of the coming conflict in a typical example of that oppression; and in a glance at Tell, the calm, strong, brave man, the unassuming, unselfish citizen, we see the cool and courageous deliverer, who later comes to the rescue, not of an individual but of a whole people. The characters are well drawn, the tension of the action is high, the setting is admirable, the close leaves us keenly expectant. It is the overture for the whole, with all the themes and motifs of the play that is to follow. The scene unites in a way all three plots of the play (cf. Introduction, p. xxix); the people and their wrongs belong to the folk plot, the rescue of Baumgarten to the Tell plot (because Tell acts as a private individual). The mention of Attinghausen suggests the nobles, whose part is developed later.

ACT I SCENE 2

Tell carries Baumgarten across the lake to canton Schwyz; Schiller takes us there in advance of them and shows us how things look before they arrive; this links the scenes together, with only time enough for the journey between them.

*Stauffacher, Tschudi's *Wernherr von Stauffach,* a historical character; the chroniclers say an influential citizen of old burgher family still living in 1341 near **Steinen,** a village some three miles from Schwyz. See map.

*Pfeifer, an invented character used here to embody and express the political views of the canton and city of Luzern, which, by right of purchase, had belonged to the counts of Habsburg (i.e. Austria) since 1291 and which feel their tyranny as much as other cantons. His well-founded advice prepares the way for Gertrud's talk with her husband.

184. Östreich, short for *Österreich;* both forms are used in the play.

185. Reich (= *das deutsche Reich*), to the Empire, whoever may be emperor; he does not say *Kaiser* because he knows the present emperor wants to enslave them. The cantons owed direct allegiance to the Empire, because that meant (1) protection against grasping neighbors, especially the Habsburg Dukes of Austria, and (2) almost complete home rule, since the Emperor was far away. When Albrecht of Habsburg was elected emperor, he declined their homage to him as Emperor and demanded their submission to him as Duke of Austria (to be governed as he chose and not by home rule), claiming the cantons as private property and thus seeking to secure them to Habsburg as vassals, even though, after his death, the imperial throne should pass, by election, to some other House. For a discussion of these important relations see Introduction, pp. xviii–xxi.

186. *will, 'is about to.'

187. Bleibt doch, 'do stay'; *doch* strengthens the invitation. — **Wirtin,** short for old Swiss *Ehewirtin,* 'wife.'

189. Viel(en) Dank (10, note), acc. absolute; 'Many thanks!' — **Gersau,** on the lake just under the Rigi.

190. Was . . . Schweres, 'whatever hardship'; *auch,* often also *nur* or *immer,* generalizes *was.* The parting of the two friends is only the end of a talk which we think of as a long, serious discussion of the whole political situation, which prepares Stauffacher to accept his wife's argument for resistance.

193. ans Reich gelangen, 'come to the throne'; because each new emperor was then elected and the choice might easily fall upon some other House than Habsburg. That is just what did happen in this case.

194. erst, 'once.' — **seid ihr's,** 'you are' ('it' = the first half-line) 'hers.'

*A bit of silent byplay that is very impressive; Stauffacher is deeply troubled, his wife watches him in silence that is eloquent of her resolve to speak out and rouse him to action.

196. seh', 'have been watching' or 'have noticed'; note this idiomatic present with *schon* and *seit*, showing that past action is still going on.

198. Herzen, we should expect the acc. — **Gebresten,** now obsolete; here 'sorrow.' We recall at once Portia's words to Brutus: "some sick offense within your mind" and "make me acquainted with your cause of grief" in Act II, sc. 1 of *Julius Caesar.* This interview is so similar to that one that Gertrud has been called the Swiss Portia. The striking resemblance may be due to a performance of *Julius Caesar* in Weimar, Oct. 1, 1803, while Schiller was writing *Tell.*

203. Scharen and **Zucht,** both subjects of **ist** (205), which, as usual, agrees with the one nearest to it. This and other passages in the scene (188, 204, 209) show strong Homeric influence.

208. neu, not "newly," but 'recently.'

210. 'Its many windows shine bright and homelike.'

212. Even yet the better Swiss houses are often adorned with such 'wise sayings'; thus the gable may bear the date, the owner's name, his coat-of-arms and perhaps also his wife's or others, while below follows the *Spruch,* usually religious, sometimes comic in tone.

218. Vollbrachte, participle as noun; the finished house.

220. Vogt, Hermann Gessler von Bruneck, legendary *Landvogt* of Schwyz and Uri. See map for his castle near Küssnacht. The historical Gesslers lived in Aargau in the fourteenth century, but no Gessler ever ruled in Uri.

221. wundernd = *sich wundernd.*

222. erhub, old for *erhob.*

229. The line is not clear. **Eures** cannot agree with **Lehen,** but we may read: *ist meines Herrn, des Kaisers, und Eures (Herrn),* 'the house is "my" lord's . . . and "yours" (= "your" lord's too)' or *ist meines Herrn . . . und Eures* (= *Euer Haus*), 'is my "lord's" house and yours (= your house)' because you represent him. Against the first we might urge: why should Stauffacher anger Gessler by reminding him that "he" too is a subject, not a sovereign; against the second: why Gessler's angry reply (231 ff.) when he has just been assured that the house is his. Again Stauffacher is not the man to conciliate Gessler with a lie. Schiller found the ambiguity in Tschudi and perhaps purposely kept it.

232. Auf . . . Hand = *auf eigene Faust* (fist), "on one's own hook," i.e. 'whenever he pleases' and without asking permission. Oppression is rife in Schwyz, as well as in Uri (177 ff.) and Unterwalden (90 ff.). Here it is an attack upon property rights and a deliberate humiliation of sterling manhood. Pfeifer's advice (183 ff.) shows the general situation in Lucerne.

233. also, 'thus'; never "also." — **frei,** pred. adj., not adverb. — **hinleb'** and **baue,** optative subjunctives; **wär',** unreal subj.

240. rühm' ich mich, "I boast myself," 'I am proud to be.' Homeric idiom, as also **vielerfahrnen.** A Konrad Iberg is mentioned as magistrate in Schwyz in the year 1311; such parentage explains her heroic nature and ripe political judgment. Again she suggests Portia.

241. saßen, customary action, 'used to sit.'

244. Pergamente, "parchments," the 'charters' granted by former emperors, Friedrich II and Rudolf of Habsburg.

254. daß . . . nicht, i.e. a hindrance resulting in his "not" doing so; *nicht* is not needed, for its idea is contained in *Hindernis.* — **der Schwyzer,** not "the Swiss," but what? — **neuen Fürstenhaus,** the Habsburgs became Dukes of Austria only about thirty years before this time.

256. gehalten und getan (*haben*), emphatic, 'have always done.'

260. dir, for usual *auf dich.*

264. So gut, the expected *als* or *wie* is often omitted in such comparisons. He held his property in fief directly from the Emperor, every *Reichsfürst* did the same, hence their equal standing.

266. Since Charlemagne's time the German emperor, crowned by the Pope as head of the "Holy Roman Empire of the German Nation," claimed to be the highest lord in Christendom.

267. Younger sons got titles or money, but no lands.

272. Noch, 'as yet.' — **erwarten,** rare for *warten* or *es abwarten.*

277. Ob, old and poetic for *wegen* with gen. or *über* with acc.

281. schafft ('is doing') **es** (= things in general), 'is acting outrageously.'

282. überm See, in Unterwalden, where Landenberg (= **der Landenberg-er,** cf. Engl. "New York-er") was governor.

284 f. Gewalt-Beginnen = *Gewalttat,* rare division of a word at the end of a line; allowed because it passes unnoticed when the lines are spoken.

286. tät', old for *wäre.* — **euer etliche** = *einige von euch.*

288. erledigen, for prose *entledigen.* Note this first suggestion of united resistance, which bears fruit later on; coming from such a source it gains our sympathy at once.

294. angesehen(*e*) **große Herrenleute,** 'prominent, influential men,' of upper burgher class. Tourists are still so called in the Alps.

295. geheim, Tschudi's word, now means 'secret,' here in old sense "intimate," 'who are intimate and trusted friends of mine.'

297. stillen, 'inmost, secret'; his heart was anything but "quiet."

299. still, 'even in secret'; goes with *denken.*

304. Wir wagten (pret. subj.) **es,** 'we should dare' ('do you mean'?), rhetorical question, expects no answer. — **Es** = line 305.

305. Herrn, cf. 266, note. — He is not a coward, but merely a prudent man who counts the cost.

312–29. Again, as in 135 ff., the short speeches enliven the dialogue.

314. Cf. 10, note; the omission of both inflectional endings is rare and highly poetic.

327. das eure, i.e. of you women.

328. Again like Portia, she does not shrink from a last resort. Apparently she has no children; even 672 does not prove it (see note on that line).

331. Herd und Hof (oftener *Haus und Hof*), cf. Engl. 'house and home.' It is one of the many alliterative couplets so common in German conversation especially. Cf. *Geld und Gut, Mann und Maus, Leib und Leben, Stock und Stein;* and in Engl. "life and limb," "kith and kin," "hide and hair," "stock and stone." In both languages such forms use two words for the emphatic expression of one idea and are relics of the old alliterative poetry.

333. fahr', 'go,' used here, perhaps, because he would naturally go by boat, though *fahren* is often used for *gehen, reisen.* — **stehnden Fußes** ("with standing foot" = "just as I stand"), adverbial gen. = Lat. ablative absolute; translate, 'at once.'

334. mir, dat. of interest, 'of mine.' — **Fürst,** Tell's father-in-law; lives in Altorf (1539 ff.), a town near the south end of the lake.

336. Bannerherrn, 'banneret'; leader of the canton's troops in battle, an important man, entitled to carry the principal banner. *Der Freiherr* ('Baron') *von Attinghaus* (short form, as often, cf. 78, 129) is historical, a leading Swiss nobleman, chief magistrate of Uri, honored for his age, wealth, and manliness, and loved for his true, unselfish patriotism.

341. weil, here in its old sense *dieweil* (= *die Weile*, Engl. "the while"); *während* is now used instead.

342. Regimént, note the accent and distinguish from Engl. "regiment."

343. Gotteshause, the monastery of St. Meinradszell at Einsiedeln near Steinen and on the main road to Italy, then as now a great pilgrim resort. Cf. 520.

346. verbirgt . . . nicht, i.e. is open to the needy. — **zu äußerst** ("on the outside") **am,** 'right out on.'

348. Weges, cf. 173, note; *Weges* has the accent here.

*While Tell and Baumgarten have been coming from the lake, two hours distant, the reader has learned the situation at Steinen, the end of their journey; their reappearance shows their escape and links the two scenes together.

349. meiner, usually acc. with *nötighaben.*

351. In all such hints at Stauffacher's qualities Schiller gradually develops the character which is to be so prominent later on.

The student should notice how well this scene is put together and realize that a good play does not "do itself" or just "happens to be that way" and not some other. The talk with his friend prepares Stauffacher for that with his wife, who then handles the situation with rare skill: (1) she says she has seen his troubles, (2) claims a wife's right to share them, (3) urges that she can understand them, (4) argues that, no matter whether he resists or submits, he is safe only when his country is rid of the tyrants, and (5) appeals thus to his patriotism as well as his own interest. The exposition, begun in scene 1, is continued. Types of other and higher classes in other cantons appear. These, too, feel the tyrant's hand; men and women alike resent it, and, though calmer and more patient, are also resolved to resist. United resistance is first suggested, not by some lawless rabble, but by a high-minded, peace-loving woman, a type of the class that has most to lose. The conservative, responsible, law-abiding citizen is roused to action and there is trouble ahead for the tyrant, for the folk plot has taken its first decisive step forward.

ACT I SCENE 3

Scenes 1 and 2 show the tyranny of the governors in Unterwalden and Schwyz; scene 3 takes us to the third canton, Uri, and gives us still further and stronger proof of it there, with further suggestion of resistance. The plot thickens. The time is later in the same afternoon as in scenes 1 and 2; Stauffacher goes at once (333) to Altorf, chief town in Uri; Tell, now bound for home in Bürglen, goes with him. We are again taken on ahead of them to see how things look before they get there; and again the scenes are closely linked together.

*sich . . . darstellt, "presents itself," 'can be seen.' — **wird** (*es*) **. . . gebaut,** "is being built," 'they are working.' — **Fronvogt,** overseer of **Frondienst** (367), enforced labor given to a feudal lord instead of taxes.

353. nicht lang gefeiert, 'don't stop so long'; such rough commands are often expressed by past participle (*zugefahren,* 354) or infinitive. — **Herbei,** compounds of *her* and *hin* also express such command, without any verb: 'Over (up) here!'

356. Das, contemptuous, 'these fellows.'

357. Heißt das geladen, '(is) do you call that a load (loaded)?'

358. Pflicht bestehlen, "rob duty," 'shirk work.'

359. doch, emphatic, 'I tell you.'

360. Twing (same as *Zwing,* 370), 'dungeon'; akin to *zwingen,* 'force,' 'compel.'

368. was meines Amtes, "what is of my office," 'my duty'; an idiomatic poss. gen. as predicate.

369. denn, 'anyhow.'

373. wollt ihr, 'do you mean to' ('think you can'); *ihr* = you Austrians. — **zwingen;** note the play on words with *Zwing Uri* (372); 'Keep Uri,' the dungeon (castle), is to 'keep down' Uri, the canton. The tyranny grows worse than in scenes 1 and 2; there it attacked individuals, here every man's liberty is in danger.

375. 'nander = *einander.* — bis ... draus wird, "until out of them is made," 'before they make.'

377. tiefsten See, 'depths of the lake.'

379. hätt', optative subj. expressing strong wish.

381. Uri had had the *Freiheit* of home rule since 1231, longer than the other cantons.

386. Flanken, sharp-cornered projections to strengthen the corners of the castle, 'bastions.'

388. Characteristic and prophetic.

389. Haus, the mountains; one of many hints that Swiss character is the outgrowth of the Nature they live in; they are part of it and just like it in their rugged simplicity; in no other play are Nature and people in such accord as in *Wilhelm Tell.*

390 f. will, soll, translate both 'means' and note that neither requires a complementary infinitive. — der Hut, archducal hat of Austria (= the Habsburgs) and symbol of Gessler's authority.

394. Aufrichten ... Säule (high-sounding word for *Stange*), the word-order adds emphasis. The proclamation is the first hint of preparation for the great scene of the apple-shot.

396. Will und Meinung, official phrase, 'will and decree.'

397. geschehen, 'be done.'

401. Verfallen, the subject is the "he" included in wer (= he, who) below.

405. dergleichen (= *der gleichen*), old gen. pl., now indeclinable adj.; 'the like.' Engl. "of that kind" is also "that kind of" as adjective. Gessler has added unheard-of humiliation to the menace of the dungeon.

406. The word-order shows emphatic contempt.

408. noch, 'only, at least.' — So, 'as it is,' 'like this.' They were ready to acknowledge imperial authority, but not that of Habsburg-Austria.

410. In castle Stein zu Baden (2966), in Aargau, where Albrecht lived when in Switzerland and where the Swiss fiefs were granted.

412. Bowing to the hat would have meant submission to Austria, and Uri was dependent directly and only on the Empire; refusal to obey is made dangerous and will provide the pretext (306) to force Austrian authority upon them. The conflict is thus made clear.

415. Ihr ... Bescheid, 'you know what I think'; reference to their talk on the political situation. Neither mentions the proclamation about the hat, perhaps because Schiller took it out of its first place at the beginning of Act II and put it here after the rest of this scene was all written. Critics suggest that it would fit in better after the exit of Tell and Stauffacher (446).

416. wo wollt ("mean to") **hin,** 'where are you going?' Again notice that *wollen* does not need the infinitive used in Engl.

417. His rescue of Baumgarten has delayed his return home.

421. 'The only thing to do now is to be patient and silent.' Such terse speeches, in striking contrast with each other, for which Schiller found his model in Greek and French drama, add great tension to the action. Cf. also 433 ff. and 136, 312, notes.

423. schnell has here its old sense "rash," "impetuous." Cf. the proverb: *Gestrenge Herren regieren nicht lange.*

425. Still custom, even law, in many parts of Switzerland.

431. doch emphasizes the opinion; translate, 'surely.'

432. Lande, the Forest Cantons.

433. könnten, subj., 'might do,' common use of modal without infin. — **zusammenstünden,** old for *zusammenständen.*

437. Note the emphatic position of **Verbunden** and the contrasts: **Verbunden — allein, Schwachen — mächtig.** The whole passage is extremely effective; it emphasizes contrasts of character and is a good example of Schiller's power of expressing truth in terse, vigorous, beautiful form and figure. He is the most quotable poet in German; of the ten lines 429–438 at least seven have become "winged words" and virtually proverbs among his people. Cf. the list on pages 185–187.

442. sollte, rhetorical question, past subj. implying emphatic denial; 'and would' (do you think).

443. was = *was auch;* cf. 190, note. Here and often Schiller takes pains to make Tell a private individual, with no part in the concerted, political action of the folk plot.

446. es . . . fehlen, 'I shall not be found wanting.' Not boastful, but quite in accord with a character whose lonely life as a hunter and whose contact with Nature and its dangers have taught him to rely on himself and not to counsel with others.

The rhyme in this passage adds great dramatic force; Schiller uses it here and often in this and other plays to show a rise of emotion and, as an element of lyric expression, to add further emphasis to an already important passage, often at the end of an act or scene.

*Berta (von Bruneck, Gessler's castle in Aargau), a fictitious character, related to Gessler, and under his guardianship. She is to take an important part later and appears here to show her love for this people and prepare us for her support of their cause. She belongs to the nobles plot.

451. Angry contempt of the idea that money could help in such a case. **euch,** ethical dative; 'you people think.' However natural his mistake, his reproach is unjust; her heart is Swiss.

458 f. Sinister prophecy from one who had many reasons for siding with the tyrants; it leaves us keenly expectant.

Along with renewed evidences of Habsburg tyranny (371, 393 ff.) which show how widespread and serious it will become, the scene shows the attitude towards it of still other and larger classes of people (artisans, townsmen). Even the daughter of nobility takes sides against her kinsman, Gessler. Citizens talk of united resistance and show a smoldering hate that may easily burst into flame, especially now that tyranny has added the prospect of political subjection for the whole people to the personal illtreatment of single individuals. Tell's brief reappearance further develops his character as a man averse to plans and counsels, but ready to act and help in time of need. The scene again unites all three plots of the play and prepares for their later development.

ACT I SCENE 4

This scene follows scene 3 at once, for Fürst lives in Altorf (333, note), and gives evidence of the cruelty of still another of the governors — Landenberg — in Unterwalden. — **Arnold,** called *vom* (not *von*) Melchtal from his home in the Melch valley, is the son of Heinrich *von* (cf. 562) or *an* der Halden.

466. Um . . . zu, 'that I should.' At once a sharp contrast is drawn between cautious age and impetuous youth, and the keenest interest is aroused for Melchtal as the important figure.

467. Dem ... Buben ('servant'), poss. dat. with **Finger** (470). — **mir,** dat. privative with **treiben;** translate 'my' with **Ochsen.** He has doubtless told Fürst all this before, but tells it here to justify himself and to let us know what he has done. The word-order is highly poetic.

471. des Vogts (pred. gen.), Landenberg's; 72, 281, notes.

474. Wie = *wie auch;* 'however.' Cf. 190, note.

475. sollt', ("surely you don't think") 'I was to.'

484. wir, even age admits the situation is desperate.

491. Prose (*es*) **ist niemand** (*da*). — **schütze** = *schützen könnte.*

492. (*Es*) **werde.** — **muß** (without infin.) **hinüber,** i.e. go home.

494. Walde, the Kernwald (1197), near which he lived; it divided Unterwalden into *Ob* (above, toward the heights) *dem Wald* and *Nid* ('neath, toward the lake) *dem Wald.* Cf. 546, 718.

499. Another suggestion of united resistance; it will not surprise us when it comes.

502. was ... schwant, 'what evil I fear' (anticipate); *schwanen,* for more usual *ahnen,* is said to come from *Schwan,* the bird of prophecy.

504. Cf. 86, note.

506. tät' ... hätten, the subj. of softened assertion; 'it would almost seem necessary'; shows the character of a people that has little use for bolts and bars even to-day and helps us feel we are there.

507. *da, 'as'; he has reached the end of his journey (333 ff.); as usual we got there first and have seen what is going on.

508. Nun, bei Gott! 'Well, I declare!' Such expressions, much more common in German than in English, rarely have their literal force; they are emphatic but not irreverent. — **werter,** 'honored.'

511. hoch, elevated style, 'most.'

514. Die, very emphatic, 'those.' — **Sieh** (interjection) **mir wird,** 'Ah! it does me good.'

515. warm geht ... auf (= "expands"), 'warms.'

517. With the return of the subject a return of the epic, Homeric style; cf. 240, note.

520. Cf. 343, note. — **Welschland,** here 'Italy'; *welsch* at first referred to the Kelts in France as foreigners, then became a generic term for anything not German.

522. frisch, a favorite word in *Tell;* here 'direct.' — **Flüelen** (pronounce *Flülen*), landing place for Altorf.

525. erstaunlich(*es*) . . . **Werk,** Zwing Uri; there is no need to name it, for it is in everybody's mind.

526. Bereiten sehen (*gesehen* becomes *sehen* with the other infin.), 'seen going on' ("being prepared").

530. fest, 'secure,' against attack or escape. Cf. 506 f.

532. verhalten = *vorenthalten, verschweigen;* 'keep from.'

538. von uralters her, strengthened form of *von alters her;* adverbial gen. also in Engl. 'from of old'; *her* adds 'on down' to the present.

541 f. *treiben* in two senses; **trieb,** cf. 62, 17, note. — **'s treiben,** 'act, carry on.'

544. noch, 'still,' before they passed away. We have here the attitude of the older nobility.

548. dem Roßberg, with the article the mountain, without it (77, 130) the castle.

551. 'He tried to wrong most shamefully.' — **der Mann,** 'her husband.'

555. doch expects affirmative answer, "of course."

556. Eidam, for *Schwiegersohn;* Tell is meant. — **übern** = *über den.* 349 ff.

558. Baumgarten has told him and thus becomes instrumental in forming the later alliance.

559. Sarnen, Landenberg's seat, near Kerns and Melchtal's home. Of course, the youth in hiding is hearing all this.

564. gilt was (= *etwas*), 'is worth something, has weight.'

565. mit, 'about.'

570. wie . . . den, 'what about him?'

573. Zur Stelle schaffen, 'bring the son before him.' The change from past to present tenses makes vivid narrative.

575. *will, 'starts to; tries to.' He suddenly remembers Melchtal, forgotten for the moment, and tries to spare him the agony of thus suddenly
learning the awful news, but he is too late. What follows is one of the
most dramatic things in all literature.

576. The change to direct quotation strongly marks his rising feeling. It
is a skillful thing to make another finish the story Melchtal had begun
(in 467 ff.).

581. *Zeichen, tremendously dramatic; he does not speak his name, for
he does not need to. It is a gripping thing, that shows how the simplest
means in a master hand can produce the profoundest effects.

585. um = *um . . . willen.* Cf. 465. Note his changed feeling, the climax
Schuld — Frevel, and the emphatic *blind — geblendet.*

587. ausgeflossen, 'run dry' ("flowed out"); a bold figure.

589. Schont, usually takes acc. — Schmerzens, now *Schmerzes.*

*The stunning, crushing effect of the blow is well indicated in his silent
suffering; well acted, it is intensely dramatic.

596. warmes, Engl. also says 'warm' = 'rich,' 'deep.' — Schmelz, the
luster of Swiss flowers.

597. roten, from the "Alpine glow." The reflected rays of the sun, before
it rises and after it sets, often color the snowpeaks a deep, rich red, while
the valleys are quite dark.

600. frische, 'good.' This whole passage is famous for its lofty poetic tone,
rendered all the more effective by the very unusual word-order (where?).
Such "reflection" may hardly fit the impetuous Melchtal; yet, dazed by
his grief, he naturally thinks first of his father's loss and suffering; 606 ff.
rouses him to thoughts of vengeance.

605. mehr, i.e. is in greater distress than simple blindness.

610. Alles geraubt, 'robbed him of all.' Note the strong emphasis of the
exclamatory participle; so also gelassen, 616.

614. *denken* with auf refers to the future, with *an* to the present or past.
His bitter, brooding grief changes to self-reproach and in **617** to reckless
thoughts of vengeance.

623. Wenn, etc., 'if I can only.'

626. Herrenburg, 'lordly castle'; at Sarnen, chief town in *Ob dem Wald.*

627. Zorns, for usual *über* with acc.

628. The remarkably poetic order **wohnt' . . . ich mache** (pres. for future) and the change from (unreal) subjunctive to indicative mark the impassioned climax to which his now frenzied feeling has risen.

629. Schreckhorn, Jungfrau, two of the highest peaks in the Bernese Oberland, in Schiller's time considered inaccessible.

630. verschleiert, i.e. by clouds; or possibly veiled in mystery; if so **seit Ewigkeit** is literally true for Schiller, for this veil of mystery was not torn from the face of the mountain till 1811, six years after his death, when it was first ascended.

632. gesinnt, participial adj. from *Sinn;* the past part. of *sinnen* is *gesonnen.*

638. frisch, 'clear.'

640 f. Not quite clear. He probably means that the torrent of Melchtal's grief and fury is at its height, while **das Äußerste** is the climax of tyranny. Note the strong and weak ending of *Äußerst* (*-e* and *-es*). — **Wollen wir,** 'shall we?' Gessler's proclamation (397) is not mentioned, though vitally important. Is it forgotten in the presence of such suffering or for the reason given in 415, note?

646. Wesen, dat. of recipient, 149, note.

650. Perhaps by accident, hardly by design.

651. Hausgenoß, house and barn are still often under the same roof in Switzerland.

654. gereizt, 'when aroused'; elliptical condition, common also in Engl. — **wetzt,** 'whets,' by tearing the earth with his horns.

659. Bünde, ancient 'compacts,' uniting the cantons in a league, renewed in 1291: each speaks for himself and his canton.

660. Freundschaft (in old sense "kindred," 'connections'), he has many relatives.

662. am andern, "in the other," 'his neighbor.'

666. Landsgemeinde, assembly or canton council, an open-air meeting of all voters to decide important questions; they are still held in some cantons.

667. Nicht, goes with **verachtet.** — **erlebte** = *erlebt habe.*

669. Prose would supply *sondern* after **Blut.**

671. Was, the whole idea of 670 is antecedent; 'a sight such as must move even a stony cliff to pity.'

672. Contrary to accepted opinion (328, note) this might imply that Stauffacher and Gertrud have children; yet Melchtal may not know, but may merely assume that both older men are fathers. At any rate Stauffacher did not know him and had to ask twice (580, 581) who he was. Line 323 is perfectly general and need not mean his own children.

675. euch, dat. of interest. — **ehre (bewache),** the sense is "a son such as would honor" or "a son to honor."

676. Leib und Gut, 'person and possessions.'

681. i.e. by standing for allegiance only to the Empire; Tschudi says Landenberg hated Melchtal's father for the same reason.

684. The pitiful distress, the passionate, heart-searching eloquence of the young man has its effect — and touches us as well.

686. Sillinen (accent first *i*), they lived near a village of the same name below Altorf on the Gotthard road.

689. Eurer, der Eure, said first to one, then to the other.

690. Währung, "standard value," "currency," here 'worth'; figure taken from coined money, as also **Klang,** 'ring,' below.

693. Was (= *warum*) **braucht's,** "why is there need," 'what need is there.'

695. Wären (subj. of strong wish) **wir doch** ('only') **allein,** i.e. would there were no nobles!

696. wollten (past subj.) = strong for *würden*. — **schon,** not "already"; its force lies here, as often, in the emphasis and assurance it adds = 'easy enough' or 'all right.'

698. Niederungen, poetic figure for the lowly common people in contrast to **Höhen,** the nobles. Has he changed his mind? Why does he not mention his intended visit to Attinghausen? Cf. 336.

702. Obmann, 'arbitrator,' standing (*ob, über*) above the two parties. The Emperor would be the logical arbitrator, but as Duke of Austria he is prejudiced and has already decided against them without even hearing the case.

704. der, 'he, who'; poetry often omits the antecedent.

706. Ihr (Stauffacher) . . . **ich** are strongly contrasted, "do you . . . I."
Such imperative, with subject expressed, is also common in Engl. When
even the over-cautious Fürst is so roused, it is strange that Stauffacher,
after his talk with Gertrud, should be so passive and take rather than
make suggestions.

709. Wem läg' . . . **an,** potential subj.; 'whom could it concern.'

711. gewähren, in two senses; here 'answer for,' 714 'give.'

718. Alzeller (282, note), Baumgarten. — **nid,** 494, note.

722. See map and introductory note to Act I, scene 1.

726. Mythenstein, 39, note. — **g**(*e*)**rad**(*e*) **über,** 'just above' or = *gerade
gegenüber,* 'just opposite' the rock.

728. Rütli (long *ü*), a small clearing (cf. next line) below Selisberg, 700 feet
above the lake, a sacred place to the Swiss, now belonging to the nation as
the gift of the school-children, who bought it for $11,000, and presented it
on Schiller's one hundredth birthday, Nov. 10, 1859. (Funke.)

737. gemeinsam, "in common," 'together.' — **das Gemeine,** 'the common
good.' Essentials thus settled, details are left for later.

739. Eure, Fürst. — **die Eure,** Melchtal.

741. Schiller purposely uses just these three for this personal compact,
which typifies the union of the *drei Lande;* each represents a different
canton (Fürst, Uri; Stauffacher, Schwyz; Melchtal, Unterwalden); each
is also a type of different age and temper: Melchtal is young and hot-
headed; Stauffacher mature and deliberate; Fürst old and over-cautious.
All three, and in them all the cantons, all ages, and classes, have directly or
indirectly suffered.

743. Länder, as individual and separate; *Lande,* 656, as united.

748. This use of signal fires on mountain heights **(Alp)** is very old and
common everywhere.

752. 'And bright shall day dawn in thy darkness!' A ray of hope amid
the general gloom. Here again the rhyme is used with fine effect in closing
the scene and marking the force of feeling. Note the dramatic skill with
which Melchtal's changing mood is portrayed, as melancholy grief (590 ff.)
gives way to ever more violent and passionate wrath (615 ff.) and then to

calm, grim resolve (745 ff.); and also the dramatic progress of the scene
from the mere expression (460–655) of opinion and feeling (helpless no
matter how strong, because it is only feeling) to calmer, and therefore more
effective, discussion (655–738), which has crystallized into the resolve to
fight, and at last to definite action in the alliance (739 ff.) of the cantons for
their defense.

The first act, usually the exposition of the play, should tell us when and
where the action passes and tell us who and what it's all about, i.e. bring
in important characters, show the nature and cause of the dramatic conflict, and array the contending forces for the clash that sets the action
going and later leads to a crisis and end. Here all these things are done —
and done very well. We know the time and place exactly; get vivid pictures of the country; see the people in their various types and leading men,
in their homes and at their work, in their ways and standards of thought
and action; see the cause of the conflict in the foreign yoke their governors
force upon them and in that increasing cruelty which has spread to every
age and class and canton; the action has gone forward in typical efforts of
individual defense and in plans for resistance which shall unite the people.
The whole people is the hero and their fight for liberty is the theme of the
play. The conflict involves great odds; the uncertain issue excites keen
interest.

ACT II SCENE 1

Some days of necessary preparation for the Rütli meeting pass between
Acts I and II. Both scenes of II fall (probably though not necessarily) on
the same day, the first in the forenoon, the second after midnight. Tschudi
puts the Rütli scene on Nov. 8, ten days after Act I.

*Freiherr, 'Baron'; 336, note. Ruins of his castle near Attinghausen are
still shown. His great age (85 years) is fictitious; Schiller makes him old
enough to have fought, when eighteen, at Faenza in 1240, in order to make
him contemporary with the charters of Friedrich II, the basis of Swiss
liberty, and thus a type of the generation now passing away. — Kuoni,
cf. 51. — Rechen, Sensen, November is too late for haying in the Alps;
the point escaped the poet's attention, and the audience doesn't think of it,
so no harm is done. Cf. also 1914. — Ulrich von Rudenz, a fictitious character, invented to embody and express the opinions of the younger Swiss
nobles.

753. Euer, Rudenz in deference uses the "polite address," his uncle the "familiar" forms — except in 754, which seems spoken more or less to all present.

755. Frühtrunk, "early drink"; unusual word, made like *Frühstück.* It is a 'morning draught,' no doubt of wine. The passage shows the patriarchal relation between the old lord and servant, in strong contrast with the ideas of the young nobleman. Again the one is very deliberate, the other impatient to get away. The contrast in costume is no less striking. It is quite like Schiller thus at once and in a few strokes to give us the essentials of character which he then develops at leisure. Cf. the first brief glimpse of Tell, 127–160.

762. enger . . . engerm, here (as often) only the second adj. has the ending which really belongs to both; 'in ever narrowing circle.'

766. Ich bring's (the drink) **Euch,** 'I pledge you' (drink your health). — **frisch,** i.e. without hesitation. — **geht** ('comes'), i.e. we drink from one cup and feel with one heart.

768. Kinder, cf. Engl. 'boys,' shows his affection.

771. Herrenburg, while Zwing Uri is building, Gessler, says Tschudi, at times occupied a tower (Schiller makes it a castle) in Altorf; his permanent seat is near Küssnacht, now in Schwyz though then outside. The map shows the ancient boundary; it used to pass by Arth.

773. Hast du's so eilig = *Hast du solche Eile;* confusion of *eilig sein* and *Eile haben.* — **Jugend** (dat. with **gemessen**), 'for you, young man.'

775. An, Engl. uses both 'on' and 'off of.'

778. 's = *es,* 'that,' namely line 777.

779. zur Fremde, 'a strange place'; with *werden* the predicate noun is often in the dat. with *zu.* — **Uli,** dimin. of *Ulrich.*

781. trägst . . . zur Schau, 'make proud show of.' — **schlägst,** 'throw.' The silk costume, peacock's feather, and red mantle all show attachment to the Austrian court. The old nobleman clings to the Swiss *Pelzwams.* Their clash is political, not personal.

787. Albrecht, called both *König* and *Kaiser,* was angry because the Swiss resisted his private, Habsburg, claims to the cantons; 185, note. Throughout the scene the old Baron feels as we have been led to expect (337, 543).

799. kostete = *würde kosten.* — **einzig**(es) **Wort,** acknowledging Habsburg-Austria's claims.

802. Augen halten (for *zuhalten*), 'keep closed'; cf. old Engl. "eyes are holden." — **ihnen,** the leaders who oppose Habsburg.

803. Daß es, 'so that they.' — **dem,** 'their own.'

805. nicht, in such case (once common in Engl. also) now dropped.

807. Wohl tut es, 'it flatters.' — **Herrenbank,** 'nobles' bench' in public meetings, to which free citizens also had the right. The cantons thus in a sense had **keinen Herrn,** but in large measure ruled themselves, since the Emperor was too far away to exert much authority.

812. Person, old sense, 'rôle, part.'

814. Landammann (from *Amtmann*, "official," "magistrate"), 'chief magistrate' in a canton, chosen once a year by all the voters. — **Bannerherr,** 336, note.

825. Fremdlinge, the Austrians with Gessler.

829. müßig still, 'idle and quiet.' — **liegen** goes with **ertrag'.**

830. bei gemeinem, 'in degrading.' The passage marks the strong contrast between the patriarchal simplicity of the older nobles and the impatient ambition of the younger generation to get away from the simple, rustic life of home into the splendors of the court and the larger opportunities of the great world.

841. Note the force of these imperatives and in 855, and the contrast between the indignation of **Geh hin** (855) and the pleading **Geh nicht** (860) as showing his deep feeling.

845. Herdenreihen, 'herd song'; he loves the *Kuhreihen,* Rudenz holds it in contempt. There is something so indescribably appealing in its plaintive melodies that the Switzer's proverbial home-sickness, **Schmerzenssehnsucht** (847), on hearing it in a foreign land is very natural.

849. Trieb, "natural impulse for," 'love of.'

852. He feels that Rudenz is loyal at heart, though at present tempted by the lure of the court, and tries to bring him to his senses. The passage suggests that the young man may think differently some day.

853. Die (emphatic demonst.) **Welt,** 'that world'; the court life.

857. Da, 'when.' — **Selbstherr,** 'your own master,' not the vassal he would become by accepting an Austrian fief.

862. Letzte, the family really lived on for several generations; Schiller makes him the last of his race so that he may be an all the more impressive figure and type of an epoch that dies with him.

864. It was an ancient custom thus to bury shield and helmet with the "last of his line."

866. brechend(*es*), "breaking," as often in older Engl., though we now say 'closing' (in death). The eye may close at the moment of death, but it "breaks" (opens slightly) soon after.

868. Give the estates to Austria, then get them back again 'in fief,' as a Habsburg vassal. — **frei,** 'as a freeman.'

871. In view of their title as Roman Emperors they claimed world sovereignty; 266, note.

872. The two alliterating verbs but emphasize one idea; 'stubbornly persist in trying to.'

873 f. Länderkette, surrounding districts under Habsburg control. — **ihm,** dat. of interest; best omitted. — **gewaltig,** 'great'; read as adj. with **Länderkette,** 'that great chain of lands with which he has surrounded us.'

875 ff. The chronicles say that Albrecht had control of the markets of Lucerne and Zug and that he gave to his sons the tolls collected on the Gotthard, the pass leading to Italy. — **ziehet,** intrans.; 'moves along.'

878. seinen, as in 873, his private, Habsburg, property; not imperial provinces.

880. The next emperor might not be a Habsburg, but, even so, could not do much with the Habsburgs or get through the *Länderkette* (873) to help the cantons.

883. Was ... auf, 'what faith is to be put in.'

885. Adlers = *Reichsadlers,* 'imperial eagle.'

886. veräußern, 'alienate from,' by giving them over to the control of powerful vassals in return for troops and moneys loaned, and then often failing to redeem them; meanwhile such mortgaged towns or provinces lost their charters and home rule rights.

890. By election; 193, note.

892. wohl verdienen um, in prose = *sich verdient machen um,* "deserve well of," 'gain the favor of.'

893. heißt, 'means.' — **in,** 'for'; to be reaped in future.

894. Willst, 'do you (claim to) think you can.'

898. Cf. Pfeifer's opinion, note at head of I, 2.

900. i.e. for taxation.

901. i.e. reserve the hunting rights for themselves.

905. Fight their battles with the help of Swiss troops, it was often done.

912. Favenz = Faenza in northern Italy. Dec. 1240–April 1241, Friedrich II, in his war with the Pope, was besieging the town. Seeing their opportunity the Schwyzer sent him 600 men in return for a charter attesting their dependence only on the Empire. Attinghausen's presence is not historical, yet Schiller makes him old enough to have been there.

913. Sie sollen, 'let them'; splendid defiance in the old man.

920. zu dir steht, 'stands by you.'

922. angebornen, natural ties binding him to home and his people.

923 f. Perhaps the most famous lines in the play; Germany's inspiration in the wars with Napoleon I. The whole speech is a patriotic appeal that might fire any heart.

928. lang', 'not for a long time now.'

936. Fräulein, same as *Ritterfräulein* (939) and originally applied only to young ladies of rank. Berta is an invented character.

941. Braut, not "bride," but 'betrothed'; the word is the same, the meaning not.

942. Unschuld, i.e. 'for you, poor innocent.'

943. Gehabt (imper. of *gehaben*) **Euch wohl,** old for *Lebt wohl!* He is mad because the old man has seen through him so clearly.

945. erhalten = *zurückhalten*, 'hold' (= "hold back").

946. Cf. 78, note.

949. strebend, construe with **Jugend; über . . . Berge,** with **reißt fort.**

951. still beglückt, 'quiet, happy.'

952. Der . . . Unschuld, 'the innocent simplicity of our lives.'

957. gewaltet und gelebt, about 'lived and labored.' These closing lines, in the tone of the disappointed prophet and patriot, who has outlived his own day and sees no hope for the future, are most impressive.

After the introduction (753–769) the main scene takes up (1) Attinghausen's reproaches, with the attempts of Rudenz to justify his course (770–893) and (2) the Baron's denunciation of Austrian policy and his appeal to his nephew to be loyal (894–942); the conclusion (942–959) gives his gloomy view of the future. The action of the play does not advance much, but we have two new and important characters, strongly contrasted and intended as examples of the older and younger Swiss nobility in their attitude towards the cantons and the Habsburgs. As part of the exposition, it really belongs in Act I and originally stood there; it was later put here to shorten Act I and to get the striking contrast it now offers with the Rütli scene. It also contrasts the united people (Act I) with the divided nobles, and the pomp of Austria with the patriarchal simplicity of Swiss life. In the conflict between *Volk* and *Vögte* there is now a new element of danger, the turning of the younger nobility to Austria, which makes the already uncertain issue even more doubtful. The scene belongs to the nobles plot, so far only hinted at (337, 543), and begins to develop the part they are to take.

ACT II SCENE 2

*Wiese, the Rütli; 728, note. For the time, see introductory note to II, 1, and line 966.

*Mondregenbogen, a very rare thing (978 f.); like that formed by the sun, but much fainter. — **Prospekt,** 'background' shut in by the mountains (across the lake) mentioned at the opening of I, 1. It is the poet's opportunity to give us another scene of marvelous natural beauty, all the more impressive for its contrast with I, 1, and he uses it well. — **Meier** (= overseer), first an office, became a common family name, as often in Engl. Cf. Snyder, Taylor, etc. — **Bühel** (hill) and **Flüe** (cliff) add local color. For all these invented characters names are taken from old Swiss documents, so also 987* and 1098*.

960–1109 serve as an introduction, filled by successive arrivals, greetings, general conversation, and personal experiences.

961. Fels, the Selisberg, above the Rütli. — **Kreuzlein,** commemorating some accident.

964. Because they are led by the impetuous Melchtal.

966. Selisberg, village high up on the mountain just mentioned.

967. Signal for early prayers in the hermit's **Waldkapelle** on the Schwyz shore. The line has six feet, but such are not uncommon; there is no pause after **Horch,** for the explanation of the bell comes at once, so we can hardly make two lines of it.

970. Gehn, zünden, subj. as softened imperative.

972. Mondennacht, also *Mondnacht; Monden* is gen. sing. weak decl. by analogy with *Sonnen,* one of the old sing. genitives still used in compounds (*Sonnen-schein*) and some set phrases. Cf. 1085, 1108. The quiet lake and silvery moonlight are a well-chosen setting.

973. als wie, colloquial; either *als* or *wie* is enough.

978. Perhaps meant to be symbolic of promise, hope, and peace.

983. erwarten (passive force), 'be waited for'; prose = *auf sich warten.*

985 f. weit umgehen (separable *úm-gehen*), 'go away round.' — **hinter-gehen** (inseparable *hintergéhen*), 'elude.'

987. *drei, a mistake for *vier;* each was to bring (735) ten men and the total is 33 (1098*). The names again are very Swiss; cf. *960, note.

991. gesogen (from *saugen*), confused metaphor; he means he has been filled with thoughts of vengeance by seeing his father's blindness.

993. Gescheh(e)nes, abstract noun; 'what has been done.' This is no time for personal vengeance. Such a stand makes him the real leader.

996. für (*die*) . . . **Sach(e);** the two friends who parted 752* meet again; their talk, naturally apart from the others, shows Melchtal's visit home and preparations for the Rütli meeting.

999. Surénnen (usually *Súrennen*), lofty ridge between Uri and Unter-walden; the Surennen pass leads from Altorf to Engelberg and is always covered with snow.

1001. Lämmergeier (Engl. has the same word), the largest bird of prey in Europe, said to be extinct in the Alps.

1003. Engelberg, mountain, also village with a monastery (1079) in Unterwalden.

1005. Gletscher Milch, milky-white water from the glaciers.

1007. einsamen, because the herdsmen had gone down for the winter (15 ff., 62 ff.); outside wooden bolts close such doors.

1012. Ehrfurcht, object of **schaffte** = *verschaffte;* poetic order.

1014. Entrüstet, construe with **Seelen,** not with **ich.**

1015. Ob, here with dat. Cf. 277, note. — **Regimént,** Landenberg's tyranny.

1022. tragen = *ertragen,* 'tolerate'; emphatic order.

1031. Euch, dat. object of **folgen.**

1035. mir die (= *meine*) **Vettern,** 'my kinsmen'; 660, note.

1039. Da brings the conclusion of the **Als** clause, 1036.

1043. Krümmen, for metrical reason; prose *Krümmungen.*

1044. ich späht' es aus, like colloq. Engl. 'but (what) I searched it out.'

1051. geben, 'yield' (crop).

1056. beiden, 'two'; as also 1067* and often.

1066. His country's cause comes before his private vengeance now.

1072. kennte, past subj. interrogative form, exclamatory force; 'who wouldn't know you?' Others come up; the private interview, its purpose accomplished (996, note), gives place to introductions, greetings, general talk.

1074. Winkelried, here made a descendant of the famous Winkelried, who, the chroniclers say, was knighted for bravery at Faenza in 1240, then, banished for murder, atoned his guilt by killing a dragon at Ödweiler near Rossberg, but died when the monster's poisonous blood touched him.

1079. hinterm Wald, beyond the Kernwald; 494, note. — **Klosterleute,** monastery servants, "hands," not monks.

1081. eigne Leute, people who are 'owned, bondmen.' Cf. *Leibeigne* and **mit seinem Leibe pflichtig** (= 'subject to'), 1085.

1084. Es . . . wer, 'let him . . . who.' — **preisen** = *glücklich preisen,* 'count fortunate.'

1085. Erden, not plural, but old weak dat. sing. Cf. 972, note.

1087. History mentions an Itel Reding, Landammann of Schwyz about 1428. — **Alt-** for *der alte*, as Engl. 'former, ex-.'

1091. It is a fine dramatic touch to make them thus bury 'personal' enmity for the sake of the common cause, which unites friend and foe, bond and free.

1092. brav, not "brave"; 'well, nobly.'

1093. A great bull's horn, blown as a signal, especially in battle. The seal of Uri shows his head. The hornblower is called the *Stier von Uri*, 2248. In view of all the secrecy previously mentioned and their danger if discovered, it is strange that the horn-blast and the fire (970) are allowed.

1097 f. The old, over-careful Fürst naturally comes last; Schiller indicates character by the order in which the leaders come. The ever grateful Baumgarten looks in vain for Tell, and such mention is not accidental. He is absent for good reason, 441–446. There is dramatic reason, too, for his absence, 443, note. He must be left free to act as an individual; so he has no part in the compact of 740 ff. and his absence is again emphasized here. — ***dreiunddreißig,** note on 987*.

1106. Lit. "as the radiant open lap" (a poor phrase for Schiller), 'as bright, open daylight.'

1107. Laßt's gut sein, "let it be well," "let that do," 'never mind.'

1108. Soll, Engl. supplies 'come.' — **Sonnen,** 972, note. Cf. the proverb:

> *Es wird nichts so fein gesponnen,*
> *Es kommt endlich doch ans Licht der Sonnen.*

1109. Though no business has been transacted they are confederates, have been such before (1156 ff.). The Swiss nation is still called *Die Schweizerische Eidgenossenschaft*. A second section of the scene (1109–1151) begins here — the organization of the meeting for business. Contrast this solemn, ghostly moonlight scenery with the smiling sunshine of the opening of Act I, sc. 1; the grim seriousness of this with the happiness of that.

1112. tagen, unlike 752; here 'deliberate.' Cf. *Reichstag*, the German Congress, and Engl. 'Diet.'

1113. '*s* = *tagen;* translate 'to do' (it).

1114. It was **ungesetzlich** in three points; they numbered only thirty-three, not the whole people; they met by night in secret, not openly, by day; they had no statute-books (1122). Cf. 666, note.

1115. entschuldige, subjunct. predicate of **Not.**

1118. Wohl, 'Well then!' so also **wohlan** (1123).

1119. Prose *obgleich es ist;* common inversion (1120, 1122,) as in conditional clauses.

1124 ff. In such meetings the Landammann sat on a low platform, two swords, symbols of his authority (1125), were stuck in the ground at his sides, two officials (*Weibel,* 1127) stood near, the people stood outside of the **Ring,** 'circle,' within which he sat.

1127. stehen, like **nehme** is subjunctive; 'let' them 'stand.'

1128. dreie, not uncommon inflected form without the noun.

1131. frei, 'voluntarily.'

1135. Römerzügen, state-journeys to Rome, made by newly elected German emperors (with title *Deutscher König*) to be crowned by the Pope as head (*Kaiser*) of the Holy Roman Empire, 266, note. The Swiss, as the emperor's vassals, furnished their part of the great procession, 1229 ff. — **uns,** dat.

1136. i.e. let Schwyz have the president, 1125.

1137. seines Stammes, Schwyz, traditionally the canton first settled (1167–1203, especially 1188 ff.) gave her name in the later forms *Schweiz* and *Schweizer* to the whole country and people, but not as early as 1307.

1146 f. Tages (1112, note) **Haupt,** 'president of the meeting.' — **dazu** = *dafür.*

1149. droben in prose would follow **Sternen.** Note the exalted and poetic solemnity of Reding's oath of office.

The organization now complete, business is taken up and we have the main body of the scene which extends, in several sections, to 1440. In its first section (1151–1204) Stauffacher, the real leader, seeks to show the unity of the Swiss people.

1155. *Each speaker stepped into the circle, 1124, note, and faced the president.

1157. Bündnis, some older compact, such as the league of 1291 or an older one, A. D. 1246. — **Väter** = *der Väter.*

1159. Ob = *obgleich.*

1163. **Liedern,** popular songs, especially the well-known 'East Frisian Lay,' authority for the purely traditional Swedish-Frisian origin of the Swiss. Cf. Introduction, p. xxi.

1167. **sich** = *einander.*

1168. **hinten,** far up, away back. — **Lande,** Sweden.

1169. **nach Mitternacht** (for *Norden*), 'to the north'; cf. **Mittagsonne** (1174), 'south.'

1171. **je der** ("ever the") **zehnte,** 'every tenth.'

1173. **Und** (*es*) **zogen,** real subject is **Männer,** etc.

1179. **Muotta,** pronounce *Muͦtta.* See map.

1182. **wartete,** rare with gen.; 'tend.' If no **Menschenspuren,** then why **Hütte** and **Fähre;** the contradiction is in the original *Ostfriesenlied.* 1180 is doubtlessly not to be taken literally.

1188. **Da,** not "there," but 'then, and so.'

1192. **Gnügen** (= *genügen* as noun) **tat,** 'sufficed' with dat. **Zahl.**

1194. **schwarzen Berg,** across the lake to the Brünig, so called from its thick woods, on the south-west border of Unterwalden. — **Weißland,** amid the snow-peaks of the Bernese Oberland, south of the Brünig.

1196. In cantons Tessin and Wallis Italian and French are spoken.

1200. Alemanni, Burgundians, Franks. They themselves were Alemanni.

1203. **Es,** expletive; **Herz** (and **Blut**) is the real subject.

1205. Sums up the theme (union) of the first part of their deliberations and ushers in that of the second (1206–1314), namely liberty and their relation to the Emperor.

1206. **Völker** (1200, note), from whom they differ in love of liberty, as in origin.

1209. **Sassen** (from *sitzen*), 'settlers'; here for *Hintersassen*, 'serfs.' — **viel**(*e*), subject of **leben.** — **fremde Pflichten tragen,** 'owe submission to foreigners.'

1215. **Schutz und Schirm,** emphatic alliterating synonyms (331, note), about = 'shield and shelter' in Engl.; i.e. direct dependence on the Empire. 912, note.

1219. **wo,** 'from whom.' — **Recht schöpfen** ("draw" as water), legal term, 'get justice.' Noble sentiment of a law-abiding people.

1222. **die** (= *diese*) **Ehr',** to be their *Oberhaupt.*

1223. i.e. of Germany and Italy, which was part of the Holy Roman Empire, 871, note.

1225. **gelobt** (from *geloben*), goes with **haben,** 1220.

1229 f. **Heribann,** old for *Heerbann,* "army summons," imperial call to vassals to take the field. — **seine,** the Emperor's.

1231. **gewappnet** (from *Wappen,* "coat of arms"), poetic for *gewaffnet.* Cf. 1135, note.

1235. **höchste Blutbann,** 'highest criminal jurisdiction,' in cases involving capital punishment.

1237. So as to be free from partisan prejudice and the temptation to assume more than his own authority. — **bestellt,** 'delegated.'

1243. **verhält sich alles,** 'it is all as.'

1246. **Pfaffen,** contemptuous. This quarrel with Einsiedeln (343, note) is historical. In 1018 Heinrich II, ignorant of the peasants' existence and ownership (1252), had given the pasture to Einsiedeln; in time quarrels arose, and in 1114 the abbot appealed to Heinrich V, who decided in his favor; the peasants refused to yield (line 1245) and when Konrad III in 1144 tried to force them, they withdrew from the Empire (line 1256) and did not return to it for eight years.

1259. **fremden Knecht,** Gessler and other Habsburg bailiffs.

1261. **erschaffen,** i.e. cleared and cultivated it; splendidly emphatic.

1265. There are many dragon stories. Cf. the Winkelried legend, 1074, note. Here, as usually, "the dragon" is disease rising from the swamps in noxious vapors. He is "killed" by clearing and draining them (1267).

1269 f. Some such work as building the Gotthard road.

1271 f. **tausendjährigen,** i.e. a very long time, though it had been nearly 1000 years since the first Alemanni came. — **Herrenknecht,** 1259, note.

1279. **greift ... getrosten Mutes** (adv. gen.) **in** 'with confidence reaches up to.' The lofty poetic tone accords with the situation.

1283. **Urstand,** 'primitive state' in which each fights for himself (1284).

1285. Zum, "for the," 'as the.'

1287. Güter höchstes is their freedom.

1295. Though a man of peace, Rösselmann is, of course, not in earnest in his "motion" or in his whole speech; but wishes to test the confederates; perhaps he shrewdly makes this most distasteful motion in order to drive them to do the opposite. Cf. 1312–14.

1297. Wir . . . schwören (also **huldigen,** 1300, **lassen,** 1301), infin. exclamation, as in Engl., showing strong feeling.

1302. Güte, Austria's first friendly approach; 185, note and 1314.

1304. sei, stronger than real passive *werde;* shows accomplished result, not action in process.

1312. 's, i.e. *frei;* the same *es* in 1303. Thus closes the second part of their deliberations. Not only are they a united people (1156–1205), but they have been and mean to remain a free people (1206–1314). Cf. 1205, note. The third part discusses the means by which they will maintain their liberty (1315–1440).

1316. auch, 'really.'

1319. A second "motion," by Reding, also lost.

1322. Auch, 'even.'

1324. (*die Reihe ist*) **an Euch** (dat.), 'now it's your turn.'

1325. Rheinfeld(*en*), once strongly fortified town on the Rhine near Basel; arbitrarily given as Albrecht's residence. Hunn and his story are founded on facts, though Schiller for dramatic reason transferred to Albrecht's reign things that came earlier.

1327 f. The charter of Friedrich II (912, note). — **sonst,** except Albrecht.

1330. schwäbischen Land, not now a separate province, but a region in southwest Germany where the Swabians (Caesar's Suevi) and their dialect are at home; 'the Swabian country.' — **Lauf,** ('course) from along.'

1331. Die, as so often, emphatic 'they'; also 1334, 1341.

1336. sonst . . . wohl, 'some other time, no doubt.'

1338. Hansen, old acc. of *Hans* (dimin. of *Johannes*). Duke John of Swabia, Albrecht's nephew, the Johannes Parricida of Act V, sc. 2, is meant.

1340. Herrn, now *Herren.* Names and story are from Tschudi.

1341. riefen = *riefen . . . zu.*

1344 f. hinterhält, for *vorenthält,* 'withholds from.' — His **Erbe** was the dukedom of Swabia from his father and lands in Switzerland from his mother, i.e. **sein Mütterliches** (*Erbe*).

1346. Er habe (subj. of indirect statement with principal verb omitted, as in 92, note; so also **wäre** and **sei,** 1349; either tense is correct) **seine Jahre voll,** 'he was, he said, of age.' He was eighteen, old enough in the opinion of his time.

1348. Was . . . Bescheid, 'what answer did he get.'

1350. Recht, concrete 'rights'; *Gerechtigkeit,* abstract 'justice.' After Hunn's report has shown what to expect from the Emperor, they see that armed resistance is the only way, and self-defense, not conquest, is their purpose.

1358. Sound biblical advice (Matt. xxii, 21; Mark xii, 17) from a law-abiding citizen.

1361. fahret, pres. indic. as imperative; as in Engl. (1363, 1365).

1362. steure, an, 'pay taxes to.' — **Herrn,** 1340, note. — **Rappersweil,** now *Rapperschwyl,* a town on the north shore of Lake Zürich.

1364. Frau zu Zür(i)ch, abbess of the *Frau-Münster,* i.e. nunnery of "Our Lady in Zürich"; founded 853 by Ludwig the German and very wealthy.

1368. Third suggestion or "motion"; adopted.

1372. Schranken, i.e. within our legal rights.

1375 f. A noble tribute to the Swiss and often quoted. — **Furcht,** 'respect.' **Volk** is subject, **sich** dat.

1377. wie comes back to his question (1353); really the great thing.

1380. wird's, i.e. *wird weichen.*

1383. uns (= Unterwalden), dat. of interest. — **Schlösser,** cf. 1386.

1386. muß, i.e. each in turn. Schwyz and Uri are not in such danger, for Zwing Uri is unfinished, the *Herrenburg* (771) is not a castle, and Küssnacht is not in Schwyz.

1394. euch, acc. Uri is meant.

1395. bieten, 'say' (lit. "offer"). The little squabble is very human.

1396. Eide, their oath as citizens, by which they swore to do nothing hurtful to the common weal; the strongest possible appeal, since refusal to obey was treason. Meier answers with a low growl that shows the same **heftigen Sinn** as 984 and 1088.

1398. weisen, *zurechtweisen,* 'reprove.'

1401. i.e. till Christmas; other chroniclers say New Year's Day, A.D. 1308.

1402. mit (*sich*), i.e. it is customary. — **Sassen,** here *Insassen,* 'tenants.' The castle is Sarnen, the *Vogt* Landenberg.

1406. Cf. 1361, note; so also in 1409, 1411, 1412. — **Eisen,** 'spear-heads.'

1415. Dirn', in old and good sense, 'girl'; not "wench" as now.

1416. betör' ich sie, "fool her into," 'induce her to.'

1417. schwanke Leiter, 'swaying rope-ladder.'

1418. erst, 'once.' — **zieh',** 'will (or can) draw.'

1419. aller, gen. pl. — (*es*) ... **werde,** 'that we postpone'; he puts the motion as president, but does not vote, hence 20 to 12.

1423. Zeichen, 748, note. — **Landsturm,** more than *Landwehr,* "militia," is every man able to bear arms. **Landsturm aufbieten** ("to call the country to arms"), 'call to arms will be read at once.'

1429. Shows his character and prepares us for later events; he is the dangerous one. 1431 f. in a way justifies his death. The question of his fate is left open.

1436. schlag' ... **Schanze,** 'will risk'; *Schanze* here not fortification, but like Engl. "take chances." Mention of Tell here significant.

1438. The proverb reads: *kommt Zeit, kommt Rat.* — **'s,** the result.

1440. Their plans are made, their business done. The scene closes with their oath and the parting admonition to watch and work and wait.

1442. Hochwacht, colors of the dawn on the peaks, like *Feuerzeichen,* 596, 748.

1444. Sammlung (from *sammeln,* "collect" — one's thoughts), 'meditation.' — **unwillkürlich;** no wonder; it is one of the grandest sights Nature has to offer. To the bow of promise at the opening is now added this sunrise of hope for a new and better day for this stricken people.

1445. zuerst, because they live in the mountains.

1450. *drei, thumb and first two; symbol of the Trinity.   That their pastor administers the oath lends a kind of consecration; this is the climax of the folk plot.

1452. den Tod, absolute acc., no verb "understood."
*wie oben, as after 1450.

1456. Freundschaft, as in 660, note. — **Genoßsame** (= *Genossenschaft,* 1109, note), 'community.'

1462. Schuld, the tyrants' debt to each and to all.

1464. das Ganze, i.e. the common cause.

1465. Raub begehen (*an* with dat., "commit theft on"), 'injures.' — **allgemeinen Gut,** 'the common weal.'   The advice of a real leader.

*fällt ... ein, 'comes in with a splendid flourish,' which, with the slowly rising sun, the sun of Swiss freedom, never fails of fine dramatic effect. — **Szene,** 'the stage.'

The scene is a masterpiece in the treatment of ensemble, showing the united people gathered in its best representatives to renew old ties and take steps for relief, and also one of the most important and carefully wrought scenes in the play.   In the detailed order of the meeting: gathering, organization, deliberation, results, oath, parting, we get still deeper insight into Swiss character and into conditions prevailing.   The action advances a long step; resistance, only vaguely suggested before, is definitely planned; hope is awakened for the cause of freedom, and the outcome is anxiously awaited.   The failure to decide what to do about Gessler increases our anxiety and leaves room for Tell's later action (cf. the *Augenblick* of 1439 and that of 2589) — a vague suggestion of the Tell plot in a scene devoted wholly to the folk plot, here brought to its climax.   The contrast between the united people and the divided nobles is made still stronger.

ACT III SCENE 1

That unanswered question: What about Gessler? goes with us as we leave the Rütli, and that vague mention of Tell in connection with it becomes more significant the more we think of it.   The central act of the play now naturally takes up these two all important figures and the fateful clash between them. Tschudi puts the hat episode on Sunday, Nov. 18, the appleshot on the nineteenth; for the year 1307 this Sunday and Monday would have to be the nineteenth and twentieth. Schiller combines the two on one day (evidently a business day, 1744), the twentieth, and thus increases the dramatic effect. Scene 1 passes about noon on that day, since, immediately afterwards, Tell goes to Altorf (1516) a mile distant, where he arrives in the early afternoon, 1744. The place is Bürglen, 126, note.

*Hedwig. Schiller gives her this name; the chroniclers say simply that she was Walter Fürst's daughter. Cf. 556. — ***Walter,** the older boy, is named for his mother's father, **Wilhelm** for his own.

1470. am, unusual for *beim;* perhaps confused with *am Morgen.* This little poem is called the *Schützenlied* and is such a favorite that it has almost become a folk song. Like the songs at the opening of the play it lends local color, characterizes the archer's son, and explains the mother's anxiety for her boys and her husband.

1472. der Weih (also *die Weihe*), generic name for large birds of prey; here, no doubt, 'eagle.'

1474. frei (adv.), i.e. unrestrained.

1475. das Weite, adj. noun; 'all space.'

1478. Was da (= *was auch*), 'whatever.' — **kreucht, fleugt** (old for *kriecht, fliegt*), pronounced in dialect *kreicht, fleigt;* the rhyme is thus preserved (so also *Beute* above).

1479. Mach' mir (in both cases dat. of interest) **ihn,** 'fix it for me'; a good example of *machen* in general sense.

1482. was, generalized *wer,* 'whoever.' Almost a proverb now.

1485. frisch will schlagen, 'stoutly make his way.' Such short, striking, proverb-like lines, of which we have so many in the scene, fill out wonderfully the character of which, so far, we have had only bold outlines. The place to study a man is in his home.

1486. keiner, neither of the boys. — **Ruh' . . . finden,** 'be satisfied, as herdsman; they want to be hunters.'

1487. Mutter, not *Frau;* a very human touch, with a world of affection in a word. It describes her well; in contrast to Gertrud she is all mother.

1490 f. erst, 'only.' — **aufs neu' erbeute** (hunter's word, "capture"), 'win anew,' by saving it from some danger. What a contrast to his wife!

1493. deiner, prose *auf dich.*

1494. Knechte, either his own farm hands or herdsmen or those of the village.

1495. sich, "each other"; omit in translation.

1497. mir (dat. of interest) **werdest,** 'lest I may never see you return.'

1500. Fehl(*fehlen,* "miss")**sprung tun,** 'making a false leap'; cf. *Fehltritt,* "mis-step."

1501. Rückspringend goes with *Gemse;* cf. 650.

1502. Windlawine, avalanche of dry, loose snow driven down by wind; they occur in fall and winter and differ greatly from the *Schlaglawinen* (1782), masses of snow mixed with ice, loosened by the summer sun, rushing down with terrible force, and striking *(Schlag)* in the valleys.

1503. Firn (38, note), treacherous because it conceals the crevasse below it.

1510. frisch, 'alertly, sharply.'

1514. auf Jahr und Tag, "for a year and a day"; old legal term for a full year — now 'a good, long time.'

1516. nach, with places, **zu** with persons. — **Vater,** her father's (Fürst).

1517. auch (introductory), 'now aren't you?'

1518. wie kommst du darauf, 'what makes you think that?' — **Es spinnt,** "something is spinning"; 'some scheme is on foot.' Rumors have reached her, hence some time must have passed since II, 2. She has heard there was a meeting, *(es)* **ward getagt** on the Rütli, but not from him; he has not told her why or even that he is going to Altorf, and she does not ask why, because she has learned to respect his reticence. Only to-day does he tell her of his meeting with Gessler (1556) or that he was not at the Rütli. Yet there is the deepest affection between them. He is by nature what he is, and his lonely life as a hunter has made him more so — not a man who could attend a Rütli meeting.

1523 f. She is wife, as well as mother, and proud of her husband.

1526. Unterwaldner, Baumgarten.

1528. Dachtest, what a human touch in this reproach!

1531. Zu schiffen, exclamatory infin., more commonly without *zu*, 1297, 1300. — **heißt,** 'is'; cf. 357, note. — **in dem,** usually acc.

1532. Gott, dat. for *auf Gott* (1511). — **Gott versuchen,** 'tempting Providence.'

1536. nicht, cf. 254, note.

1540. willst (without infin.) **mit,** 'want to go along (go, too)?'

1545. Cf. the proverb *Tue recht und scheue niemand.*

1546 f. Die, 'Those who.' — **eben die,** 'just those.' — **an ... kommen,** 'get at.'

1551. Schächental, Bürglen is in it; see map.

1553. (*es*) **nicht auszuweichen war,** 'where there was no escaping' a meeting on the narrow path.

1556. gegen ... daher, 'along towards.' The meeting is invented to explain Gessler's hate.

1559. Herre, old for *Herr.* — **mein** (gen.) **ansichtig ward,** 'caught sight of me.'

1561. Helps explain their personal relation. Cf. *grollt,* 1543.

1562 f. sah ... kommen, 'saw ... come striding along.' — **Gewehr,** his cross-bow. — **verblaßt',** usually of things, *erblassen* of persons.

1566. (*es*) **jammerte ... sein** (= *seiner,* gen.), 'I pitied him.' Cf. 486. Shows Tell's generous nature and sympathy with any distress.

1568. keinen armen (= *geringen,* 'little') **Laut,** 'not a single word.'

1575. dort = *von dort.* — **lieber jagen,** her anxiety (cf. 1492–1509) is less than her fear of Gessler. Her feminine intuition is better than all his masculine logic.

1578. Weil's, 'just because.' "Just like a woman"? Her intuitive fear is ground enough. A subtle touch, as is also her yielding, when she learns he has promised.

1583 f. bring ... auch (*et*)**was,** 'Oh! but I'll bring.' — **vom Ehni,** 'from Grandpa's.' Such touches of nature "make all the world akin" and have a dramatic grip that is splendid. Cf. Wilhelm's emphatic **ich.**

1585. *Hoftor,* i.e. as far as she can go. — **den Abgehenden,** dat. pl. with *folgt.* Simple, but effective means of showing her deep anxiety, for all her heart is in her eyes.

A beautiful picture of Swiss home life, developing further the character of Tell, the man, the husband, and father, and showing what the mothers in Swiss homes feel in such trying times. While the *Eidgenossen* have planned to fight, Tell's wish is to be let alone. Hedwig's anxiety hints that he may not have his wish and is a foreboding of ill that serves further to heighten the tension. The scene develops the Tell plot only barely suggested before. It emphasizes the purely personal, not political, relation of Tell to Gessler (as man to man), explains Gessler's hate and later cruelty to him, and gives us the basis of Tell's later action. Hedwig's distress at the close, in such contrast to the happiness at the beginning, fills us with deep concern.

ACT III SCENE 2

The place is near Altorf, for while Tell is coming from Bürglen, Rudenz and Berta meet and talk and then reach the town soon after he does; so the time is about the same as in III, 1.

*eingeschlossene, by sheer cliffs. — *Staubbäche, 'dust (= fine spray) brooks,' little streams, rushing over high cliffs and dashed into spray by the fall.

1587 ff. Fräulein, 'My Lady.' Note that at the very start the lyric tone of the scene is emphasized by rhyme, which is also used in several important passages later (1682, 1686, 1696).

1592. dort hinaus, 'gone that way'; gives the opportunity, desired by both, for him to declare his love, for her to win him back to his people.

1600. in . . . Reih' . . . stellen, "take my place among" = 'compare myself with.'

1601. Euch umwerben, 'surround you as suitors.'

1604. Der . . . an, 'who are faithless in'; we might have *der Ihr werdet,* because the antecedent *(Ihr)* is usually repeated, the verb then agreeing in person; if, as here, the antecedent is not repeated, the verb is third person; *treulos* usually has simple dat. without preposition.

1612. naturvergeßnen, past part. with active force; i.e. forgetting the place and duty natural to him; 'degenerate, renegade.'

1613. sich . . . machen, "make himself into," i.e. 'become.'

1617. sein, beschirmen, subject infin. for meter's sake with and without *zu.*

1622. Es anticipates real subject **Herz.**

1631. (*will ich*) **ihm . . . Frieden** (*bereiten* = *geben*).

1633. Schloß, 'stronghold,' i.e. the Forest Cantons.

1635. versteht sich ("knows its mind") **auf** ("as to"), 'understands its.'

1639. Tät' = *wenn ich tät'.* — (*es*) **wäre.** — **den . . . sehen,** 'to see him despised'; i.e. by his own people and by the Austrians whose dupe he was.

1643. einem, emphatic; 'one and the same.'

1650. alles, predicate. — **läßt,** "makes," 'enables'; agrees with *Liebe.*

1652. (*das*) **wozu** = Engl. "whereunto."

1653. Erfüllt = *füllt aus.* — **wohin,** verb implies motion.

1658. der Verwandten (pl.), of Gessler especially; as Gessler von Bruneck he is made a relative, to whose care she is entrusted and who seems anxious to marry her himself (1611, 1720). — **Wille,** that he side with Austria.

1660. Cf. 446*, note; Schiller transfers them to identify her interests with those of the Swiss.

1661. 's = **frei;** can marry whom she chooses, as evident in what follows.

1665. Erb', Habsburg possessions; their greed is historical. Cf. 1343 ff.

1670. Dort, goes with **hin,** implying direction.

1672. harren mein (= *meiner,* gen. of *ich*), 'await me.' Again the rhyme.

1676. in (= 'out into') **das Weite,** 'for the great world.'

1686. Weiten, 'larger spheres.'

1688 f. feste Mauer breiten, 'extend their strong wall.' — **allein,** goes with **Himmel,** i.e. be clear and open only above.

1691. du (not *Ihr* as above), said to the accepted lover. — **ahnend,** she as well as Attinghausen (852) had thought him loyal at heart.

1697. leben, in his memory as old friends.

1700. fehlte, 'would be lacking.' He gives himself rather too much credit; as yet her love is more important than all else. — **Erden,** old gen. sing.

1701. Insel, the fabled Isles of the Blessed, land of bliss.

1703. heimisch wohnt, emphatic union of *heimisch ist* and *wohnt.*

1705. trübt ("troubles" = 'disturbs'), **entfliehen,** presents with future force.

1710. wie ... König wirkt, 'like a king ruling.' — **Reichen,** pl. to get the rhyme, which at this climax is more frequent than ever.

1711, aller Frauen, 'of all womanhood.' — **seh'** goes with the four infinitives below.

1719. Wie ... mich, 'how would it be with me?'

1720. Ritter, probably Gessler; 1658, note.

1727. Was ... werde, 'whatever may come of it.' She has courage for both.

The scene is a bright chapter in the sad story of oppression, whose shadow has fallen even upon these two. With a fitting background of grand romantic scenery it is full of poetic beauty and lyric passion, expressed by unusual word order and frequent rhyme. The action takes a long step forward when Rudenz is won back to his own people. Berta, the girl of noble, foreign family, is thus made the companion-piece to Gertrud, the mature Swiss matron of humbler birth; each inspires the man she loves to open conflict with tyranny. The Swiss cause seems more hopeful, for with the help of the younger nobility the cantons can better cope with Austria. The scene is not so "unnecessary" as many think. It belongs to the nobles plot, carries it on, and prepares for the part Rudenz takes later.

ACT III SCENE 3

The scene connects directly with III, 1 and takes place soon after; scene 2 gives Tell time to come from Bürglen, a mile away.

*Wiese bei (near) **Altorf,** 395 says *mitten in Altorf;* cf. also 1743. The monument supposed to mark the spot stands on the square in the town.

*Bannberg (from *bannen*, 'put under the ban,' 'protect by law'), mountain, overlooking Altorf, whose thick woods protect the town from falling stones and avalanches (1783 f.). Even yet it is forbidden to cut the trees on it; hence *die Bäume sind gebannt*, 1778.

*Frießhard ('fright-hard') and **Leuthold** (really *Liut-wald*, 'ruler of the people'; mistaken for 'kind to people') indicate contrasting characters.

1737. Popanz (accent **o**), 'that scare-crow.' He means Gessler's hat. They have been on guard some three weeks (393 ff.) and he is tired of it.

1739. uns zum Verdrieße (old for *Verdrusse*), 'to annoy us.'

1740. Was = *alle welche.* — **rechte Leute,** 'decent' (better class) 'people.'

1742 f. den halben, 'half the'; perhaps as agreed in 414. — **beugten,** 'would bend.'

1744. With what follows gives the time, not long after noon. Leuthold seems to have been away for a while and now hears what happened while he was gone; so do we.

1749. Hochwürdigen, 'Host, sacramental wafer.' Really an act unworthy of him and of the sacrament, but done to save his people.

1752. Monstránz, 'monstrance'; glass box containing the sacrament, really used only in church. The sacristan's **Glöcklein** calls attention to its presence, and devout Catholics kneel as it passes.

1753. Es fängt . . . deuchten, 'I begin to feel as if we were standing.'

1755. doch, 'after all'; here and in 1759 merely adds emphasis.

1761. Inversion common in exclamations, especially with **doch,** 'you know,' implying that contradiction is impossible.

1764. Mag, 'let.' — **wer da** (= *wer auch*), 'whoever.'

1766. ihr, pl. of *du.* The line is bitter mockery.

1767. Wollt's Gott, 'wish to goodness'; lit. "O that God willed it" = "would (to) God."

1768. "It would not on that account be worse for"; 'the country wouldn't be the worse for it.'

1769. Wollt . . . Platz, 'Will you get away from here!' — **Verwünschtes . . . Weiber,** 'You confounded women-folks!'

1770. fragt nach, 'cares about.'

1771. Mut sticht, about equivalent to 'notion strikes 'em.'

***Tell,** while he has been coming from Bürglen we have seen what is going on at the end of his journey; this connects the scenes. — ***vordere Szene,** 'front of the stage.'

1773 f. bluten, old superstition. — **führte,** condit. subjunc. 'should deal.'

1776. Gebannt, 'charmed'; 1778 'protected'; cf. note on *Bannberg* at head of scene.

1777. dem seine, colloquial for *dem die* = 'his.'

1779. Hörner, sharp snow-peaks, cf. *Schreckhorn,* 629.

1782. Schlaglawinen, cf. note on 1502.

1786. Landwehr ("defense of the land"), 'bulwark'; now usually 'militia.'

1790. Doubtless Germany, towards which Schächen, Reuss, and Rhine flow.

1793. nach . . . Himmelsräumen, 'in all directions.'

1798. Statt daß (= *statt* with *zu* and infin.), 'instead of' with pres. participle.

1803. i.e. to the Church and the State.

1807. The sale of salt was a state monopoly.

1812. 'I feel oppressed in that broad land,' when I think how things are there; **eng** and **weit** form effective contrast.

1813. Da, 'then,' 'in that case,' 'if that's so.'

1815. *wollen, 'are about to.' Here ends the introduction to the scene. It has shown that Gessler's demand of obeisance to the hat is still in force and that Tell is not only the loving father but also a real comrade of his boy. The main part of the scene (1818–2050) follows at once and gives us Tell's arrest, the resulting tumult, Gessler's cruel order, Berta's interference, Rudenz' defiance, the shot, and the impression it makes.

1817. Was kümmert, 'what do we care about?' A much disputed line. Why Tell's question? According to 1771* he has already passed the hat without seeing it, busy with Walter's questions. Now that his attention is called to it he may not realize that it is Gessler's hat or, if he does, is unwilling to linger, lest he should have to bow to the hat or openly defy Gessler's order. But the watching Friesshard wants a victim and arrests him anyhow.

1818. *greift in, 'lays hold of.'

1822. After his first burst of anger the formal *Ihr* gives way to the good humored *du*.

1823. *in die Szene, 'towards the background.'

1824. Herbei, 'Here!'

1826. Was legst = *warum legst.* — **du,** natural word for the pastor.

1829. *Fürsten, old acc. Such names are rarely declined now.

1830 f. geschieht, 'is being done.' — **haltet,** doubtless said to both guards.

1835. hätt', 'What! (do you mean) Tell has', cf. 1072, note. — **Das lügst,** 'that's a lie, you scoundrel.' Melchtal is apt to be emphatic.

1840. unsers Amtes, cf. 368, note.

1844. andern, dat. pl., 662, note.

1847. schon, expresses his self-confidence; 'never mind, I'll.'

1855. was . . . werden, 'what will come of this!' He knows his Gessler.

*den Falken, adverbial acc. (with) "a falcon"; they are returning from the hunt (1592), Berta and Rudenz having joined them. — Rudolf der Harras, fictitious character here, though the name occurs in old records. This, Gessler's first appearance, is most impressive. He is the only *Vogt* who does appear, so the cruelty of them all seems concentrated in him; having seen him so far merely in the effects of his tyranny and through the eyes of others, we are all the more impressed when, thus late, he emerges from the background. On horseback and splendidly attended, he is an imposing figure. His first harsh words show his whole character; at once judge and tyrant he quiets the tumult and overawes the people in a moment.

1860. Gestrenger Herr (Engl. "dread sovereign") lost its original force and became a term of respect; 'Your Lordship.' — **dein** is by no means "familiar"; older literature applies it even to kings.

1862. über (= *auf*) **frischer Tat,** 'in the very act,' 'as.'

1866. Gessler calls him by name at once. Why? Cf. 1556 ff. — **Kaiser,** the hat meant Habsburg, not imperial, authority, 409; Gessler purposely identifies them.

1872. Verachtung Eurer (= *Euer*, gen. of *Ihr*), 'contempt of you.'

1873. Many efforts, differing as widely as the critics themselves, have been made to explain Tell's name and with it the meaning of this line. It goes back to Tschudi's *wär ich witzig, so hieß ich nit der Tell* and seems to mean that he is heedless, not deliberate, and if he were otherwise (*besonnen*) he wouldn't be himself, for "the foolish," "simple" is his nickname.

1874. begegnen, 'happen.' — *einigem ('some'), 'a moment's'; there are several of these tense dramatic pauses, 1857, 1865; here some cruel plan is ripening.

1878. dir, ethical dative; 'shoot you an apple.' Schiller puts this boast in the mouth of the boy that it may attract Gessler's attention and suggest the cruel idea of making the father shoot the apple from the son's head. The lines were added in response to a hint from Goethe, who may have felt that the general purpose to punish Tell, evident in 1875, should have some reason for taking this particular form.

1879 ff. Such apparent interest is in glaring contrast with the fiendish cruelty of 1887.

1890. An intentional shot wide of the mark is made impossible.

1893. nein doch, very emphatic; 'No, Oh! no.' — **kommt ... zu** (usually *in den*) **Sinn,** 'you cannot mean that?' The broken speech shows him stunned with astonishment. The grim seriousness of what follows is in telling contrast with the easy-going humor at the opening of the scene. Hedwig was right (1573); Gessler is taking vengeance.

1896. wirst, this future (and 1900 pres.) indic. as imperative is strong.

1904. 'Ah Tell! Why! you are'; fiendish gloating; also **eigen,** 'special,' 1908.

1909. wohl, 'no doubt.' — **drückst ... zu,** not literal, but bitter irony; (you're such an archer) 'you'll just shut your eyes and go at it.'

1913. Kurzweils (usually fem.), prose would have acc. She seems to think it all a cruel joke, as does Harras until 1920.

1914. *The vivid dramatic action makes us forget that Nov. 20 is too late for apples on the trees in Switzerland.

1918. ihrer (partitive gen. with *hundert*), 'of them,' i.e. *Schritte*. It was Walter who had said so.

1921. Es gilt (from *gelten*, 'be a question of,' 'be at stake,' used in many idioms), here about = 'all is at stake'; 'it's now or never.'

1922. Haltet an Euch, 'control yourself.' — **drum,** 'for it'; **to** (do it). The Rütli meeting had voted to postpone any uprising.

1924. also (never 'also'), 'thus.'

1929. lernen = *gelernt* changed to inf. by *kennen;* cf. *hat tun wollen.* — **Stunde,** gen. with **denken** (for *gedenken*), 'remember.'

1931 f. Gasse, here narrow space between two lines of people, who are thus ordered to 'make way.' — **Verwirkt,** 401 f. The unfeeling torture continues, shows his character, and explains Tell's later acts.

1938. Hier gilt es (1921, note), 'now's your chance.'

1943. i.e. whose feeling (heart) does not make eye dim or hand shaky.

1945. lasset ... vor (= *für*), 'let mercy go before justice.'

1949. hinstehen = *mich hinstellen;* 'go stand.'

1950. Begin with **ja,** 'Why!'

1951. fehlen auf, i.e. miss the apple and strike the heart.

1954. Rede stehen, 'give account'; each one's speech shows his character.

1964. Frisch, 'Come!' or 'Quick now!' — **'s** = the rest of the line.

1965. 's, 'that you can do it.'

1966. Dem ... Verdrusse, 'to vex the tyrant.' 1739, note.

1971. 's = driving out the tyrants. — **mit frischer Tat,** 'right away'; without the delay agreed on in 1401 ff. Yet it was Unterwalden that suggested it.

1979. Freut's (conditional) **euch** ('you people'), hits the others through Tell.

1980. Ziel, the apple, of course. Some think Schiller wished the audience to see a second, prophetic meaning in the word, not even thought of by the speaker, that Gessler himself is later to be the *Ziel* of Tell's arrow. There are several such cases in the play: 1542, *geht* i.e. from Altorf and to his death; 1991, *alle* = Baumgarten and all the people; 2073, *zweimal*, once with Baumgarten and again out of Gessler's boat. It is hard to decide the question.

1985. This last appeal is splendidly dramatic.

1988. kannst ja, 'Why! you can do.' Gessler wants neither his life nor the shot, but seeks to humble the archer and torture the father and wreak cowardly vengeance for 1559–71; to the punishment of 1887 he adds the cruelty of 1900, the jeers of 1909, and the gloating of 1987 ff.

1990. zu retten gilt, 'when it means saving somebody'; bitter reference to Tell's rescue of Baumgarten.

*The strong contrasts between the beginning (III, 1) and the end of Tell's journey, between his quiet happiness (1772 ff.) and his present agony, greatly increase the dramatic tension — made all the more tense by our actually seeing this supreme example of the governors' cruelty, while we know others only by hearsay. We have here the turning-point of the whole play; it is just this **fürchterlicher Kampf,** between the father-heart and the independent manhood Gessler was trying to crush, that ripens Tell's resolve to take Gessler at his word and 'save everybody' from such a tyrant. Such a stage-direction is a whole drama in itself.

1992. schieß zu, 'shoot on.' — **es muß,** 'it must be.' His two offers of his life have been vain, all protest vain; there is no other way out. He is not the "unnatural" father some suppose.

***mit Gewalt gehalten,** 1922, note. Rudenz, now knowing Berta's feeling and brought to see his duty by this inhuman cruelty, at last takes his people's part.

1999. darf's = *darf reden;* the nobleman's right.

2004 ff. still, unnecessary, but idiomatic with *schweigen.* Without intending deception Rudenz gives himself credit he does not deserve; his response (770 ff.) to his uncle's entreaties was not patriotic, but Berta has already taught him much; and Gessler more. — **Sehend,** he might have seen, but would not.

2011. Ihr, not *du* as in 1691; she is not yet ready for others to know of her love.

2016. Da ... befestigte, "in that I strengthened," 'by strengthening.'

2020. war daran, 'was about to.'

2021. in bester Meinung, 'with the best intentions.'

2022. deinem, change from *Ihr;* said as to a subject, not to an equal.

2029. Antwort, 'satisfaction,' in a duel.

2031. da, 'here.' — **die,** 'these,' i.e. the peasants. This skillfully developed clash compels attention to Rudenz and Gessler and spares the spectator the pain of actually seeing Tell shoot at the boy, gives time for an apple with an arrow through it to be thrown from behind the scenes, and marks the climax of the nobles plot, for Rudenz now fights for his people. 2012–32 seem to be a later addition, for Berta's intervention is mentioned twice (2010* and 2032*) and forty lines between the aim (1992*) and the shot (2032) is a long interval.

2036. Wußt' ich's ja, 'Why! I knew'; emphatic inversion.

2037. *stand, 'has been standing.' The stage-direction is another of those vividly dramatic pictures that Schiller drew so well.

2039 ff. Even in these exclamations of natural surprise, the poet draws character: Tell collapses when the awful strain is over, the danger past; Leuthold and Harras praise the wonderful shot (2039–42); Berta and Fürst rejoice (2035, 2038) that the father's anguish is over; the boy, knowing nothing of such suffering, is proud of his father's skill (2036); the pastor, incensed at Gessler, calls down God's wrath upon him (2045); Stauffacher is happy that Tell is free (2047); Gessler is surprised and angry that Tell has shot (2034) and, failing in one plan, seeks another (2050).

2050. stecktest . . . zu dir, 'put in your doublet.' Cf. 1991*. Here begins the third and last section of the scene; the sudden change from frozen horror to melting joy is now changed again; Tell is rearrested and carried off to prison; the defeated tyrant triumphs.

2054. lass' . . . gelten, 'let pass, accept.'

2055. wird . . . wohl, fut. perf. shows confident opinion, 'no doubt it meant.'

2056. frisch und fröhlich, 'freely and frankly.'

2057. sich(e)r(e), 'assure'; note the acc. of the thing and dat. of the person, which is the usual construction of the simple verb; 2059, 2064 use acc. (person) and gen. (thing), where prose would have *mich (dich) versichert.*

2061. durchschoß, past indic. instead of plup. subj. of conditional. It gives Tell's words a terrible emphasis, further strengthened by the contrast with his previous humble attitude (1985 f.) and puts the result (2063) beyond doubt.

2063. Eurer (for *Euer*), gen. (1919 acc.) with **fehlen,** cf. 1996.

2073. As it were a mocking challenge flung in the face of God Himself; it seals his doom.

2075. Sogleich, 'in a moment.'

2077. Characteristic of the pastor, who knows all about the charters; it was unlawful to imprison or try a man outside of his canton, but Gessler ignores privileges not confirmed by the present Kaiser. Cf. 1325–36.

2081. Kaisers, meter omits *des.*

2086. *Berta follows, not from choice but because her guardian, Gessler, has authority over her. Rudenz is, of course, unwilling to leave her.

2089. warum mußtet Ihr, 'why did you have to.'

2090. 'Let him control himself who'; his feeling is beyond expression.

2091. From the sturdy Stauffacher and in spite of the Rütli oath in which Tell had no part! Shows how they regard Tell.

2097. Sag' ich, 'shall I take no message to your wife.' These closing lines have a grip that must be felt, it cannot be described.

This is aptly called the *Meisterszene* of the whole play. First, it shows careful dramatic structure; in spite of its many characters and incidents it is a unit whole of which each part easily and naturally leads up to and into the next — the introduction describes the guards (1733–55), the father and son (1772–1817); the main action (1818–2050) shows the arrest, the coming and cruelty of Gessler (1855–1910), the resulting conflict in Tell (1910–92), the interference of Rudenz (1993–2031), the shot (2031–50); the conclusion gives us Gessler's new plan, with the helpless protests against it, and, as fitting close, the father's love for his boy and the strong man's trust in his God, whose instrument he becomes. Schiller's contrasts are here most emphatic and dramatic. Secondly, the scene shows greater dramatic variety than any other: whimsical humor, rude jest, indignation, anxiety, fear, horror, hate, sympathy, inhuman cruelty, exultant joy, and splendid defiance are all combined to fill and thrill the heart. Again, the scene shows greater dramatic intensity than any other, and it brings the action of the whole play to a crisis in Tell's fearful struggle and his terrible oath, while the confederates are incensed almost beyond control. It has been too much. Revenge must come, though it is delayed by Tell's arrest. All three of the plots are brought together in the presence of their chief figures and further development of the action is admirably held in suspense.

ACT IV SCENE 1

After the crisis of Act III, Rudenz and the confederates move to resist;
Tell acts for himself; this begins the declining action of all three plots.

*Östliches Ufer, of the lower arm of the lake near Sisikon, 2121, note.
The scene passes, very soon after III, 3, an hour or so later in the afternoon
of the same day.

*Kunz (for *Konrad*) **von Gersau** (see map), fictitious character put in here
to connect this scene with what precedes and follows. Just from Flüelen
(2106), he tells what has happened since the close of the last scene and
brings news of Attinghausen (2116) that prepares us for the next scene.

*Fischer, Schiller told Iffland, the actor, that Ruodi is meant. We are to
suppose that, after I, 1, he and Jenni went to his other hut, doubtless his
permanent home (115) across the lake.

2103. gelten ... für, usually simple *gelten,* 'if there should ever be a fight.'
Cf. 1990, note.

2105. eben d(a)ran, cf. 2020, note.

2114. Mannes, Tell, if he should get free again; prepares for what is
coming, which **gerechte** makes just.

2116. am Tode, *im Sterben;* 'at the point of death.'

2121. Dorf, Sisikon probably, three miles from Flüelen.

2125 ff. Mund der Wahrheit, Attinghausen. — **seh'nde Auge,** probably
also to Attinghausen, whose eye he assumes **geblendet** in death; possibly
to Rudenz, after his uncle their natural protector, who though seeing is
blind to their interests (Bellermann). Kunz may not have mentioned his
clash with Gessler. The first seems best. — **Der Arm,** evidently Tell.
Without these all seems lost. It is strange that he regards the Baron's
death as such a loss to the Rütli cause; Attinghausen has not even heard
of the meeting.

2133 ff. Such elevated language from a fisherman seems out of place; it
is thought Schiller had in mind the famous passage in *King Lear* (III, 2,
1–9):

> Blow, winds, and crack your cheeks! rage! blow! ...
> Crack Nature's moulds, all germens spill at once.

2136. Wüste (gen.), cf. Stauffacher's account, 1261 ff.

2141. geboten, from *gebieten.*

2142 ff. Again (cf. 182, note) Nature is almost made one of the active characters of the play; so close do these people live to her, that they feel as if she too must share their righteous anger against the tyrants.

2148. Klüfte, the walls of the gorges.

2153. daß (*es*) **gebetet werde,** impersonal passive, 'that prayer be offered' — by all who hear this signal of distress; a beautiful custom.

2155 ff. The frequent alliteration is striking.

2159. Busen, 'bay.' — **gewährte,** potential subj., 'might give.'

2160. Handlos, "handless," offering no hold to be grasped like a hand; 'cliffs, rising steep and inaccessible, stare him in the face.' Personification, alliteration, and poetic order combine in a fine passage.

2165. sich erst verfangen, 'has once been caught'; the lake is here an immense gorge with 700 feet of water in it and cliff banks 800 feet high. These lines are again vivid personification.

2171. Herrenschiff (like *Herrenbank*, 807, and *Herrenburg*, 771), 'the governor's boat.' It showed red (Habsburg color) deck or awning and flag.

2175. Verbrechen, 'his crime, sin'; hardly Tell, its victim, as some think. To be sure Kunz told him Tell is on board (2104, cf. also 2215–18), but, in his pleasure over Gessler's danger, he seems to have forgotten it, tells the boy **bete nicht,** 2180, and needs the reminder of 2183.

2178. geben nicht (usually *nichts*, as object) **auf,** 'yield not to,' 'heed not.'

2181. 'Stay not the Judge's arm' by your prayer.

2183. mit (i.e. with the others), 'also.' Note the skill which shows us, through the watching boy, action off the stage; Tell actually in the storm and on the journey started in 2098.

2186. mitsamt, the double preposition is emphatic. Reminded of Tell's presence on board, he changes the *Rächer* of 2176 and the *Richter* of 2181 to *Unvernunft*, 2184. — The **Steuermann** can hardly be Tell; the boy does not say so, and Ruodi (2101, 2110) has thought of him in chains and still thinks so (2198), so it seems best to take *Steuermann* in a general sense; "ship and crew" must perish to punish one guilty one (Vos).

2188 ff. Buggisgrat, Hackmesser, Axenberg, dangerous cliffs on the east shore; **Teufelsmünster,** on the west. See map.

2194. Fluh (also *Flüh, Flüe*), Swiss word for bald, steep rock; used in many compounds: *Flüelen, Klaus von der Flüe;* cf. *960.

2196. If they would only use him. He has seen Tell handle a boat, 151 ff.

2197. könnt', unreal condition. — **einer** = *irgend einer.* — **doch dem . . . ja,** 'but then his.' The contrast between his desperate situation in the boat and his sudden appearance so soon after is splendidly dramatic; so also the silent expression of his feeling in the stage-direction. The first section of the scene (to 2199) shows the helpless, hopeless despair that follows Act III; the second (2199–2283) gives the details of Tell's escape.

2199. Sieh, 'Look!' — **wer,** 'who' (do you suppose); or 'Wonder who' (Vos).

2211. Seid = *wie seid Ihr.*

2212. Hört an, 'Listen!' Schiller thus makes the opportunity to let us know the details of his escape.

2215 f. Daß, connects with **wißt,** for he does not stop for Ruodi's answer. — **fahen,** old for *fangen.* — **zu,** 'at.'

2218. entkommen, add *seid.*

2220. aufgegebner, "given up," 'despairing.'

2227. Gransen ("beak"), pointed end of a boat; **am hintern Gransen,** 'at the stern'; *der vordere Gransen* is the prow.

2229. kleinen Axen, lower part of the Axenberg. In simple faith these sturdy souls feel that God is fighting on their side.

2231. Gäh(for *jäh-*)**lings herfür**(for *hervor*)**brach,** cf. 109, 875, notes. Schiller uses many of the old forms of Tschudi's chronicle, from which this account was taken; cf. 2194, 2215, 2239, 2247, 2258.

2238 f. wissen sich . . . nicht Rat, "know not counsel for themselves" = 'know not what to do.' — **Für,** old for *vor;* cf. Engl. "for fear," "for very joy." — **des Fahrens . . . berichtet,** 'not skilled in steering.'

2242. sein (gen., prose acc.) **brauchten,** 'should make use of.'

2244 f. Getrautest, preterite subj.; 'if you felt you could.' — **möchte,** 'might.'

2247. hiedannen = *von dannen, von hier weg;* Tschudi's expression. — **'s,** 'that,' i.e. the last half of 2244.

2249. fuhr redlich hin, Tschudi again, 'rowed steadily on.'

2252. auftät', cf. Engl. "open up," 'might present itself.'

2257. Geht's an, 'it goes up.' — **abzureichen** = *vom Schiff ab zu erreichen.*

2258. Schrie, goes on with 2253 and shows his excitement. — **handlich zuzugehen,** 'to pull hard.' Tschudi's *hantlich zugind* (= *zögen,* from *ziehen,* 'pull') was mistaken for *zugingen* (= "go at").

2259. vor, Tschudi's *für* = *über hinaus,* past. — **kämen,** 'should come,' or 'came'; like **sei,** subj. of indirect discourse with **schrie.**

2266. Platte, Tell's Platte, see map; a flat, jutting rock; now has a chapel, with frescoes illustrating Tell's deeds, on it. Surely we cannot blame Tell for his so called "desertion" of Gessler.

2274. hin, direction of motion; no infin. "understood," though Engl. needs 'go.'

2275. A fact that makes Tell's later deed self-defense, not murder.

2279. über Schwyz, 'by way of Schwyz,' the town.

2281. denkt's = *gedenkt* ('intends') *es zu tun.*

2283. Shows his fearless manhood, implies some grim purpose, and begins the third section of the scene. The shortest way leads along the south shore of Lake Lowerz, while Gessler kept to the north through Schwyz, Steinen, and Arth. See map.

2291. So, 'well then.' He feels he may ask it in view of 2290. — **tut...** **an,** 'do me the favor.'

2295. Schwäher, he thinks Fürst has taken Walter back home.

2297. Muts, pred. gen.

2229. ein Weitres, 'something further'; a significant hint.

2301. Ist, 'when it is.' — **zur Rede** (usually *Sprache*) **kommen,** 'be told.' Just like the Tell 419, 445. His plan to kill Gessler seems to be already made.

The despair of the whole people is further expressed by the fisherman. In spite of the Rütli meeting there seems no hope now — why is not made clear. But hope beats high again when Tell escapes. The action, purposely retarded by his rearrest, can go on again; the end is awaited with ever growing tension for we know something decisive is coming.

ACT IV SCENE 2

After the apple-shot, when Tell has been led away, Fürst, Stauffacher, and Melchtal hasten to Attinghausen a mile away, we may suppose to advise with the old Baron or upon the news of his illness. They find him critically ill, but doubtless tell him of Tell's fate. Walter naturally goes with Fürst; Hedwig has heard the news, of course, and her presence explains itself. The scene passes while Tell is on his way up the lake on the boat.

2304. hinüber, "across," 'he is gone'; no participle needed.

2305. Feder, of down, to show if breath has stopped.

2313. Just, though vain remonstrance; nothing could stop her.

2314 f. mir (both lines), ethical datives, best omitted. — **Auch,** 'really.'

2317. Any mother would feel the same way; not even her own father's word makes the least difference.

2320. Cf. 1921, note. Strange he does not tell her the boy's life was also at stake.

2325. Wie's ... können, 'how it might have (come) been.'

2326. achtzig, general, like Engl. "a hundred." — **seh',** pres. for vivid future.

2327. gebunden, she has heard an exaggerated report, or, more likely, just imagines it, as an anxious mother might.

2328. The mother says *mir*, not *ihm*.

2332. setzen = *setzen ... ein,* 'stake,' as in a game of chance. So far the mother-heart has run away with her head and she does Tell gross injustice, forgetting, if she had heard it, that his own and the boy's life depended on the shot. 2329 may well have given her a very wrong idea of the situation.

2336. *großen, wide with surprise and reproach. Reminded of her husband's suffering, it is now the wife that speaks, and that with loving pride.

2337. du (= Baumgarten), full of effective reproach, thus said to a stranger.

2338. ihr, all the others. It is not strange that she knew their passiveness in Altorf; such news spreads rapidly.

2344. dir, Baumgarten, as a special example.

2351. Her father, else she would have given him, too, a piece of her mind.

2353 f. 'We all miss him, he misses us.' — **vor,** 'from.'

2356. erkrankte, pret. subj. exclamatory, 'should get sick.'

2358. Alpenrose, not a rose, but a rhododendron growing only in the higher altitudes.

2361. Balsamstrom, 'balm of the breezes.' How well she knows him!

2370. rettete, pret. subj., 'could have saved.'

2374. Junker, name for young noblemen, before they are knighted; here Rudenz.

2375. gesendet (*worden*), 'he has been sent for.'

2378. Warum, cf. 2526 ff.

2383. Sense of pain is a sign of life; pain is gone, so death is near.

2390 f. Mußt' ich, (to think) 'that I had to!' — **um,** 'only.'

2397. He naturally thinks only the nobles can do it.

2398. sich, 'to each other,' at the Rütli.

2401. Es (impersonal) **wird,** 'action will be taken.'

2402. Eh' noch, emphatic, 'even before.'

2415. harren, "wait for"; 'expect, count on.' — **wenn es gilt,** 'when the time comes' to fight. Cf. 1921, 1990, 2103, notes.

2418. Mittel, the plural is generally used.

2420. unserer (for *unser*, gen. with **bedarf**), the nobles. This is the conclusion of the conditional sentences 2417 and 2419.

2422. Es, either perfectly general, 'there will be (new) life,' or anticipating **das Herrliche,** i.e. love of liberty will live. — **Andre Kräfte,** i.e. the people, burghers.

2424. Reference to Walter as type of the coming generation of yeomen, that in his prophetic vision is to give freedom to the country. He has been told of the apple-shot as well as of the change in Rudenz. Cf. 2464 f. Note the contrast with the pessimism of 944–959.

2431. Political and social tendencies already begun, the greater importance of the citizen class, allegiance of the nobles to the cities.

2433 ff. Ücht("morning-gray")**land,** between the Bernese Alps and the Jura; named from its fog-covered swamps, later reclaimed. **Bern** and **Freiburg** were its chief towns (here fem. because personified). Bern, early an important city, is now the national capital. — **Thurgau** ("district of the Thur"), much larger then than now, included nearly all of northeastern Switzerland. **Zürich,** its chief town, now the largest in the country, was important commercially, hence **die rege.**

2437. In fruitless attacks by the Habsburgs, especially Albrecht II, in 1351–52. In the illumination of death (**Strahl,** 2430) his prophetic vision becomes ever clearer. — **Zum,** 'into a.' — **Es,** anticipates the real subject **Macht.**

2439 ff. Refers to wars with the Austrians and Burgundians.

2442. (*es*) **wird gekämpft,** 'there is a life and death struggle'; at Morgarten in 1315, Laufen in 1339, Sempach in 1386, Näfels in 1388, Granson and Murten in 1476.

2443 f. Paß, Morgarten (see map) and Näfels, directly east, below Lake Zürich. — **Landmann,** reference to Arnold von Winkelried (of course, not the one in the play) and his heroic death in the battle of Sempach. Legend says he made an opening for his comrades by seizing as many as he could of the enemy's lances and forcing them into his own breast.

2451. So that the members may come together quickly.

*entseelt, 'in death.' The whole patriarchal system he stands for is pictured once more as he (and it with him) sinks into the grave.

2453. *hin, towards the body.

2455. Because it has another owner, Rudenz.

2460. Da, 'while.'

2462 f. Schuld, his treatment of his uncle in II, 1. — **dahinscheiden,** 'die.'

2478 f. Vater, said to Fürst; **die Eurige,** to Stauffacher.

2483. (*als*) **nichts geachtet** = *verachtet.*

2484. **wessen,** 'what shall we expect of you,' lit. "for what is one to look to you." Melchtal has reason to hesitate, cf. **766 ff.**

2485. **denket,** in prose *gedenkt* or *denkt* with *an* and acc.

2489 f. **Manneswort,** '(true) man's pledge.' — **Stand,** "rank," 'class.'

2493. **ihren . . . befruchtet,** 'makes it fertile.'

2500. **'s vergleichen,** 'settle our differences.' — **schon,** 'readily.'

2513. **ward,** 'has become.'

2516. **Wartet,** with subject expressed, strong imperative, do you 'wait.' — **wolltet,** pret. subj. indirect question, 'you mean you would.'

2526. There is a good deal of self-interest still in his patriotism.

2528. **hätte,** like *wolltet,* 2516. — **Edle,** cf. *Ritterfräulein,* 936, note, 939. — **der Tyrann** (= *der Wütende,* 2533) is, of course, Gessler, who, to make sure of her for himself (1658, note, 1720) or enraged by her defense of Tell (1923), has had her secretly imprisoned; 2075 gave him time for the order.

2534 f. 'What criminal force they will make bold to use.' **Band,** cf. 1669.

2544. Unter . . . hervor (= "out"), 'from under.'

2547. Ob, i.e. 'to see if.'

2551. Das Ungeheure, Gessler's treatment of Tell. Under the changed conditions his Rütli oath no longer binds him to delay; other confederates doubtless join him, but are not named.

2553. der = *daß er,* 'that he could; as to.'

2558. seht ihr, as in Engl. 'if (= when) you see.'

2559. The prose order is: *Dann stürzt,* etc.

The scene gives Tell time for the journey begun 2294 and shows developments among the others meanwhile, with Hedwig's joy and sorrow, Attinghausen's prophecy and death, Rudenz-Melchtal's alliance, as essential features. If Tell's mind is made up, Rudenz, too, awakens to his new responsibility after his uncle's death, and, for personal reason also, is roused to the fighting point. Prince and peasant have joined hands for instant action, because the latest cruelties (against Tell and Berta) show tyranny will stop at nothing and must be overthrown ere it is too late. So from two sides, individual (Tell) and general (Rudenz and confederates), the blow is about to fall, which shall set this people free. The old patriarch, Attinghausen, though he has never suffered as the rest, gives their cause his dying blessing; so it must be a just cause. The scene again unites all three plots, for Hedwig and Walter represent Tell. Through the leaders gathered here the dying blessing and prophecy are given symbolically to the whole people. It is not clear why Baumgarten is here; Rösselmann is absent perhaps because "his presence would have required a religious setting out of harmony with the scene as planned." (Vos.)

ACT IV SCENE 3

*Connects directly with IV, 1 (2300 ff.); during sc. 2 Tell has come from the lake; we find him late in the afternoon of the same day. In reality the distance is too great for that, but neither poet nor spectator here thinks of such things. The **hohle Gasse,** 'hollow way' (= sunken road), then a deep, narrow road between overhanging rocks and trees, has been partly filled up by a good modern turnpike; the place, half a mile from Immensee, is marked by another Tell chapel. The first division of the scene, the monologue, is used to show Tell's inmost heart and thought and to justify his awful purpose already formed; he thinks he can (to 2577) and must (to 2590) kill his enemy, and feels it is right to do so (to 2597); his reasons are the everlasting instincts of nature roused beyond control by ruthless outrage.

2563 ff. Such deliberate choice of an ambush has been called cowardly, yet: (1) he must now kill or be killed without mercy, (2) an attack in the open is a risk of failure, which would mean his death before he could ever get another chance, (3) such necessity knows no law or chivalry, but must choose a method certain to succeed, (4) Schiller must be true to his sources in so important a matter as the manner of the tyrant's death. We should remember these things — and think as we must.

2568. Uhr (= *Sanduhr*) . . . **abgelaufen,** refers to the running sand of the hour-glass, 'thy hour has come.' Such direct address, as if face to face, is very dramatic.

2571. Mord (repeated 2622–30–35), he does not deny it or seek to gloss it over; to him it is willful killing, but needs no defense.

2572. heraus-geschreckt, cf. 284, note, 'roused out of.'

2574. Milch, cf. Engl. "milk of human kindness," here turned to the rankling poison of hatred and revenge.

2575. zum, for usual *an* with acc.

2577. After his own feeling comes his thought of his family suggested by 2576; each paragraph has a new theme.

2584. ohnmächtig ("powerless," 'vainly') **flehend rang,** 'as I writhed in vain entreaty.'

2585. Damals takes up again the *Da* of 2580.

2589. It is the *Augenblick* also of 1439.

2590. He has two grounds for his action: (1) natural and necessary defense of himself and his family, for Gessler would soon wreak vengeance as Landenberg had done; (2) the sacred obligation of keeping the oath wrung from him in his agony by Gessler's cruelty. He acts as an individual, not from the motives of the confederates. He does not contradict 2061–62, for he had even then determined to kill him, but then meant to wait for a good chance — which has now come.

2595. der, demonst., "that," 'such.' The passage arraigns Gessler.

2596. Dich erfrechen (with gen.), 'make bold to do.'

2598. du, in apostrophe to the arrow, which he now takes out. There are several of these apostrophes in the monologue, 2567, 2598, 2603, 2623.

2601. undurchdringlich (figure of arrow and target), 'inaccessible to.' — **fromme Bitte,** requests of the people, himself among them (1985).

2604. Freude Spielen (= *Freudenschießen*, 2649), 'happy sports.'

2606. nur jetzt noch ("only now still"), 'only this once more.'

2609. keinen zweiten, possibly literal (the arrow of 2051), for though he took his bow he may have left his quiver in the boat (hardly likely from 2226 and 2265); he probably means he will have no second chance at Gessler.

2610. dieser, this famous line is often quoted as an instance of Schiller's "bad grammar"; *auf* with verb of motion does take acc., but **sich setzen** has here force of *Platz nehmen,* 'sit,' hence the dát.

2612 ff. treibt . . . rasch . . . vorüber, 'each hurries past the other (like a stranger) carelessly.' — **seinem,** the other's.

2616. leicht geschürzte ("lightly girt"), figurative, 'easy-going.' Note the contrast with **sorgenvoll,** also **andächtig, düster, heiter.** These "reflections" have been criticized as out of place here, but they are by no means unnatural, for the merest trifle will often momentarily occupy the heart in distress.

2620. führt, one to another, that to another, and so on; "all roads lead to Rome."

2622. Geschäft brings him back to his own, to which he refers with utter frankness, as before; 2571, note.

2625. Prose *ohne daß er . . . bracht'*, 'without bringing you something.'

2626. War's, 'either it was . . . or.'

2627 f. Ammonshorn, 'ammonite'; fossil shell, so called because it looks like the ram's horns on the head of Jupiter Ammon. — **Wie es,** 'such as.'

2632. lieben, weak declension, still used in plural address, though the strong form is the rule; 2623.

2633. Cf. 2590, note.

2637. Läßt sich's (usually with *doch*) . . . **verdrießen,** 'does not let it weary him'; invented for emphasis, not conditional.

2641. This story that the hunter cuts open the ball of the foot to glue himself to the steep rocks with the congealing blood is, of course, not true.

2642. Grattier, a kind of chamois living only on the highest crags, redbrown in color and smaller than the kind that lives on the wooded slopes.

2650. das Beste, 'the best prize,' the victor's reward in the shooting-match. Lest we think it cowardly murder, Tell's deed must be put to us as it seems to him, as an act of righteous self-defense. He is not just now reaching his decision, of course, but, as he sits waiting he is thinking of what he has determined to do, and the monologue is the poet's device to give us his thoughts and show us the change wrought in him by the *Kampf* of 1991*.

*Hochzeit, "wedding," here 'wedding party.' This second division of the scene (2652–2697) gives us the news of Gessler's escape from the storm, emphasizes Tell's grim purpose by contrasting him with the talkative Stüssi, keeps us in suspense as to whether Gessler is really coming, and provides the wedding which is to contrast so strongly with Gessler's death. The gay party also secures the separation of Gessler from his retinue (2778), necessary to insure Tell's escape, and explains the very dramatic presence of the people at the tyrant's death. — **Stüssi,** Swiss dimin. of *Justus.*

2652. Klostermeier, overseer of monastery farm work and property; cf. note at head of II, 2. — **Mörlischachen,** on the lake near Küssnacht.

2653. Brautlauf hält, 'is getting married.' *Brautlauf* ("bride-race"), so called because in old German weddings, as a relic of the ancient marriage by capture, a race with the bride was actually run; the word, outliving the custom, has come to mean *Brautzug* (2898*), fetching the bride to her new home in gay procession.

2654 f. Senten, a *Sente* is a small herd tended by a *Senne* (15) in the Alps. — **zu** ("at"), from Imisee, same as Immensee (see map).

2656. (*es*) **wird . . . geschwelgt** (general sense), 'there'll be reveling.'

2660. Nehmt mit, 'take whatever (pleasure) comes' (along with other things).

2661. leicht ergreifen, 'be quick to take.'

2662. wird gefreit, impersonal and general, as in 2656; 'here they're marrying.'

2663. Stüssi does not understand such mysterious references (also 2658 and 2686), the reader does — which greatly increases the dramatic tension.

2664. nun, not "now," but introductory 'Well!'

2665 f. Ruffi, Swiss name for the often dangerous landslides occurring mainly in spring; 'there's been a landslide in Glarus.' — **Glärnisch,** cluster of peaks rising above Glarus, capital of the canton of Glarus, east of Schwyz.

2670. Da sprach, 'For instance, I met (spoke with) a man.' — **Baden,** cf. 410, note and *Stein zu Baden,* 2966.

2677. Man deutet's auf, "point it to"; 'they say it means' (cf. 614, note).

2684. *Höhe, top of the slope (on the road) over which he is restlessly expecting Gessler to appear; a very dramatic touch.

2685. Gehabt, cf. 943, note. His question and the answer are splendidly dramatic.

2687. aus Uri, his dialect has shown that.

2689. Increases the dramatic suspense after the line before.

2692. Sucht... an ihn, cf. *Gesuch an ihn richten,* which explains the unusual *an* with acc. here; 'have you something to ask of him?' This Armgard episode, a third section of the scene (to 2786) used to give new evidence of Gessler's past cruelty and threats of future tyranny, still further justifies Tell's deed and connects it with the cause of his people, since, in killing his own enemy, he also strikes one thus the more evidently theirs.

2698. *vordern Szene, 'front of the stage.'

2703. mein Lebtag = *meinen (mein'n, mein) Lebtag* or *mein(e) Lebtag(e),* "all the days o' my life"; 'as long as I live.'

2704. muß voraus, 'must go on ahead'; no infin. is "understood."

2706 f. Wär'n, condition; **wär's,** conclusion, 'would have gone to the bottom' [**in** (= *in den* = *in'n* = *in*) **Grund**] 'with all on board' (**mit Mann und Maus,** 331, note).

2708. dem, emphatic contempt, 'such.' — **bei**(*kommen*), "get at," 'hurt'; the infin. is often omitted, as here.

2709. kam... hin, 'has gone; did... go.'

2713. ihm (= *Volk*) **sanft zu tun,** 'deal gently with them.'

2714. Streit, 'question'; close of a talk in which Harras, his own partisan, has been urging moderation.

2716. bring'... an, 'bring up'; state her request.

2719. kenn'... längst, pres. for perfect, 'have long known.'

2721. Mir, ethical dat., not indirect object; omit.

2727 f. Die, 'them.' — **Werk... Werden,** 'in progress and planned'; it is hard to preserve such alliteration in Engl.

2730. begonnen, what Rudolf of Habsburg (reigned 1273–1291) had done for his House. — **will,** 'means to.' — **Sohn,** Albrecht.

2732. So oder so, 'whether (willingly) or no.'

2734. dringt, for *drängt.*

2735. in, cf. 2706, note.

2739. Wildheuer, poor peasants, with no pastures of their own, cut free grass on dangerous heights. — **Rigiberge,** near by; see map.

2740. überm ... weg, 'from over.'

2745. Was ... Schweres, 'whatever crime.'

2747. Euch ... werden, cf. 149, note.

2750. den Mann, 'my husband.'

2751. in ("into") **... Mond** (= *Monat*), 'going on six months.'

2754. From entreaty she goes over to demand, then to scathing accusation (2769) and threat (2773); her changed tone uses *du* for her earlier polite *Ihr*, and *Vogt* for *Gestrenger Herr.*

2756. so ... so, 'as ... so.'

2758. Schafft, 'Get this ... out of my sight!'

2763. nichts (emphatic *nicht*) **fragen,** 'care nothing for.'

2766. Da, 'There!'

2770. Tratest ... doch, very emphatic; 'Well! you have long since, etc.'

2772 f. Prepares us for Tell's shot.

2775. 'Somebody get her away from here.'

2776. mich reuet, "will repent me," 'I'll regret.'

2781 f. soll, 'shall be.' — **es soll ... werden,** 'things shall be different.'

2786. Ich will (four times in four lines) — **Gott sei mir gnädig,** his cruelty reaches its climax in terrible threats; with fine dramatic effect, after steady rise in tension, Schiller chooses this best of all opportunities to cut him down; just as he has laid bare his cruel heart and unfolded his plans for worse things to come, the arrow cuts short his vow to crush this people, if he cannot break their spirit; his last act of cruelty, riding down a helpless mother and her children, so enrages the reader that Tell's shot appears only as just retribution, the defense of his life, his home, and now of his people. The close of the scene (2787–end) shows the effects of Tell's deed in the changed attitude of the people and in their hopes of liberty.

*fährt ... Hand, 'puts his hand'; natural gesture, which also allows the actor to straighten up the dummy arrow already in his doublet, so it can be seen.

2794 ff. Tell came to kill the enemy of his own home, but, after hearing Gessler's threats and seeing his treatment of Armgard and her children, he now realizes that he has struck down not only his own (individual, personal) enemy, but also the enemy of his country, the oppressor of innocence everywhere. He has solved the problem of 1429 ff.

2798. *geht fort, 'continues'; intended, telling contrast with this scene of death.

2800. Said rather about him than to him, hence *du*, for *Ihr*.

2803. Rast (not "rage"), 'have these people gone mad?'

2804. Musik, as accompaniment. — **Laßt,** 'make them.'

2805. Ihr, said to Gessler (again conscious) instead of *du* as in 2800.

2808. Laßt . . . Irdische, 'forget earthly things.'

2810 f. tritt . . . an, "approaches," 'lays hold of.' — **Gebrochen,** 866, note.

2811. The manner of the elders and the contrast between these innocent children and the dying tyrant are intensely dramatic. And what a companion-piece to the death of Attinghausen!

2815. Leget Hand an, 'Take hold.' — **Steht . . . bei,** 'will . . . help?'

2818. Wagt es, 'Just you dare (it)'; the moment the tyrant is gone, they change their tone, for Tell's shot has set them free.

2831. (*Es*) **ist . . . zu vertrauen,** 'there is no faith to be put.' — **Treu,** dat., 'in . . . fidelity.'

*Barmherzige Brüder, 'Brothers of Mercy,' an order founded in 1540 by Juan Ciudad di Dio in Seville, Spain. Schiller probably thought it much older. (The audience knows no better, so nobody's illusion is disturbed.) Their dress was black, hence Stüssi's rude reference to them as **Raben** around a corpse.

2836. Es (indefinite, supernatural) **stürzt ihn,** "something hurls him," 'he is overthrown.' — **mitten in,** 'in the midst of, in mid career.'

2837. Es (as above) **reißt,** 'he is hurried away.'

2839. stehen (i.e. *treten*) implies motion, hence acc. **Richter.** Cf. *hinstehen*, 1949, note. This chorus, so like that in Greek tragedy, which Schiller had imitated the year before in his *Braut von Messina*, is a very solemn and impressive close to the scene. It reminds us of the famous thirteenth century Latin funeral chant: "In the midst of life, we are in death," and is intended to soften the impression of the awful thing we have seen.

The expected catastrophe has come; the individual blow has been struck and proves to be that by which Swiss liberty is almost won (Rudenz' expedition being still in doubt). It is another of those great scenes that have made the play famous and is worthy of the events it describes. Not only are the beginning and end, monologue and chorus, very impressive, but its many situations are also intensely dramatic, and its striking contrasts — Tell and Stüssi, *der ernste Gast* and *das Hochzeitshaus*, the *Mord* and *Musik*, the threatening Gessler and the stricken governor, the innocent children and the dying tyrant — are most effective.

ACT V SCENE 1

The scene is again laid in Altorf, before Zwing Uri (I, 3); Tschudi gives the time as the morning after Gessler's death, but here it must be at least two nights and a day later. After 2086* Berta is sent to Sarnen (Nov. 20), later that afternoon Rudenz and Melchtal start to capture the castles; Rossberg was taken (2874–76) the night (Nov. 20) before Sarnen fell (Nov. 21); there must also be time for the news of Gessler's death to reach Altorf (2856, 2930) from Küssnacht and for Tell, Rudenz, Melchtal, and Berta to get back. If III and IV occupy Monday, Nov. 20 (cf. note at head of III, 1), Act V begins at the very earliest at daybreak (**Morgenanbruch**) on Nov. 22.

2840 f. Feúersignále, those of 1423, 2555. — **Wald,** in Unterwalden.

2842. Burgen, Rossberg and Sarnen.

2843. Like the average man that he is, Ruodi is very brave now.

2846. Joch, Zwing Uri; cf. 371.

2848. Stier von Uri, 'Bull of Uri'; 1093, note.

2849. Hochwacht, high 'signal point' (station); not as in 1442, 2450.

2853. Very like the old, over-cautious Fürst.

2858. 'Have we not enough in these?'

2865. im Lauf, "on its course"; i.e. they have begun. Numbers take part.

2867. gebrochen, 'stormed.' Impetuous Melchtal brings the news.

2869. Lande (and **Land** 2872), the three Forest Cantons.

2877. Schloß, Sarnen.

2880. Bub = *Knappe*, his servant; doubtless one of several who had brought Berta here to Landenberg's castle — to hide her. Cf. 498, 2883; 2528, note.

2881. Bruneckerin, 'the lady of Bruneck'; cf. 281 f., note.

2884. erhub, for usual *erhob*, from *erheben*.

2888 f. Da galt (cf. 1921, 1990, notes), "that was the time for"; 'that meant.' — **Edelmann,** i.e. feudal lord.

2890. i.e. would have hesitated and taken no risk.

2892. Berta is subject of **ehrte.** — **setzten . . . dran,** 'cheerfully risked.'

2900. Attinghausen's prophecy come true; prince and peasant in symbolic union.

2903. Über den (acc. of implied motion) **Brünig** (pass), see map; 1194, note.

2904. Nicht . . . mir, 'it was not my doing (or fault).'

2906. Nach jagt', vivid poetic word-order. The passage shows splendid magnanimity and self-control. Cf. 1375–76.

2911. Urfehde, 'a solemn oath'; oath not to avenge injury, to keep the peace.

2918. damit werden, 'be done with it.'

2919. Not really true; he stood under the linden.

2923. ewig Zeichen, has been so from ancient times; cf. our "Cap of Liberty."

2927. Not complete because their ultimate enemy, the Habsburg emperor, may interfere. Act V must remove this danger and assure us that their liberty is complete and permanent.

2931. Vertriebnen, Landenberg.

2939. Skillful introduction of a new theme, the murder of the Emperor. Its bluntness rouses interest anew.

2947. Bruck (also *Brugg*), town on the Aar, some twenty miles from Zürich; the ruins of the ancestral Habsburg castle still stand near by.

2949. Schiller intends this as a tribute to his friend, the great Swiss historian, Johannes von Müller, born in Schaffhausen (lived 1752–1809), whose personal letters and history of Switzerland were of great help in writing the play.

2953. He was the son of Rudolf, Albrecht's brother, and is the *Herzog Hans* of 1338 ff. and the *Parricida* of V, 2. The murder was done May 1, 1308. By changing the date Schiller helps to condense into three weeks action to which Tschudi gave twenty-one months.

2954. Vatermords, here (like Lat. *parricidium*) the murder of any near relative; hence the name *Parricida* (3165).

2955. väterliche [Hunn mentions *sein Mütterliches* (1344, note); Tschudi speaks of both], the duchy of Schwaben.

2957. Es hieß, 'It was said; they said.' — **darum kürzen,** 'cut him out of.'

2958. abzufinden, 'put him off with the empty dignity.'

2959. Wie dem . . . sei, 'Be that as it may.'

2966. Stein zu Baden, cf. 2670, note. *Stein* is common in castle names.

2967. Gen (= *gegen*) **Rheinfeld(en),** cf. 1325, note.

2968. Hans, his nephew (2953). — **Leopold,** his son.

2975. Stadt, old Roman (hence **Heiden**) town Vindonissa (now Windisch), a border fortress against the Germans, later one of the capitals of Helvetia; destroyed by the Franks in 594.

2977. Habsburg, short for *Habichts*(= Hawk's)*burg*, the home of the Habsburgs, the Royal House of Austria.

2983. den Seinen, 'his own kin.' — **dem Seinen,** 'his own land.'

2989. frühes, i.e. 'untimely'; he was fifty-eight years old.

2993. Stand (= *Reichsstand*, 'Estate'), commonwealth, duchy, county, canton, even city; any self-governing member of the Empire.

2997. Bannes, ban of outlawry; cf. 3213.

2998. Albrecht's oldest daughter, widow of Andreas of Hungary.

3001. Unbelievable stories are told of her vengeance; that the castles of the murderers were destroyed and hundreds, **ganze Zeugungen,** killed. Modern history gives her a much better name.

3006. Walking barefoot in May dew was supposed to give health and beauty; blood is substituted here.

3010. um ... sehen, 'never to see again.'

3011. Prepares for his appearance in the next scene.

3013. sich (dat.) **selbst,** cf. Shakespeare's "doth make the meat it feeds upon."

3019. Their liberty is now secure.

3023. Nov. 1308, the Electors did assert their independence of Habsburg by choosing Heinrich of Luxemburg Emperor (Heinrich VII, reigned 1308–1313).

3024. was, anything about the probable successor of Albrecht.

3025. Impossible, of course, in Nov. 1307; Schiller changed the history, 2953, note. — **mehrsten** = *meisten.*

3027. hoffen; Heinrich VII did (in 1309) confirm the charters of Schwyz and Uri and gave a similar one to Unterwalden.

3034. Elsbet, Albrecht's widow. — **Gutes** = *Gute.*

3037 f. Worein, "in(to) which," 'where-in.' — **Hinscheid** = *Hinscheiden.* — **versetzt** (*hat*); note the stilted official style.

3042. versieht sich, 2484, note. The usual gen. is replaced by **Daß.**

3043. Abscheu ... vor, 'aversion for.'

3050. empfangen (*haben*).

3052. Vater, Albrecht's father, Rudolf, who reigned 1273–1291.

3053. wessen rühmen wir, 'what (favor) can we boast.'

3058. Cf. 1327 ff. 'Did he even deign to?'

3063. rührte ... an = *hätte angerührt* in force.

3065. konnte sein, 'could have been'; the indic. is emphatic.

3068. Die 'those whom.' — **gemehrt,** *Mehrer des Reichs* was in his title.

3069. Falls, gen. for usual *über* with acc.

3074. will (adds great emphasis) ... **gebühren,** i.e. 'can't' be right.

3075. will ("insists" on being) ... **sein,** 'must be.'

3077. nichts weiter, i.e. no further obligation.

3078-80. Und ... So, 'and even if ... still' (at the same time).

3081 f. eben diesem, 'this very same.' — **Tränen,** of sympathy.

After the Rudenz-Melchtal success the scene shows that the triumph of liberty is complete and permanent, that danger from within and without is past. This is one purpose of Act V; another is to get, in Albrecht's death, a wider historical background; another still is to show us Tell after Gessler's death and the effects of his deed on him and his people. Act V is not so "unnecessary" as many think.

ACT V SCENE 2

*Hausflur, usually "hall," "entry"; here 'living-room.'

*zeigt ins ("points into") **Freie,** 'affords a view outdoors.' The place is the same as in III, 1; the time as in V, 1.

3088. alles, 'everybody.'

3093. hart vorbei, "hard by," i.e. came near hitting me.

3100. wird, future of probability, 'is no doubt asking.'

3104. *zerstört, for *verstört*, 'with wild, haggard look.'

3109. Herr, 'husband'; *Mann* is the modern word.

3110. was ist Euch, 'what's the matter with you?' At once her woman instinct tells her something is wrong.

3112 f. auch (both lines) generalizes, 'ever.'

3114. zugesagt, i.e. assured me of protection.

3117 f. Very ancient invocations of hospitality; add: "I conjure (implore) you."

3120. Her feminine intuition and mother fear again.

3125. 'Your look frightens me' ("oppresses my heart").

3126. *will nach, 'starts to follow.' — **hält ... an,** 'holds to something' to keep from falling.

3134. der Freude, 'for joy.'

3136. Meinigen, cf. 2983, note.

3139. Common custom; there is no ground for the statement here, but it shows he does not think himself a "murderer."

3145. frei, with clear conscience; her doubts give this opportunity for Tell's own view of his deed. Compare his manner with Parricida's.

3146 f. vergaß, 'had forgotten.' — **mir graut,** 'I am afraid.'

3159. wäret, the subj., after the indic. **seid,** powerfully expresses Tell's horror; 'you are, can it be that you are.'

3162. einem, 'the same.' — **wohnen,** here 'stay.'

3163. Herzog von Österreich, another name for the same *Herzog* of 2953, called in history (as here also, when his identity is established) Johannes Parricida. Cf. 2954, note.

3168. Euch, dat.

3171. Tell's contempt makes him change to **du.**

3176 ff. This passage shows the real purpose of the scene — so to contrast the deed of Parricida with that of Tell as to make the one murder, the other self-defense.

3183. heilige Natur, nature's sacred instinct to defend one's own.

3184. teil', 'have in common.' In the monologue he called his own deed *Mord.*

3192 f. So jung, he was eighteen years old — **Enkel Rudolfs,** i.e. of Rudolf of Habsburg, unlike Albrecht, much esteemed by the Swiss.

3195. Des . . . Mannes (expands **meiner**), 'a poor man like me.'

3198. konnte werden, instead of *hätte werden können;* I was able to, but didn't. Indic. (as also **bezwang**) adds intense emphasis.

3201. Leopold, Albrecht's second son, also born 1290.

3208. weisen Schluß, is disturbing; it was greed, not wisdom (2957).

3213. Usual phrase of the imperial ban; friends were forbidden to shelter him, enemies allowed to kill him. — **erlaubt** (*bist*).

3217. Eignes Schrecknis, 'a terror to myself.'

3218. vor mir selbst, 'at the sight of myself.'

3221. From now on Tell's sympathy brings him back to greater respect, so *du* changes back to *Ihr.*

3223. Mensch der Sünde, general, 'sinful mortal.'

3230. entdeckt, shortened condition, 'if discovered.'

3234. Stadt, Rome, city of the Pope, St. Peter's successor.

3235 f. Papst, Clement V. — **löset,** get absolution after confession.

3244 f. wildes (for *wilden*) **Laufes,** adv. gen., 'in wild course.'

3253. This **Schreckensstraße** runs along the Reuss through the wild gorge of Schöllenen to the Devil's Bridge = **die Brücke welche stäubet,** i.e. 'the spray-covered bridge.'

3254. Windeswehen ("drifts"), avalanches from the summit (**Joch**); frequent and dangerous.

3259. reißt . . . auf, 'opens suddenly.' This 'rocky gateway' is the *Urner Loch,* once a mere cleft, since 1707 a good tunnel over 200 feet long.

3261. The Urseren valley with open, green pastures, in marked contrast to the gloomy gorges just described.

3265. Boden, Canton Tessin and Italy, part of the Holy Roman Empire. Cf. 266, note.

3267. Small lakes of constant (**ew'gen**) depth on the Gotthard Pass, fed by the rains and snows of the high Alps.

3270 f. muntern, cf. the strong form of the adj. in 3244. — **ein andrer Strom,** the Ticino (pron. *Ticheéno*), with its source in the lakes above. — **Euch** ('for you') **das gelobte,** 'the Promised Land.'

3281. *bedeutet ihn,** makes a sign (gesture) to him, cutting off his thanks. — **kommen gezogen,** 'come marching.' — **drängen nach,** 'crowd after.'

3286. mein Recht, 'my cause.' — **Rechte** (3289), 'right hand.

3291. Knechte, 'serfs'; cf. 1081, 1143, 1209, notes. Appropriate ending for this drama of freedom.

Scene 2 is criticized as unnecessary to the action, for that was already finished, yet Schiller felt the need of justifying still further the deed of Tell by comparing it with that of Parricida, whose murder of the Emperor is all the more vivid in the murderer's presence. Tell vindicates himself to others as he has already done to himself. It is, however, an open question whether any latent doubt in the mind of the reader may not rather be roused by this second defense. His somewhat pharisaical air hardly accords with his usual simplicity, his harsh condemnation with his usual ready sympathy. Again the three plots are brought together in this bright picture of liberty, union, fraternity for all classes of one happy people.

VOCABULARY

This vocabulary attempts to give the student only what he may really need, hence proper names and many every-day words are omitted. The declension of nouns is shown by the endings of gen. sing. and nom. pl. Where no pl. is given, there is none in common use. In the principal parts of strong verbs the pres. indic. third pers. sing. is given last. The auxiliary is **haben** unless **sein** is indicated by **s.** Transitives are indicated (*tr.*), intransitives not. Separable verbs are distinguished by the hyphen (-).

The adverbial use of adjectives is not noted.

Stress is indicated by the acute accent ('), and, as a further aid in pronunciation, long and short vowels are at times marked; figures refer to the lines of the text; (*) shows stage-directions; other abbreviations explain themselves.

A

ab *adv. and sep. pref.* off, down, away; exit, exeunt

ab-brechen (brach, gebrochen; bricht) break off, stop

ab-drücken *tr.* (*lit.* press off), let fly (*arrow*), shoot

ab-fahren (fuhr, gefahren; fährt) s. start, leave, set sail

Ab'fahrt *f.* –en departure

Ab'fall *m.* –s, ⁼e desertion

ab-fallen (fiel, gefallen; fällt) s. desert, be faithless to

ab-finden (fand, gefunden) *tr.* put off, pay off

ab-führen, *tr.* lead off (away), carry away

ab-gehen (ging, gegangen) s. go off (away), depart; leave (the stage)

ab-gewinnen (gewann, gewonnen) *tr.* win from (*dat.*)

Ab'grund *m.* –s, ⁼e abyss, gulf, precipice

ab-holen *tr.* fetch, go for

ab-laufen (lief, gelaufen; läuft) s. run down

ab-mähen *tr.* mow (cut) off

ab-messen (maß, gemessen; mißt) *tr.* measure off, survey

ab-nehmen (nahm, genommen; nimmt) *tr.* take off

ab-platten *tr.* flatten (down); *past part. as adj.* flat

Ab'rede *f.* –n agreement; — **nehmen** take counsel

ab-reichen *tr.* reach

Ab'scheu *m.* –s abhorrence; — **tragen vor** feel aversion for

Ab'schied *m.* –s, –e parting, leave, farewell

ab-senken *refl.* slope, descend

Ab'sicht *f.* –en intention

ab-stoßen (stieß, gestoßen; stößt) push (shove) off (from shore)

Abt *m.* –(e)s, ⁼e abbot

ab-treiben (trieb, getrieben) *tr.* drive off; throw (shake) off

ab-trotzen *tr.* (*dat. pers. and acc. thing*) extort from

ab'trünnig *adj.* faithless, disloyal (to **von**)

ab-wägen (**wog, gewogen**) *tr.* weigh, consider well

ab-warten *tr.* wait for, await; *also intr.* wait, delay

ab-wehren *tr.* ward off, avert

ab-weiden *tr.* graze over (bare)

ab-wenden (**wandte** *or* **wendete, gewandt** *or* **gewendet**) *tr., refl.* turn away; avert (*face*); alienate, 681

ab-werfen (**warf, geworfen; wirft**) *tr.* throw (cast) off

Acht *f.* ban of outlawry

ach'ten *tr.* think, consider; esteem, regard as, heed; *with* **auf** *intr.* listen to, heed

acht-geben (**gab, gegeben; gibt**) give heed to (**auf,** *acc.*); look out

a'ckern *tr.* plow, cultivate

A'del *m.* **-s** nobility, nobles

a'delig *adj.* noble

Ad'ler *m.* **-s,** — eagle; Imperial Eagle

Ahn *m.* **-s** *or* **-en, -en** forefather, ancestor, grandfather

ah'nen *tr. and intr.* (*impers. with dat.*) forebode, anticipate; *part. as adj.* prophetic

all *adj. and pron.* all; each, every, any; **alles** everybody, everything

allein' *adj.* alone; *adv.* only; *conj.* but, however

al'lerwegen *adv.* everywhere

allgemein' *adj.* general, common, public

allgerecht' *adj.* all-righteous; merciful, 582

all'zu *adv.* all-too, too

all'zustraff *adv.* too tightly

Alp *f.* **-en** mountain pasture; peak; *pl.* the Alps

Al'penblume *f.* **-n** Alpine flower

Al'penjäger *m.* **-s,** — Alpine hunter

Al'pentrift *f.* **-en** Alpine (mountain) pasture

Al'penwasser *n.* **-s,** — Alpine stream, torrent

Alp'horn *n.* **-(e)s,** **˝er** alphorn (*wood, six feet long*)

als *conj.* as, when; (*with comp.*) than; (*with neg.*) but, except, save, 1677; **als** (**ob**) as if

alsbald' *adv.* immediately

al'so *conj.* so, then, therefore; *adv.* so, thus

alt *adj.* (**älter, ältest**) old, ancient; *as m. noun* old man; *neut.* the old order, 953

Al'ter *n.* **-s,** — age, old age

alt'gewohnt *adj.* long accustomed

Alt'landam'mann *m.* **-s,** **˝er** old (former, ex-) landammann, chief magistrate

Alt'vordern *m. pl.* ancestors, forefathers; *for* **Vor'fahren**

Alzel'ler *indec. adj.* of (from) Alzellen; *as noun m.* **-s,** — the Alzeller

Am'mann *m.* **-s,** **˝er** ammann (*Swiss magistrate*)

Amt *n.* **-(e)s,** **˝er** office, duty

an *prep.* (*dat. or acc.*) *sep. pref., and adv.* on, by, towards, at, near, to, of, against *in many idioms;* **denken an** think of; **an mir** on my part; **an Euch** (*dat.*) your turn; **an ... hin** along; **an ... vorbei** past

an-befehlen (**befahl, befohlen; befiehlt**) *tr.* (*dat. and acc. or inf.*) direct, command, bid

An'blick *m.* **-s, -e** sight

an-blicken *tr.* look at, regard

an-bringen (**brachte, gebracht**) *tr.* bring up, mention (*a request*)

an'dächtig *adj.* devout, reverent

an'der *adj.* another, other, different, next, following; else

än'dern *tr. (and refl.)* change

an'ders *adv.* otherwise, different(ly)

an'dersdenkend *part. as adj.* thinking otherwise, of different opinion

an'derswo *adv.* elsewhere

An'fang *m.* –s, ⁼e beginning

an-fangen (**fing, gefangen; fängt**) *intr. and tr.* begin, commence

an'fangs *adv. (gen. of* **Anfang***)* at first

an-fassen *tr.* seize, lay hold of

an-flehen *tr.* entreat, implore

an-führen *tr.* lead (on)

an-füllen *refl.* to fill up with

an'geboren *part. adj.* inborn, innate, hereditary; natural

an-gehen (**ging, gegangen**) *s.* ascend, rise

an'genehm *adj.* pleasant, charming, kind; good

An'ger *m.* –s, — field, green, meadow

an'gesehen *part. adj.* prominent, influential

an'gestammt *part. adj.* natural, innate

an-greifen (**griff, gegriffen**) *tr.* lay hold (of ; go at

Angst *f.* ⁼e anxiety, anguish; — **des Todes** mortal terror

angst'befreit *part. adj.* freed from anxiety

äng'stigen *tr.* alarm, make uneasy; *refl.* worry

ängst'lich *adj.* anxious

an-halten (**hielt, gehalten; hält**) stop; *refl.* steady (check) oneself

An'höhe *f.* –n height, hill

an-hören *tr.* listen to, hear

An'ker *m.* –s, — anchor

an-klagen *tr.* accuse; cry to

an-klingen (**klang, geklungen**) sound, strike the ear

an-kommen (**kam, gekommen**) *s.* arrive (at **bei**), approach

an-legen *tr.* lay (to) on; **Hand** — set to work; *intr.* take aim, 1992*; aim at, 2583

an-leimen *refl.* glue oneself on

an-liegen (**lag, gelegen**) lie near, concern, interest

an-locken *tr.* entice, draw on

An'mut *f.* grace, charm

an-nehmen (**nahm, genommen; nimmt**) *tr.* accept; assume

an-pochen knock at (**an** *acc.*)

an-rufen (**rief, gerufen**) *tr.* call to; call upon, invoke

an-rühren *tr.* touch; move (*to sympathy*), 3063

an-sagen *tr.* speak, say on, tell

an-schließen (**schloß, geschlossen**) *refl.* attach oneself (to **an**)

an-sehen (**sah, gesehen; sieht**) *tr.* look at (on), see, regard

an'sichtig *adj. (with gen.), with* **werden** become aware of, catch sight of

an-siedeln *refl.* settle

an-sinnen (**sann, gesonnen**) ask (expect) of, demand of

an-sprengen *s.* gallop up

An'spruch *m.* –s, ⁼e claim; **in** — **nehmen** lay claim to

an-steigen (**stieg, gestiegen**) *s.* rise, ascend

an'stellig *adj.* fit (good) for (**zu**)

an-stemmen *tr.* push, press

An'teil *m.* –s, –e part, share

Ant'litz *n.* –es, –e face

an-treten (**trat, getreten; tritt**) *tr.* approach

an-tun (**tat, getan**) *tr.* do to, offer; **Lieb'** — do kindness; **Schmach** — insult

Ant'wort *f.* –en answer

an-wachsen (wuchs, gewachsen; wächst) s. grow on, increase

an-ziehen (zog, gezogen) tr. draw (put) on; draw, pull; attract

An'zug m. -s, ᵘe approach; im — coming, gathering

an-zünden tr. set fire to, kindle

Ar'beit f. -en work, labor, task

ar'beiten tr. and intr. work; refl. (make) force one's way

Ar'beiter m. -s, — workman

arg (ärger, ärgst) adj. bad

Arg'wohn m. -s suspicion

arm (ärmer, ärmst) adj. poor

Arm'brust f. ᵘe cross-bow

arm'se'lig adj. poor, wretched, paltry

Arm'sessel m. -s, — armchair

Ar'mut f. poverty

A'sche f. -n (very rare) ashes

A'tem m. -s breath

a'temlos adj. out of breath

at'men breathe

auch adv., conj. also, too, even; really, 301, 1316, 2315; with wer, was wie, wo ever; — nicht not even; although, 1122; so — however; wenn — even if; — nur even so much as

Au'e f. -n field, meadow

auf prep. (dat. or acc.) upon, on, to, toward, at in many idioms; — immer or ewig forever; — Tod und Leben for life and death; against, 259; for (cf. page 1); interj. Up! Away!; as sep. pref. and adv. up, open

auf-bauen tr. build up, erect

auf-bewahren tr. keep, preserve, put away

auf-bieten (bot, geboten) tr. call out, call to arms

auf-blühen s. begin to bloom; fig. grow up

auf-fahren (fuhr, gefahren; fährt) s. start up, flare up

auf-finden (fand, gefunden) tr. find out, discover

auf-fordern tr. call upon, ask, summon

auf-geben (gab, gegeben; gibt) tr. give up, resign

auf-gehen (ging, gegangen) s. go up, rise; open, swell

auf-halten (hielt, gehalten; hält) tr. hold up, stop, detain

auf-hangen (hing, gehangen; hängt) (now usually aufhängen) tr. hang up

auf-heben (hob, gehoben) tr. lift (take) up, raise

auf-hören stop, cease

auf-lachen break out laughing

Auf'lauf m. -s, ᵘe tumult

auf-legen tr. lay (put) on

auf-lösen tr. loosen; fig. dissolve (bond)

auf-merken listen (closely)

auf'merksam adj. attentive

auf-nehmen (nahm, genommen; nimmt) tr. take up, receive, harbor; es mit (dat.) — cope with, be a match for

auf-passen keep watch

auf-pflanzen tr. set up

auf-rauschen s. surge up

auf'recht adj. upright, erect

auf-reißen (riß, gerissen) tr. tear open; refl. open suddenly

auf-richten tr. raise, set up; refl. rise, get up

auf-rufen (rief, gerufen) tr. call upon, ask

Auf'ruhr m. -s tumult, riot

auf-rühren tr. stir up

Auf'satz m. -es, ᵘe essay

auf-schieben (schob, geschoben) tr. postpone, delay

auf-schlagen (schlug, geschlagen; schlägt) tr. lift up; open

Auf'schub m. -s delay

auf-setzen *tr.* put on (head)
auf-springen (sprang, gesprungen) **s.** spring (leap) up
Auf'stand *m.* –s, "e tumult, commotion
auf-stecken *tr.* set (put) up
auf-stehen (stand, gestanden) **s.** stand (get) up, rise
auf-steigen (stieg, gestiegen) **s.** go up, rise, ascend
auf-tauen **s.** thaw, melt
auf-treten (trat, getreten; tritt) **s.** enter, appear
auf-tun (tat, getan) *tr.* open; *refl.* disclose (present) itself
auf-wecken *tr.* wake up, rouse
Auf'zug *m.* –s, "e act
auf-zwingen (zwang, gezwungen) *tr. dat. and acc.* force upon
Au'genblick *m.* –s, –e moment
au'genblicks *gen. as adv.* at once
au'genlos *adj.* sightless
aus *prep. with dat.* out of, of, by, from, through = because of; *adv. and sep. pref.* out, over, past
aus-breiten *tr.* spread out
auseinan'der-fliehen (floh, geflohen) **s.** flee, scatter (*in flight*)
auseinan'der-gehen (ging, gegangen) **s.** separate, disperse
auseinan'der-treiben (trieb, getrieben) *tr.* drive apart, scatter
aus'ersehen (ersah, ersehen; ersieht) *tr.* select, designate
aus-fechten (focht, gefochten; ficht) *tr.* fight out, settle
aus-fließen (floß, geflossen) **s.** flow out, cease to flow
aus-gehen (ging, gegangen) **s.** go out (forth), start from
aus-gießen (goß, gegossen) *tr.* pour out, empty
aus-liefern *tr.* deliver up
aus-löschen *tr.* put out (*fire*)

aus-reuten, aus-roden *tr.* root (out) up, clear away (*forest*)
Aus'rufer *m.* –s, — crier
aus-ruhen *intr. and refl.* rest, stop to rest
aus-sehen (sah, gesehen; sieht) look, seem
au'ßen *adv.* outside, without
au'ßer *prep.* (*dat.*), out; except, save; — sich beside oneself; *with gen.* out of
äu'ßerst (*superl. of* äußer) *adj.* utmost, extreme; *as noun* the worst, 641; *adv. phrase* zu — right out
Aus'sicht *f.* –en view, prospect
aus-sinnen (sann, gesonnen) *tr.* (*acc. and dat.* sich) think out, devise
aus-spähen *tr.* spy (search) out
aus-sprechen (sprach, gesprochen; spricht) *tr.* speak out, express
aus-stellen *tr.* put out, set
aus-suchen *tr.* pick out, choose
aus-treten (trat, getreten; tritt) **s.** step out; overflow
aus-üben *tr.* exercise; Gewalt — do violence (an to)
aus-weichen (wich, gewichen) **s.** step aside, evade
aus-ziehen (zog, gezogen) **s.** set out, go forth, depart
Axt *f.* "e ax; battle-ax

B

Bad *n.* –es, "er bath
ba'den *refl.* bathe
Bahn *f.* –en way; course
Bah're *f.* –n bier
bald *adv.* soon, easily; — ... — now . . . now
Bal'ken *m.* –s, — beam, timber
Bal'samstrom *m.* –(e)s, "e balmy (stream), breeze

Band *n.* −es, −e tie; bond, union; fetter, chain

Band *n.* −es, ⁼er band, strap

bän'digen *tr.* tame, subdue

bang(e) *adj.* afraid, anxious, alarmed (for)

Bank *f.* ⁼e bench, seat

Bann *m.* −es ban of outlawry

ban'nen *tr.* preserve (game); enchant, 1776

Ban'ner *m.* −s, — banner

Ban'nerherr *m.* −n, −en banneret

bar *adj.* bare, without (gen.)

Bär *m.* −en, −en bear

barmher'zig *adj.* merciful, compassionate; −e Brüder Brothers of Mercy

Barmher'zigkeit *f.* −en mercy, pity, charity

Bau *m.* −(e)s, −ten building, structure

bau'en *tr.* build (an *dat.* on)

Bau'er *m.* −s or −n, −n peasant

Bäu'erin *f.* −nen peasant woman

Bau'ernadel *m.* −s peasant nobility

Bau'gerüst(e) *n.* −(e)s, −e scaffolding

Baum'zweig *m.* −(e)s, −e branch, twig

bebau'en *tr.* cultivate

be'ben tremble, shiver, quake

Be'cher *m.* −s, — cup, beaker

bedau'ern *tr.* pity, be sorry for

beden'ken (bedachte, bedacht) *tr.* think over, ponder; discuss, 246; consider, remember, 2313; *refl.* hesitate

bedeu'ten *tr.* mean, signify; make a sign to

Bedeu'tung *f.* −en significance

bedrän'gen *tr.* oppress, afflict; *past part. as noun,* 140, 351

bedür'fen (bedurfte, bedurft; bedarf) *intr.* (with gen.) and *tr.* need, be (in) need of

bedürf'tig *adj.* needy

beeist' *part. adj.* ice-covered

Befehl' *m.* −s, −e command, order

befeh'len (befahl, befohlen; befiehlt) *tr.* (dat. of pers.) command, order, bid

befe'stigen *tr.* strengthen; *refl.* fortify

befin'den (befand, befunden) *refl.* find oneself, be

befle'cken *tr.* stain, spot

beflü'geln *tr.* wing, speed

befol'gen *tr.* follow

beför'dern *tr.* further, promote

befrei'en *tr.* free, rescue

befrie'digen *tr.* appease, satisfy

befruch'ten *tr.* make fertile

bege'ben (begab, begeben; begibt) *refl. with gen.* give up, 1426; betake oneself, come, 1734; happen, come to pass, 2214

begeg'nen s. (dat.) meet; happen to, befall; treat, 539

Begeg'nung *f.* −en meeting

bege'hen (beging, begangen) *tr.* commit

begeh'ren *tr.* (acc. and gen.) demand, ask for, desire, covet

Begei'sterung *f.* enthusiasm, inspiration

Begier'de *f.* −n eagerness, desire

begin'nen (begann, begonnen) *intr. and tr.* begin

beglei'ten *tr.* accompany

beglü'cken *tr.* bless, make happy

begra'ben (begrub, begraben; begräbt) *tr.* bury; *past part. as noun,* 1505

begren'zen *tr.* bound, border

begrü'ßen *tr.* greet; *refl.* exchange greeting

Begrü'ßung *f.* −en greeting

behal'ten (behielt, behalten; behält) *tr.* keep

behan'deln *tr.* treat

behar'ren (bei, auf *with dat.*) stand by, remain steadfast

behaup'ten *tr.* maintain, affirm

bei *prep. with dat., adv., and sep. pref.* by, with, at, near, in, among, at the house of, on, upon; **bei mir** at my house; **bei eröffneter Szene** after the scene opens, *1; **kann... bei** get at, hurt, 2708

beich'ten *tr.* confess

bei'de *adj. pl.* both

bei-legen lay on, hurry

beisei'te *adv.* aside

Bei'spiel *n.* –s, –e example, parallel

bei'spiellos *adj.* unparalleled

Bei'stand *m.* –s help, support

bei-stehen (stand, gestanden) help, stand by

bei-zählen *tr.* count among

bejam'mernswürdig *adj.* pitiable, wretched

bekannt' *part. adj.* known, acquainted; — **machen** introduce

bekla'gen *tr.* bewail; *refl.* complain (of **ob**)

beklem'men *tr.* grieve, distress

bekom'men (bekam, bekommen) *tr.* get, receive

bekrie'gen *tr.* make war upon

bela'den (belud, beladen; belädt or beladet) *tr.* laden, load

bele'ben *tr.* enliven, cheer

belebt' *part. adj.* animate

belei'digen *tr.* insult, offend

beloh'nen *tr.* reward, enrich

bema'len *tr.* paint, decorate

bemer'ken *tr.* observe, notice; catch sight of; record, 1216

bequem' *adj.* comfortable, convenient

beque'men *refl.* submit to (*dat.*)

bera'ten (beriet, beraten; berät) *refl.* confer with

berau'ben *tr.* rob, plunder

bereit' *adj.* ready, prepared

berei'ten *tr.* prepare, make ready

ber'gen (barg, geborgen; birgt) *tr.* hide, shelter

Berg'weg *m.* –s, –e mountain path

Bericht' *m.* –(e)s, –e report

berich'ten *tr.* report; *past part.* (informed), skilled in

ber'sten (barst, geborsten; birst or berstet) *s.* burst

beru'fen *part. adj.* of repute; **wohl** — well spoken of, 1083

beru'higen *refl.* calm oneself

berüh'ren *tr.* touch

beschäf'tigen *tr.* employ, occupy; *past part.* busy, 2303 *

Bescheid' *m.* –s, –e information, answer; — **geben** tell, 2918; — **wissen** know definitely; **zum** — **werden** be given (receive) as answer, 1348

beschei'den (beschied, beschieden) *tr.* destine for, assign; *refl.* control oneself

beschei'den *adj.* modest; *older sense* discreet, prudent, good, 554, 3032

beschei'dentlich *adv.* modestly

beschei'nen (beschien, beschienen) *tr.* shine on

beschir'men *tr.* defend, protect

beschlie'ßen (beschloß, beschlossen) *tr.* decide, settle, resolve

beschrei'ben (beschrieb, beschrieben) *tr.* describe

beschüt'zen *tr.* protect (**vor** from) defend

Beschüt'zer *m.* –s, — defender, protector

beschwö'ren *tr.* swear (to)

bese'hen (besah, besehen; besieht) *tr.* look at, examine, inspect

beset'zen *tr.* occupy, fill, cover

besie'gen *tr.* conquer, subdue

Besin'nen *inf. as noun, n.* **-s** reflection, thought

Besitz' *m.* **-es** possession

besit'zen (besaß, besessen) *tr.* possess

beson'der *adj.* individual

beson'nen *part. adj.* discreet, prudent, thoughtful; **schnell —** with quick presence of mind

bespre'chen (besprach, besprochen, bespricht) *tr.* discuss

best *(superl. of* **gut)** *adj.* best; *as noun* welfare, good, interest; best prize, 2650

bestä'tigen *tr.* confirm, ratify

beste'hen (bestand, bestanden) exist; last, endure; *(with* **auf)** insist on, 1306

besteh'len (bestahl, bestohlen, bestiehlt) *tr.* steal from, shirk

bestel'len *tr.* appoint, delegate, 1236; cultivate, 2681

besteu'ern *tr.* tax

bestimmt' *part. adj.* certain, appointed

Besuch' *m.* **-(e)s, -e** visit

be'ten pray, offer prayer

betö'ren *tr.* beguile, induce

betrach'ten *tr.* look at, view

betrü'ben *tr.* trouble, harm

betrü'gen (betrog, betrogen) *tr.* deceive; *refl.* delude oneself

beu'gen *tr.* bow, humble, conquer; *refl.* bow, submit

Beu'te *f.* booty

bewa'chen *tr.* watch, guard

bewach'sen *part. adj.* overgrown, covered with

bewaff'nen *tr.* arm, equip

bewah'ren *tr.* keep, guard, protect

bewäh'ren *tr.* prove, show

bewe'gen *tr.* induce; *refl.* stir, move; **bewegt** stormy

Bewe'gung *f.* **-en** movement; commotion

bewei'den *tr.* graze, pasture (on)

bewei'sen (bewies, bewiesen) *tr.* show, prove; do, make

bewoh'nen *tr.* inhabit, occupy

bewun'dern *tr.* admire

bezäh'men *tr.* *(and refl.)* tame, restrain

bezeich'nen *tr.* mark, indicate

bezwin'gen (bezwang, bezwungen) *tr. and refl.* subdue, conquer; force, capture; control

bie'der *adj.* true, good, worthy

Bie'dermann *m.* **-es, "er** good, true man

bie'gen (bog, gebogen) *tr.* bend; *fig.* pervert, 1246

bie'ten (bot, geboten) *tr.* offer; do to, 1260; say to, 1395

Bild *n.* **-es, -er** form, image

bil'den *tr.* form, make; *refl.* be formed

bil'lig *adj.* just, reasonable

Bin'de *f.* **-n** bandage

bin'den (band, gebunden) *tr.* bind

bis *prep.* (*acc.*), *adv., conj.* to, as far as; till, until

Bi'schof *m.* **-s, "e** bishop

Bi'schofshut *m.* **-(e)s, "e** bishop's hat = bishopric, 2958

bisher' *adv.* till now, hitherto

Bit'te *f.* **-n** request, entreaty

bit'ten (bat, gebeten) *tr.* ask, beg; *with* **um** ask for, 1874

bla'sen (blies, geblasen, bläst) *tr. and intr.* blow

blaß (blässer, blässest *or* **blasser, blassest)** *adj.* pale

blei'ben (blieb, geblieben) *s.* remain, stay; *as noun*, 612

bleich *adj.* pale, white

blei'chen (blich, geblichen) *s.* grow pale, fade

blen'den *tr.* blind; dazzle

Blick *m.* **-(e)s, -e** look, glance; sight, 992; prospect, 1662

bli′cken look

Blitz *m.* −**es, −e** lightning

blit′zen (*impers.*) flash, gleam

bloß *adj.* bare, mere; *adv.* simply, only, just

blü′hen bloom; prosper, 202

Blut′bann *m.* −**s** criminal jurisdiction

Blü′te *f.* −**n** flower, bloom

blu′ten bleed

Blut′schuld *f.* blood-guilt = murder

bluts′verwandt *part. adj.* akin by blood; *as noun* kinsman

Bo′den *m.* −**s** ground; **zu** — down (to the ground)

Bo′gen *m.* −**s,** — *or* ⸚ bow; arch, 2861

Bo′gensehne *f.* −**n** bowstring

Bo′genstrang *m.* −(**e**)**s,** ⸚**e** bowstring

boh′ren *tr.* bore, thrust (into)

Bord *m. and n.* −(**e**)**s, −e** board, shipboard; edge

bös(e) *adj.* bad, wicked, evil, ill; *masc. noun* wicked man; *neut. noun* evil, wrong, harm

bös′mei′nend (*part. adj.*) *adv.* with evil purpose

Bo′te *m.* −**n, −n** messenger

Bo′tensegel *n.* −**s,** — messenger-sail, dispatch boat

Bot′schaft *f.* −**en** tidings, news

Brand *m.* −**es,** ⸚**e** brand, firebrand

bran′den dash, break, surge

Bran′dung *f.* breakers, surf

Brauch *m.* −**es,** ⸚**e** custom

brau′chen *tr.* want, need; *with gen.* use, make use of, 2242; *intr. with gen.* be need of, 693

bräuch′lich *adj.* customary

brau′sen roar; *as noun* roaring

Braut *f.* ⸚**e** betrothed, promised bride

Braut′lauf *m.* −**s,** ⸚**e** wedding

Braut′zug *m.* −**s,** ⸚**e** wedding-party (procession)

brav worthy, good, noble; brave, 2102

bre′chen (**brach, gebrochen; bricht**) *tr. and intr.* (**s.** *and* **h.**) break, destroy (wreck, 2192); rush out, 1412; *fig.* gather, 3017; *refl.,* 2437; (*of eye*) close, grow dim

breit *adj.* wide

brei′ten *tr.* extend, spread

bren′nen (**brannte, gebrannt**) *tr. and intr.* burn, blaze

Brief *m.* −**es, −e** letter, charter

brin′gen (**brachte, gebracht**) *tr.* bring; take, 2049; pledge (*in drinking*), 766

Brin′ger *m.* −**s,** — bringer, bearer

Brü′cke *f.* −**n** bridge

Bru′der *m.* −**s,** ⸚ brother; monk, 3099; **Barmherzige Brüder** Brothers of Mercy

brül′len bellow, roar, low

Bru′neckerin *f.* the lady of Bruneck

Brun′nen *m.* −**s,** — spring

Brünn′lein *n.* −**s,** — little spring

Brust *f.* ⸚**e** breast

Brut *f.* −**en** brood

Bu′be *m.* −**n, −n** boy, servant, 471; fellow, rascal, 476, 1835

Buch′handlung *f.* −**en** (book-)publishing house. *Cf. page 1*

Bucht *f.* ⸚**en** bight, bay, inlet

bü′cken *tr. and refl.* bend, bow

buh′len (*with* **um**) court, woo

Büh′ne *f.* −**n** stage

Bund *m.* −**es,** ⸚**e** union, league, covenant, confederation

Bünd′nis *n.* −**sses, −sse** covenant, league, compact

bunt *adj.* bright, gay-colored

Burg *f.* −**en** castle, fortress

bür′gen go (give) bail

Bür′ger *m.* −**s,** — citizen, burgher

Bür′gereid *m.* −(**e**)**s, −e** civic oath

Bür′gerin *f.* −**nen** (female) citizen

Burg′glocke *f.* −**n** castle bell

Bürg′schaft *f.* security, bail; — **leisten** give (go) bail

Burg′verließ *n.* –es, –e keep, dungeon

Burg′vogt *m.* –s, ⁻e bailiff

Bu′sen *m.* –s, — bosom, breast; bay, inlet, 2159

Bu′ße *f.* punishment, penalty

bü′ßen *tr. and intr.* pay for, atone for, suffer for; punish, 566, 1561; satisfy, 273

C

Chri′stenheit *f.* christendom

Christ′fest *n.* –es, –e Christmas

Cot′ta′schen, J. G. *proper adj.* J. G. Cotta's (*publishers*). *Cf. page 1*

D

da *adv.* there, here then; *conj.* when, while; since, as; *with* **wer, was** ever; *for* **darum** and so, then, 1813; that, 1550

dabei′ *adv.* thereby, therein; present, 1521, 2289; in that, 372

Dach *n.* –es, ⁻er roof; awning *or* deck, 2172

dage′gen *adv.* against (it, them)

daheim′ *adv.* at home

daher′ *adv. and sep. pref.* hither, from there; along, on

daher-kommen (kam, gekommen) s. come along

dahin′ *adv. and sep. pref.* thither, there, away; **bis** — till then, 1459; — to this (that), 2822; gone, 2461

dahin-fahren (fuhr, gefahren; fährt) s. go (row) along (on)

dahin-gehen (ging, gegangen) s. go away, depart; *with* **über** pass over, 2766

dahin-scheiden (schied, geschieden) s. depart, die

dahin-wandern s. wander along (thither)

da′mals *adv.* then, at that time

damit′ *adv.* therewith, with (by) it (that, them); *conj.* so that

dämp′fen *tr.* muffle, soften

dan′nen *adv.* (*with* **von**) thence, away, from there

d(a)ran′ *adv.* thereon, thereby, on (at, by, in) it (them); — **sein** be about to, 2020, 2105

d(a)rauf′ *adv.* thereupon, upon (to) it (that, them), then, after that

darauf-kommen (kam, gekommen) s. come to think of, 1518

d(a)raus′ *adv.* from (of, out of) it (that); — **werden** come of it

d(a)rob′ *adv.* thereat, about it

dar-reichen *tr.* reach (stretch) out

dar-stellen *refl.* show itself, be seen

d(a)rü′ber *adv.* over (beyond, more than) that (it); at (about) that

d(a)rum′ *adv.* thereabout, for (about) it (that); of it, 2957; therefore, for that reason

d(a)run′ter *adv.* under it (that); among them; down there, 981

Da′sein *n.* –s existence

davon′ *adv. and sep. pref.* thereof, of it (that), therefrom; away

davon-tragen (trug, getragen; trägt) *tr.* carry away (off)

dazu′ thereto, to (*or* for) it (*or* that)

dazwi′schen *adv.* between (among) them; at intervals, now and then

de′cken *tr.* cover, defend

dein *poss. adj. and pron.* thy, thine, your; *pl.* your people, 792, 859, 931

Denk′art *f.* –en way of thinking, nature, character

den′ken (dachte, gedacht) *tr. and intr.* (*with gen. or* **an, auf, über** *with acc.*) think (of, about);

remember, 1930, 1953, 2485; intend, 2281, 2957

Denk'mal *n.* **-s,** **"er** monument, emblem

denn *conj.* (*stands first*) for, because; *adv.* then, therefore

den'noch *adv.* anyhow

der (die, das) *def. art.* the; *demonst. adj. and pron., pers. pron.* this (that) one, he, she, it; *rel. pron.* who, which, that; **das** (356), these fellows

dereinst' *adv.* some day (time)

derglei'chen *indec. adj.* (the) like, such (as), that kind

dersel'be (dieselbe, dasselbe) *adj.* (*pron.*) the same

deuch'ten *impers.* (*dat. or acc.*) seem, appear

deu'ten *tr.* explain (*with* **auf**) say it means, 2677; *intr.* point, make a sign

dicht *adj.* dense, close; *adv.* close (upon), 71, 2697

die'nen (*dat.*) serve (for **zu**)

Die'ner *m.* **-s,** —— servant

Dienst *m.* **-es,** **-e** service

dienst'fertig *adj.* officious

die'ser [**diese, dies(es)**] *adj. and pron.* this (one), that (one); he; the latter

dies'mal *adv.* this time

Dir'ne *f.* **-n** maid, girl

doch *adv. and conj.* yet, but, 119, 521; though; anyhow; surely, 555; *emphatic* do (pray), 187, 392; would that (only), 695; Well! 2770; you see; after all; really

Dolch *m.* **-s,** **-e** dagger

Don'ner *m.* **-s,** —— thunder

don'nern *intr. and impers.* thunder; *inf. also as noun*

Don'nerschlag *m.* **-s,** **"e** peal (clap, roll) of thunder

dop'pelt *adj.* double; *as noun,* 357

dort'hin *adv.* there, that way

Dra'che *m.* **-n,** **-n** dragon

Dra'chengift *n.* **-s,** **-e** dragon's poison, venom

dran = daran

Drang *m.* **-es** oppression, tyranny

drän'gen *tr.* oppress, distress; *refl.* press (crowd) up to (*with* **an,** 1555 ***); *with* **in** force oneself into, 2504.

Drang'sal *n.* **-s,** **-e** oppression

drauf = darauf

draus = daraus

drau'ßen *adv.* outside, without

drin'gen (drang, gedrungen) *s.* press, force way; be urgent, 149, 2512; *refl. for* **drängen,** 2734

drin'nen *adv.* inside, within

dritt *num. adj.* third

drob = darob

dro'ben *adv.* above, up there, on high

dro'hen *tr. and intr.* (*dat.*) threaten, menace; be about to, 2033***

drü'ben *adv.* over there (yonder)

drü'ber (= **darüber**) more than that, over that

Druck *m.* **-(e)s** oppression

drü'cken *tr.* press, oppress, afflict; *past part. as noun,* 1277; *intr.* (**auf** *dat.*) weigh upon, 198

drum = darum

drun'ter = darunter

dul'den *tr.* bear, tolerate, suffer

duld'sam *adv.* patiently

dumpf *adj.* dull, heavy; deep, 480

dun'kel *adj.* dark, gloomy

dün'ken *impers.* (*dat. or acc.*) seem

durch *prep.* (*acc.*), *sep. and insep. pref.* through, by, by means (because) of, during; *adv.* through

durchboh'ren *tr.* bore through, pierce

durchdrin′gen (durchdrang′, durch-drun′gen) *tr.* pierce through, penetrate

durch-gehen (ging, gegangen) go (pass) through

durchren′nen (durchrann′te, durch-rannt′) *tr.* run through, pierce

durchschau′en *tr.* see through, understand

durchschie′ßen (durchschoß′, durch-schos′sen) *tr.* shoot through

dür′fen (durfte, gedurft; darf) *modal aux.* dare, may, be allowed, have right to

Durst *m.* **-es** thirst

dü′ster *adj.* gloomy, sullen

E

e′ben *adj.* even, flat, smooth; *adv.* even, just, just now

echt *adj.* real, true, genuine, sterling

E′cke *f.* **-n** corner

e′del *adj.* noble; *as noun (pl.)* nobility; *f. sg.* noblewoman, 2529; *neut.* nobleness, 1644

E′delhof *m.* **-s,** ″**e** nobleman's seat, castle

E′delmann *m.* **-(e)s,** (″**er** *or*) **Edel-leute** nobleman

E′delsitz *m.* **-es, -e** nobleman's seat (castle)

E′delstein *m.* **-s, -e** jewel, precious stone

eh(e) *conj.* ere, before

E′he *f.* **-n** marriage, wedlock

e′her *adv. (comp. of* **ehe**) sooner, rather, before

E′hewirt *m.* **-s, -e** (*old for* **Mann, Gatte**) husband

Eh′ni *m.* **-s** *Swiss dim. of* **Ahn** grandfather; **zum (vom)** — to (from) grandpa's

Eh′re *f.* **-n** honor

eh′ren *tr.* honor, revere, respect

Eh′rengruß *m.* **-es,** ″**e** salute of honor, homage

Eh′renmann *m.* **-(e)s,** ″**er** man of honor, (good) true man

Ehr′furcht *f.* reverence, respect

Ehr′geiz *m.* **-es** ambition

Ehr′sucht *f.* ambition

ehr′würdig *adj.* venerable, esteemed, worthy

ei *interj.* why! well! oh! ah!

Eid *m.* **-es, -e** oath

Ei′dam *m.* **-s, -e** son-in-law

Eid′genoss(e) *m.* **-n, -n** confederate

Eid′schwur *m.* **-s,** ″**e** oath

Ei′fer *m.* **-s** zeal, ardor

eif′rig *adj.* zealous, eager

ei′gen *adj.* own; peculiar, special; **auf** —**e Hand** on his own (hook) account, 232; —**e Leute** bondmen, serfs, 1081, 1143

ei′gensinnig *adv.* willfully, stubbornly

Ei′le *f.* haste, hurry

ei′len h. *or* **s.** hurry, hasten

ei′lends *adv.* hastily, hurriedly

eil′fertig *adv.* in haste

ei′lig *adj.* hasty; **Hast du's so** —**?** Are you in such haste?

einan′der *indec. recip. pron. (dat. or acc.)* one another, each other; **′nander = einander**

ein-brechen (brach, gebrochen; bricht) s. break (in, down), give way

ein-fallen (fiel, gefallen; fällt) s. fall in; begin (*of music*); occur to, 1576

ein′förmig *adj.* monotonous

Ein′gang *m.* **-s,** ″**e** entrance

Ein′geweide *n.* **-s,** — bowels (of mercy) = heart, feeling

ein-holen *tr.* overtake, catch

ei′nig *adj.* one, united; *pron.* some (*generally pl.*) a few

ein-kaufen *tr.* buy, purchase

ein-kehren s. turn in, stop (*at an inn*), lodge

ein'mal *adv.* once, some day; **auf** — all at once, suddenly, 1462; **sonst** — some other time, 1336

ein-reißen (**riß, gerissen**) *tr.* pull (tear) down

ein'sam *adj.* lonely, solitary; alone, 1181

ein-schiffen *refl.* take ship, embark, start (*by boat*)

ein-schlafen (**schlief, geschlafen;** **schläft**) s. fall asleep

ein-schließen (**schloß, geschlossen**) *tr.* shut in, confine, surround

ein-schränken *tr.* shut in

ein-schreiben (**schrieb, geschrieben**) *tr.* write in, engrave

ein-sinken (**sank, gesunken**) s. sink in, give way

ein-stürzen s. fall in (down)

Ein'tracht *f.* union, harmony

ein-treten (**trat, getreten;** **tritt**) s. enter; **im** *with inf. as noun,* 2938 * on entering

ein'zeln *adj.* single, individual

ein-ziehen (**zog, gezogen**) *tr.* draw in; *intr.* s. enter, come in

ein'zig *adj.* only, single, alone; **for einig** united, 1449

eis'bedeckt *part. adj.* icy, ice-covered

Ei'sen *n.* **-s,** — iron = spearhead, 1406

Ei'senstab *m.* **-s,** ⁼e iron rod

Eis'gebirge *n.* **-s,** — ice mountains

Eis'palast *m.* **-(e)s,** ⁼e ice palace

ei'tel *adj.* vain, empty, idle

e'lend *adj.* wretched, miserable; *m. noun* wretch, 613

E'lend *n.* **-s** misery

empfan'gen (**empfing, empfangen;** **empfängt**) *tr.* receive

empfin'den (**empfand, empfunden**) *tr.* feel, experience

empö'ren *tr.* stir up; *past part.* indignant, 2007; *refl.* rebel, revolt, 2143

Empö'rung *f.* **-en** revolt, rebellion

empor-heben (**hob, gehoben**) *tr.* lift (up)

empor-ragen rise (tower) above (**über** *dat.*)

en'digen end, stop

end'lich *adj.* final; *adv.* at last, finally

eng(e) *adj.* narrow; — **werden** feel oppressed, 1812

En'ge *f.* **-n** narrowness

En'kel *m.* **-s,** — grandchild, grandson, descendant

entbeh'ren (*acc., gen.*) be without, do without

entbin'den (**entband, entbunden**) *tr.* release (from **von**)

entblö'ßen *tr.* bare, uncover

entde'cken *tr.* discover, catch sight of; tell, disclose, 2300

entfer'nen *refl.* retire, withdraw; depart (differ, deviate) from, 1150, 1906

entflie'hen (**entfloh, entflohen**) s. flee, fly, pass (*of time*)

entge'gen *prep.* (*after dat.*) *and sep. pref.* towards, against, to meet; up, 3243

entge'gen-eilen s. run to meet, hasten towards

entge'gen-gehen (**ging, gegangen**) s. go to meet (towards)

entge'gen-kehren *tr.* turn towards (against)

entge'gen-starren stare at (in the face)

entge'gen-treten (**trat, getreten;** **tritt**) s. step towards, go to meet

entgeg'nen *tr.* answer, reply

entge'hen (**entging, entgangen**) s. escape

entkom'men (entkam, entkommen) s. escape (from *dat.*)

entlas'sen (entließ, entlassen; entläßt) *tr.* dismiss, let go

entle'digen *tr.* (*acc. and gen.*) free, release from, relieve of

entrei'ßen (entriß, entrissen) *tr.* tear away, wrest (from *dat.*)

entrich'ten *tr.* pay, discharge (*a duty*)

entrin'nen (entrann, entronnen) s. escape, fly from

entrü'sten *tr.* provoke, enrage

entsa'gen (*dat.*) give up, renounce

entschei'den (entschied, entschieden) *tr. and intr.* decide, settle

Entschei'dung *f.* –en decision

entschlie'ßen (entschloß, entschlossen) *refl.* determine, resolve

entschlos'sen *part. adj.* determined, resolved

Entschlos'senheit *f.* decision, resoluteness

Entschluß' *m.* –sses, ⁻sse resolve, determination

entschul'digen *tr.* excuse, justify

entseelt' *part. adj.* lifeless

Entset'zen *n.* –s horror

entsetz'lich *adj.* wretched, dreadful

entsin'ken (entsank, entsunken) s. drop (fall) from; fail, 2232

entsprin'gen (entsprang, entsprungen) s. escape; *as noun,* 2252

entste'hen (entstand, entstanden) s. arise; *old sense* fail, be wanting, 700

entwei'chen (entwich, entwichen) s. withdraw (from *dat.*)

entwi'schen s. escape, get (slip) away (from *dat.*)

entzie'hen (entzog, entzogen) *refl.* (*with dat.*) forsake, desert

entzwei' *adv.* in two, broken

entzwei'en *refl.* quarrel

erbar'men *tr.* touch, move to pity,

671; *refl.* (*with gen.*) take pity on, be merciful to, 111, 143; *impers.* (*with acc.,* 2094, *and gen.,* 3191) regret, be sorry (for)

erbärm'lich *adj.* wretched, miserable

Erbar'mung *f.* mercy

erbau'en *tr.* build, make

Er'be *n.* –s inheritance

erbe'ben s. tremble, shake

er'ben s. (*with auf acc.*) descend to (*by inheritance*)

erbeu'ten *tr.* capture (get as booty), win

Erb'herr *m.* –n, –en hereditary lord, sovereign

Er'bin *f.* –nen heiress

erbli'cken *tr.* see, catch sight of, discover

erbrau'sen s. roar, surge up

erbre'chen (erbrach, erbrochen; erbricht) *tr.* break open (*letter*)

Erb'stück *n.* –(e)s, –e inheritance (*land*)

Er'de *f.* –n earth, ground; soil, 848; **auf** —n (*old dat. sg.*) on earth, 1085, 2668; **der** —n (*old gen. sg.*), 1700; land, 1223

erdul'den *tr.* bear, endure, tolerate

Ereig'nis *n.* –sses, –sse event

erer'ben *tr.* inherit

erfas'sen *tr.* grasp, get hold of

erfle'hen *tr.* beg, entreat

erfor'schen *tr.* sound, question

erfre'chen *refl.* (*with gen.*) make bold (dare) to do

erfreu'en *tr.* please, delight

erfri'schen *tr.* refresh

erfül'len *tr.* fill; fulfill, accomplish

Erge'bung *f.* submission

erge'hen (erging, ergangen) s. go forth, be proclaimed, 1229; *with* **vor** (*acc.*) take (go out) in place of, 1945; *impers.* fare, be

ergie'ßen (ergoß, ergossen) *refl.* spread, be shed

ergrei'fen (ergriff, ergriffen) *tr.* seize, lay hold of (= *fig.* touch); accept, take; *part.* touching

erhal'ten (erhielt, erhalten; erhält) *tr.* get, receive; keep (hold) back, restrain, 945; *refl.* preserve (maintain) itself, 2423

erhe'ben (erhob (*older* **erhub), erhoben)** *tr.* lift up, raise; *refl.* rise, arise; revolt

erhel'len *tr.* brighten, cheer; light up, 3260

erin'nern *refl.* (*with gen. or* **an** *with acc.*) remember

erja'gen *tr.* hunt (bring) down

erken'nen (erkannte, erkannt) *tr.* see, recognize (by **an,** *dat.*); acknowledge; **zu — geben** make itself known

Er'ker *m.* **-s —** balcony, bay-window

erklä'ren *tr. and refl.* explain *or* declare (oneself)

erkran'ken s. get (fall) sick

erküh'nen *refl.* grow bold; *with gen.* make bold (dare) to do

erkun'den *tr.* explore, examine

erlan'gen *tr.* reach

erlas'sen (erließ, erlassen; erläßt) *tr.* (*acc. and dat.*) release (excuse) from

erlau'ben *tr.* allow, permit

erle'ben *tr.* live to see, meet with, experience

erle'digen *refl.* get free, release oneself from (*gen.*)

erlei'den (erlitt, erlitten) *tr.* suffer; tolerate, endure

erlö'schen (erlosch, erloschen; erlischt) s. go out, be extinguished; *as noun,* 2429

ermäch'tigen *refl.* (*with gen.*) get possession of, seize

ermor'den *tr.* murder

ermü'den s. get tired, tire

erneu'ern *tr.* renew

ernst *adj.* earnest, grave, solemn, serious

Ernst *m.* **-es** earnestness, seriousness

ernst'haft *adj.* earnest, serious

ern'ten *tr.* reap, harvest, gather

ero'bern *tr.* take, capture

eröff'nen *tr.* open, begin

erqui'cken *tr.* refresh

erre'gen *tr.* rouse, stir up

errei'chen *tr.* reach, get to; overtake

erret'ten *tr.* save, rescue

Erret'ter *m.* **-s, —** deliverer

errich'ten *tr.* set up, erect

errin'gen (errang, errungen) *tr.* get by force, win

ersäu'fen *tr.* flood, drown

erschaf'fen (erschuf, erschaffen) *tr.* create

erschal'len (erscholl, erschollen) s. spread abroad, resound

erschei'nen (erschien, erschienen) s. appear

erschie'ßen (erschoß, erschossen) *tr.* shoot, kill (*by shot*)

erschla'gen (erschlug, erschlagen; erschlägt) *tr.* slay, kill

erschlei'chen (erschlich, erschlichen) *tr.* get by fraud; *part. adj.* fraudulent, 1253

erschöpft' *part. adj.* exhausted

erschre'cken (erschrak, erschrocken; erschrickt) be (alarmed) startled

erschre'cken *tr.* frighten, alarm

erspa'ren *tr.* save, spare; *with* **an** (*dat.*) save at expense of

erst *adv.* first, once (194, 701, 1418, 2165), only (382, 1490); not until, just; *adj.* first

erstau'nen s. be surprised

Erstau'nen *n.* **-s** astonishment

erstaun'lich *adj.* astonishing

erstei'gen (erstieg, erstiegen) *tr.* climb, scale

ersti'cken *tr.* stifle, smother, choke

ertö'nen ring

ertö'ten *tr.* kill, destroy

ertra'gen (**ertrug, ertragen; erträgt**) *tr.* bear, suffer, stand

ertrin'ken (**ertrank, ertrunken**) *s.* drown, be drowned

ertrot'zen *tr.* extort, force from

erwa'chen *s.* awake, wake up

erwar'ten *tr.* await, expect, look for; *for intr.* **warten** wait, 272, 493, 641

Erwar'tung *f.* –en expectation

erwe'cken *tr.* awaken, inspire

erweh'ren *refl.* (*with gen.*) ward off, defend oneself from

erwer'ben (**erwarb, erworben; erwirbt**) *tr.* get, acquire; produce, 2000

erzäh'len *tr.* tell, relate

erzei'gen *tr.* show, do

erzit'tern *s.* tremble

erzwin'gen (**erzwang, erzwungen**) *tr.* enforce, extort

es'sen (**aß, gegessen; ißt**) *tr.* eat

et'liche *adj. pron.* some

et'was *indec. pron.* some, something

eu'er (*or* **Euer**) *poss. pron.* your, yours; *dat.* to your friends (family), 2686

eu'rig (*or* **Eurig**) (**der, die, das** —**e**) *poss. pron.* yours

e'wig *adj.* eternal, everlasting; *adv.* forever

E'wigkeit *f.* –en eternity

F

fa'hen (*old and poetic for* **fangen**) *tr.* take, seize

Fah'ne *f.* –n flag, banner

Fahr (*old and poetic for* **Gefahr**) *f.* –en danger, peril

fahr'bar *adj.* navigable

Fäh're *f.* –n ferry, ferryboat

fah'ren (**fuhr, gefahren; fährt**) *s.* go, row, ride, travel; *Swiss for* **treiben** drive, 17; **aus dem Weg** — get out of the way; **fährt sich** is rowing, about, *1; *as noun* rowing, 2239; **mit der Hand** — put one's hand; *tr.* carry, bring up, 360

Fähr'mann *m.* –s, –er *or* **Fährleute** ferryman, boatman

Fahrt *f.* –en trip, journey

Fahr'zeug *n.* –s, –e boat, craft

Fal'ke *m.* –n, –n falcon

Fall *m.* –s, –e fall

fal'len (**fiel, gefallen; fällt**) *s.* fall; — **in** fall upon, seize; **in Straf'** — incur a penalty; **ins Land** — invade country

fäl'len *tr.* fell, cut down

Falsch *m.* –es (*old and poetic*) deceit, guile

Falsch'heit *f.* –en baseness, falsehood

Fall'strick *m.* –s, –e snare, trap

fal'ten *tr.* fold, wrinkle (*brow*)

Fang *m.* –(e)s, –e catch, haul; — **tun** make a catch (haul)

fan'gen (**fing, gefangen; fängt**) *tr.* catch, take prisoner; *part. as adj. or noun* prisoner, captive

fas'sen *tr.* seize, grasp, take hold of; *refl.* (come to) compose oneself, be calm

fast *adv.* almost

Fast'nachtsauf'zug *m.* –s, –e carnival procession

faul *adj.* lazy, idle

Faust *f.* –e fist, hand

fech'ten (**focht, gefochten; ficht**) fight

Fe'der *f.* –n feather

feh'len *tr. and intr.* miss; *with gen.*, 2063; — **auf** miss thing aimed at and hit something else, 1951; *intr.* fail, be wanting, missing

Feh'ler *m.* –s, — fault

Fehl'sprung *m.* **–s, ⸗e** false leap; **— tun** miss one's leap

Fei'erabend *m.* **–s, –e** quitting (resting) time

fei'ern stop work, be idle

feig'(e) *adj.* cowardly

feig'herzig *adj.* fainthearted

feil *adj.* for sale, to be bought

Feind *m.* **–es, –e** enemy

feind'lich *adj.* hostile

Fels *or* **Felsen** *m.* **–en** *or* **–ens, –en** cliff, rock

Fel'senkluft *f.* **⸗e** rocky gorge

Fel'senplatte *f.* **–n** flat ledge of rock

Fel'senriff *n.* **–s, –e** ledge *or* reef of rock

Fel'sensteig *m.* **–s, –e** rocky path

Fel'sentor *n.* **–s, –e** door (gateway) in the rock

Fel'senufer *n.* **–s, —** rocky shore

Fel'senwall *m.* **–s, ⸗e** wall of rock

Fel's(en)wand *f.* **⸗e** wall of rock, precipice

Fen'ster *n.* **–s, —** window

fer'n(e) *adj., adv.* far, far off, away; from afar

Fer'ne *f.* **–n** distance

fe₁n'her *adv.* from afar

Fer'se *f.* **–n** heel

fer'tig *adj.* ready; done, finished

Fes'sel *f.* **–n** fetter, bond

fes'seln *tr.* fetter, bind

fest *adj.* fast, firm, strong; secure; fortified; *as noun,* 2542, definite, certain

Fest *n.* **–(e)s, –e** feast, festival; **— des Herrn** Christmas

Fe'ste *f.* **–n** fortress, stronghold

fest-halten (hielt, gehalten; hält) *tr.* hold fast to; *intr.* hold fast (= unbroken), 2606; **with an** hold fast (cling) to

fest-knüpfen *tr.* tie (knit) fast

fest-stehen (stand, gestanden) stand fast, be stable

feucht *adj.* damp

Feu'ersignal' *n.* **–s, –e** signal fire, beacon

Feu'erwächter *m.* **–s, —** night watchman

Feu'erzeichen *n.* **–s, —** beacon fire

fin'den (fand, gefunden) *tr.* find; *refl.* be found, be

fin'ster *adj.* dark, gloomy; *as noun* darkness, gloom, 595

Fin'sternis *f.* **–sse** darkness

Firn *m.* **–es, –en** glacier, snowpeak (field)

Fi'scherkahn *m.* **–s, ⸗e** fisherman's boat

Flan'ke *f.* **–n** flanking (side, corner) wall, bastion

Fle'cken *m.* **–s, —** village, hamlet

fle'hen entreat, beg (**um** for); *tr.* (*with* **um**) beg (*person*) for; *part. as noun* suppliant

Fleiß *m.* **–es** diligence, industry

flie'gen (flog, geflogen) s. *or* **h.** fly

flie'hen (floh, geflohen) s. flee

flie'ßen (floß, geflossen) s. *or* **h.** flow

Flit'terschein *m.* **–s** tinsel, false glory

Flö'te *f.* **–n** flute

Fluch *m.* **–es, ⸗e** curse

Fluch'gebäude *n.* **–s, —** accursed building

Flucht *f.* **–en** flight

flüch'ten *tr.* save by flight, rescue; *refl.* flee, take refuge

flüch'tig *adj.* fugitive, fleeting, transient; **wurde —** fled

Flücht'ling *m.* **–s, –e** fugitive

Flug *m.* **–(e)s, ⸗e** flight; **im —** on the wing

Fluh *f.* **⸗e** rocky wall, cliff

Flur'schütz *m.* **–en, –en** ranger, field-guard

Flut *f.* **–en** flood, waves

Föhn *m.* **–(e)s, –e** Föhn (*south wind bringing storm*)

fol'gen s. (*dat.*) follow; *part. as noun*, 2438 *
Fol'terknecht *m.* –s, –e torturer
for'dern *tr.* demand, claim, call (ask) for; — **lassen** summon
for'schen ask, inquire
fort *adv. and sep. pref.* forth, away, gone; — **und** — continually; on, 1021; *interjec.* Away!
fort-bestehen (bestand, bestanden) go on, continue
fort-eilen s. hurry away
fort-fahren (fuhr, gefahren; fährt) continue, keep on
fort-führen *tr.* lead (take, carry) away (off)
fort-gehen (ging, gegangen) s. go away; continue, 2798 *
fort-helfen (half, geholfen; hilft) (*dat.*) help one get away
fort-reißen (riß, gerissen) *tr.* tear (carry) away
fort-setzen *refl.* continue
fort-ziehen (zog, gezogen) s. go on, proceed
Fra'ge *f.* –n question
fra'gen *tr.* ask (about), inquire (for **nach**); *with* **nach** care for, heed, mind, 1770, 2764
Frau *f.* –en woman, wife; Mistress, 517, 2308; **große** — "Our Lady," 1364
Fräu'lein *n.* –s, — girl of noble birth, lady; *in address* my lady
frech *adj.* bold, insolent, shameless
frei *adj.* free; unclaimed, 2741; voluntarily, 1131; *superl. m. noun*, 1217; *neut. noun* the open, 2129, 3087 *
frei'en (*with* um) woo; *tr.* marry, 2662
Frei'heit *f.* –en freedom, liberty
Frei'heitsbrief *m.* –(e)s, –e charter
Frei'herr *m.* –n, –en baron; **Herr** — my lord

frei'lich *adv.* of course, to be sure, certainly
frei'willig *adj.* voluntary
fremd *adj.* foreign, strange; a stranger, 852, 2449; a stranger's, 1037; as a stranger, 2613; *as noun*, 950
Frem'de *f.* strange (foreign) land
Fremd'ling *m.* –s, –e stranger, foreigner
fres'sen (fraß, gefressen; frißt) *tr.* eat (*of animals*), feed on
Freu'de *f.* –n joy, delight
Freu'denhaus *n.* –es, –er house of joy
Freu'denkunde *f.* –n glad tidings
Freu'denschießen *n.* –s, — shooting-match
Freu'despur *f.* –en glad memory
freu'dig *adj.* glad, joyful
freu'en *impers. tr.* please; if you like to, 1979; *refl.* rejoice; *as noun* rejoicing
Freund'schaft *f.* –en friendship; kindred, 660, 1456
Fre'vel *m.* –s, — crime, outrage
fre'veln commit crime; *part.* outrageous, criminal, 1534
Fre'veltat *f.* –en crime, deed of violence
Frie'de(n) *m.* –ns, –n peace
fried'gewohnt *adj.* peaceful
fried'lich *adj.* peaceable, peaceful; *as noun*, 429
frisch *adj. and adv.* fresh, brisk, new; quick(ly), 96; promptly, 738, 2659; vigorous(ly), 176, 1485, 2261; sound, good, 600, 678; freely, without hesitation, 766, 2056; alertly, 1510; **eben** — just fresh, directly, 522; **über** —**er Tat** in the very act, 1862; **mit** —**er Tat** with prompt action, at once, 1971; — **nach** right after, 960; *interjec.* Quick! Come! 103, 353, 364, 1931, 1964

Frist *f.* –**en** respite, time

froh *adj.* glad, happy

fröh'lich *adj.* joyful, glad, happy; frankly, 2056

froh'locken exult (rejoice) over (*gen. or* **über** *with acc.*), 3069; *as noun,* 3281*

fromm (frömmer, frömmst) *adj.* good, worthy; *adv.* devoutly; *superl. as noun,* 2683, most peaceable

Fron'dienst *m.* –**es,** –**e** enforced labor

Fron'vogt *m.* –**s,** ⁼**e** overseer, taskmaster

Frucht *f.* ⁼**e** fruit

früh *adj., adv.* early; untimely

Früh'ling *m.* –**s,** –**e** spring

Früh'trunk *m.* –**s** morning drink (cup)

fü'gen *tr.* put (fit) together; decree; *refl.* submit to, 474

füh'len *tr. and intr.* feel; —**d** groping, 594

fühl'los *adj.* unfeeling, cold

füh'ren *tr.* lead; conduct, 341; bring, 511; take, 2075; handle, manage, wield, carry, 134, 313, 1973; strike (*blow*), 1774

Fül'le *f.* plenty, abundance

fül'len *refl.* be filled

für *prep.* (*acc.*) for; — **sich** aside; independently, 1160; **was** — what kind (sort) of

fur'chen *tr.* furrow (*brow*)

Furcht *f.* fear, fright; dread; respect, 1375

furcht'bar *adj.* fearful, terrible

fürch'ten *tr.* fear, dread; *refl.* be afraid (of **vor** *with dat.*)

fürch'terlich *adj.* frightful, fearful

furcht'sam *adj.* timid

für'der *adv.* (*old for* **ferner**) further; **nicht** — never again

Für'sehung *f.* (*old for* **Vorsehung**) Providence

Fürst *m.* –**en, –en** prince

Für'stengunst *f.* princes' favor

Für'stenhaus *n.* –**es,** ⁼**er** princely house (= family)

Für'stenknecht *m.* –**s,** –**e** princes' slave

fürwahr' *adv.* indeed, verily

Fuß'stoß *m.* –**es,** ⁼**e** (foot) thrust, kick

G

Ga'be *f.* –**n** gift

gäh'lings *adv.* (*Swiss for* **jählings**) abruptly, suddenly

gäh'stotzig *adv.* (*Swiss for* **jähstotzig**) steep

Gang *m.* –**es,** ⁼**e** course, manner

ganz *adj.* whole, all; *adv.* quite, entirely, wholly; *as noun* the whole

gar *adv.* quite, very; *with neg.* emphatic at all; even, 2663

gä'ren (gor, gegoren) *tr.* ferment; *part. adj.* rankling, 2573

Gas'se *f.* –**n** narrow way, passage, *cf.* 1931, note

Gast'freund *m.* –**es,** –**e** good (intimate) friend

gast'lich *adj.* hospitable

Gast'recht *n.* –**s** right of hospitality

Gat'tin *f.* –**nen** wife

Gebälk' *n.* –**s,** –**e** timbers

gebä'ren (gebar, geboren; gebiert) *tr.* bear, give birth to

ge'ben (gab, gegeben; gibt) *tr.* give; yield, 1051; pass, make, 1307; furnish, 1129; *with* **auf** put faith in, 883; heed, 2178; **zu erkennen** — make known, 1203; **was gibt es** what's the matter? what is there? **ins Herz** — put into my heart; **es gibt (gab,** *etc.*) there is (was, *etc.*).

gebie'ten (gebot, geboten) *tr.* command, govern, rule

Gebir′g(e) *n.* −(e)s, −e (*collect.*) mountains

gebo′ren (*past part. of* **gebären**) born, natural

gebor′gen (*past part. of* **bergen**) safe, sheltered, hidden

Gebot′ *n.* −s, −e command, order

gebrau′chen *tr.* use

Gebre′sten *n.* −s, — sorrow

gebüh′ren (*dat.*) be due, belong to; *refl.* be proper, becoming

Geburts′land *n.* −es, ″er native land, country

Gedächt′nis *n.* −sses, −sse memory; **zum** — in memory

gedämpft′ *part. adj.* softened

Gedan′ke *m.* −ns, −n thought

gedei′hen (**gedieh, gediehen**) **s.** grow, thrive; progress, advance

gedenk′ *adj.* (*for* **eingedenk**) mindful of

geden′ken (**gedachte, gedacht**) (*gen. or an acc.*) think of, remember; intend to do

Geduld′ *f.* patience

gedul′dig *adv.* patiently

Gefahr′ *f.* −en danger

gefähr′lich *adj.* dangerous; *neut. noun*, 1517

gefal′len (**gefiel, gefallen; gefällt**) (*dat.*) please

Gefäng′nis *n.* −sses, −sse prison

Gefie′der *n.* −s (*collect.*) game birds

Gefol′ge *n.* −s, — (*collect.*) retinue, attendants

Gefühl′ *n.* −s, −e feeling

ge′gen *prep.* against, towards, about, to (= as compared with), contrary to

Ge′gend *f.* −en region, scene

Ge′genteil *n.* −s, −e contrary

gegenü′ber *prep.* (*dat.*) *and adv.* over against, opposite

geha′ben *refl.* fare; **gehabt Euch wohl** Farewell!

gehäs′sig *adj.* spiteful; — **sein** to hate

geheim′ *adj.* (secret); intimate

Geheim′nis *n.* −sses, −sse secret

Geheiß′ *n.* −es command, order

ge′hen (**ging, gegangen**) **s.** go; get loose, fall, 2665; **geht nicht** can't be done, 104; **hoch** — run high, 109; — **um** (*acc.*) concern, be a question of, 112; **meines Wegs** — go my way, 1570; **zu Rate** — take counsel, 287

Gehöft′ *n.* −(e)s, −e farm

Gehölz′ *n.* −es, −e woods, forest

gehor′chen (*dat.*) obey

gehö′ren (*dat.*) belong to

gehor′sam *adj.* obedient, dutiful; *pl. as noun*, 400

Gehor′sam *m.* −s obedience

Gei′ßel *f.* −n scourge

Geist *m.* −es, −er spirit, heart, mind, soul

Gei′sterstunde *f.* −n ghost (midnight) hour

Geiz *m.* −es greed, avarice

Gelän′der *n.* −s, — railing

gelan′gen s. get to, reach

gelas′sen *part. adj. in exclam.* Quiet! Be calm!

Geläu′t(e) *n.* −s ringing of bells; bell, set of bells, 47, 49

Geld′not *f.* ″e(n) financial distress

Gele′genheit *f.* −en opportunity

Geleit′ *n.* −es, −e escort

gelenk′ *adj.* agile, nimble

geliebt′ *part. adj.* loved, dear; *as noun*, 2532

gelo′ben *tr.* promise, vow; *refl.* pledge, 1225; **das gelobte (Land)** the Promised Land

gel′ten (**galt, gegolten; gilt**) *intr.* be worth, be of (have) value (weight), 564; pass, 2054;

pass (stand) for, 1111; *tr. impers.* life is at stake, 1921, 2320; be a question of, 1938, 1990, 2388, 2643; when the time comes, 2103, 2415

Gelüb'de *n.* **-s,** — vow

Gelü'sten *n.* **-s** *(inf. noun)* desire, purpose

gemäch'lich *adv.* easily, 141; slowly, 1792

gemah'nen *tr.* **(an** *acc.*) remind of

gemein' *adj.* common, general, 435; common, mean, 830; *as noun* common good, 737

Gemein'de *f.* **-n** community; meeting, 1129

gemein'sam *adv.* together, in common

Gem'se *f.* **-n** chamois

Gem'senhorn *n.* **-s,** **⁼er** chamois horn

Gemüt' *n.* **-s,** **-er** mind, heart

gen = **gegen** towards

genie'ßen **(genoß,** **genossen)** *tr.* enjoy

Genos's(e) *m.* **-en,** **-en** companion, confederate

Genoß'same *f.* **-n** community

G(e)nü'gen *n.* **-s** *(inf. noun)* enough; — **tat** sufficed

Genuß' *m.* **-sses,** **⁼sse** enjoyment

g(e)ra'd(e) *adj.* straight; honest, 1014; *adv.* just, directly

Gerät' *n.* **-s,** **-e** *(collect.)* tools

gerecht' *adj.* just, righteous, legitimate, merited; good, worthy, 1069

Gerech'tigkeit *f.* justice

Gericht' *n.* **-es,** **-e** judgment; court; **zu** — **sitzen** hold court

gering' *adj.* small, insignificant

ger'n(e) *adv.* gladly; *with verbs* like to, be glad to

Gerü'st(e) *n.* **-(e)s,** — scaffolding

Gesang' *m.* **-es,** **⁼e** song

Geschäft' *n.* **-s,** **-e** business, affair

Geschäf'tigkeit *f.* **-en** activity

gesche'hen **(geschah,** **geschehen;** **geschieht)** *impers.* **s.** happen, be done (shown, 397); *neut. part. noun,* 993

Geschenk' *n.* **-s,** **-e** gift, present

Geschick' *n.* **-s,** **-e** fate, lot

Geschlecht' *n.* **-s,** **-er** generation; sex, 3000

Geschmei'de *n.* **-s,** — jewels

Geschöpf' *n.* **-(e)s,** **-e** creature

Geschoß' *n.* **-sses,** **-sse** arrow

geschwind' *adv.* quickly

Geschwind'sein *n.* **-s** quickness

geseg'nen *(old for* **segnen)** *tr.* bless

Gesel'l(e) *m.* **-en,** **-en** fellow-workman; comrade, 1753

gesel'len *tr. and refl.* join

gesel'lig *adv.* in company, together

Gesetz' *n.* **-es,** **-e** law

Gesicht' *n.* **-(e)s,** **-er** sight, view; face, look

Gesin'del *n.* **-s** rabble

gesinnt' *part. adj.* minded, disposed

Gespann' *n.* **-s,** **-e** span, yoke

gespannt' *part. adj.* eager

Gespräch' *n.* **-(e)s,** **-e** discourse, conversation

Geß'lerisch *adj.* Gessler's

Gesta'de *n.* **-s,** — shore, bank

Gestalt' *f.* **-en** shape, form

gestal'tet *part. adj.* formed, shaped

geste'hen **(gestand,** **gestanden)** *tr.* confess

Gesträuch' *n.* **-(e)s** *(collect.)* bushes

gestreng' *adj.* stern, dread; **—er Herr** my lord, 1860, 2737

gesund' *adj.* sound, healthy

Getön' *n.* **-(e)s** *(collect.)* clang

getrau'en *refl.* *(dat.)* trust oneself, dare

getreu'lich *adv.* faithfully

getrost' *adj.* confident, cheerful, courageous

getrö'stet *part. as adv.* with confidence

gewa'hren *tr.* discover; *with gen.* become aware of, 2253

gewä'hren *tr.* give, grant; *intr.* answer (vouch) for (**für**), 711

Gewalt' *f.* **-en** power, authority; oppression; violence

Gewalt'beginnen *n.* **-s** act of tyranny

Gewalt'herrschaft *f.* despotism

gewal'tig *adj.* mighty, vast; *adv.* by violence

gewalt'sam *adj.* violent; *adv.* with might, 949

Gewalt'tat *f.* **-en** deed of violence, outrage

Gewehr' *n.* **-s, -e** weapon

Geweih' *n.* **-(e)s, -e** horns

Gewer'be *n.* **-s, —** business

Gewinn' *m.* **-s, -e** gain, profit

gewin'nen (gewann, gewonnen) *tr.* win, gain, get; capture

gewiß' *adj.* sure; certain, 2726; *adv.* no doubt, 2152

Gewit'ter *n.* **-s, —** storm

gewöh'nen *tr.* accustom to

gewohnt' *part. adj.* used (accustomed) to (*acc.*, 539; *gen.*, 1913)

gift'geschwollen *part. adj.* swollen with poison

gif'tig *adj.* (poisonous), malignant

Gip'fel *m.* **-s, —** height; worst

Git'ter *n.* **-s, —** grating, cage

Glanz *m.* **-es** brightness, splendor; show, 840, 916; glow, 2428

glän'zen shine, gleam; *part. adj.* bright, brilliant

glanz'voll *adj.* radiant, resplendent

glatt *adj.* smooth, sleek

Glau'be(n) *m.* **-ns** faith, belief

glau'ben *tr.* believe, put faith in (*dat. or* **an** *acc.*)

glau'benswert *adj.* trustworthy

gleich *adj.* like, same; *as noun* the same, *pl.* equals; even, 1023; *adv.* at once, directly (= **sogleich**); equally, 1882; right, 1886; *conj.* (= **obgleich**) although, 1119–20

glei'chen (glich, geglichen) (*dat.*) be like, resemble

gleich'falls *adv.* likewise, also

gleich'förmig *adv.* uniformly

gleich'wie *conj.* just (like) as

glei'ten (*usually* **glitt, geglitten,** *here weak*) **s.** *or* **h.** glide, slip

Glet'scher *m.* **-s, —** glacier

Glet'scherberg *m.* **-(e)s, -e** snow mountain

Glo'cke *f.* **-n** bell

Glöck'lein *n.* **-s, —** little bell

glor'reich *adj.* glorious

Glück *n.* **-(e)s** fortune, prosperity, happiness

glück'lich *adj.* happy, fortunate; *adv.* successfully, safely; *as noun, pl.* 3275, *sg.* 3284

glückse'lig *adj.* happy, safe

Glücks'stand *m.* **-(e)s** fortune

glü'hen glow

Glut *f.* **-en** glow, flame, heat

Gna'de *f.* **-n** mercy, pardon

gnä'dig *adj.* gracious, merciful

Gnü'gen = Genügen

Gol'ler (for **Koller**) *m.* **-s, —** doublet

gön'nen *tr.* grant

go'tisch *adj.* Gothic

Got'teshaus *n.* **-es, "er** house of God, monastery

Grab *n.* **-es, "er** grave

gra'ben (grub, gegraben; gräbt) *tr.* dig

gra'de = gerade

Graf *m.* **-en, -en** Count

Gram *m.* **-s** grief, sorrow

Gran'sen *m.* **-s, —** (*lit.* beak); **der hintere —** stern (*of a boat*)

Gras *n.* **-es, "er** grass

gräß'lich *adj.* terrible, dreadful; *often as noun*
Grat'tier *n.* –(e)s, –e chamois
grau *adj.* gray, grizzly
grau'en *impers.* (*dat.*) dread, be afraid (of **vor** *dat.*); *as noun* terror
grau'envoll *adj.* terrible, awful
grau'sam *adj.* terrible, cruel
Grau'samkeit *f.* –en cruelty
Grau'sen *n.* –s horror, dread
grau'senvoll *adj.* terrible, awful
grei'fen (**griff, gegriffen**) *tr. and intr.* catch, seize; *with* **in** *and acc.* reach, 1278; lay hold of, 1818 *, 2758 *; check, stay, 2181; *with* **nach** *and dat.* reach out after; *with* **zu** *and dat.* take up, have recourse to
greis *adj.* hoary
Greis *m.* –es, –e old man
Gren'ze *f.* –n border, limit
gren'zenlos *adj.* boundless
Greu'el *m.* –s, — outrage
greu'lich *adj.* horrible, shocking; *comp. as noun,* 558
Grimm *m.* –(e)s fury, wrath
Groll *m.* –s enmity, grudge; *with* **auf** (= **gegen**), 259
grol'len (*dat.*) bear a grudge
Groß'vater *m.* –s, ⸗ grandfather
Gruft *f.* ⸗e crevasse, grave, 1505; dungeon, 2363 (*pl.*)
Grund *m.* –es, ⸗e ground, reason; foundation; *pl.* gorges, 1550; **in** — to the bottom
grün'den *tr.* establish
gründ'lich *adj.* thorough
grü'nen grow green; grow, flourish, 2425; *part. adj.* green
gruppie'ren *tr.* group; *refl.* be grouped
grü'ßen *tr.* greet; *refl.* exchange greetings
Gunst *f.* favor; **zu** —**en** in favor of

gün'stig *adj.* favorable
Günst'ling *m.* –s, –e favorite
gür'ten *tr.* gird, belt
Gut *n.* –es, ⸗er goods, property, estate, possessions
Gü'te *f.* kindness
gü'tig *adj.* kind, gracious
Gut'tat *f.* –en act of kindness

H

Ha'be *f.* goods, property
ha'ben (**hatte, gehabt**) *tr. and aux.* have, possess; **was habt Ihr?** what's the matter with you? **eilig** — be in a hurry
Ha'fen *m.* –s, ⸗ haven, harbor
ha'geln *impers.* hail
Hahn *m.* –es, ⸗e cock
Halb'kreis *m.* –es, –e half-circle
Hälf'te *f.* –n half
Hal'le *f.* –n hall
Hals *m.* –es, ⸗e neck
hals'gefährlich *adj.* dangerous (to life)
hal'ten (**hielt, gehalten; hält**) *tr.* hold; keep (stop), 619; keep shut, 802; celebrate, 2653; — **für** regard as; — **von** think of; *intr.* hold, keep; halt, wait, 1409, 1831, 2853; hold, last, 1514; **an sich** — restrain oneself
Hand'bube *m.* –n, –n boy, servant
han'deln act, take action; *with* **an** *and dat.* act toward, treat
hand'haben (**handhabte, gehandhabt**) to handle, wield
Hand'langer *m.* –s, — laborer
hand'lich *adv.* vigorously
hand'los *adv.* inaccessibly
Hand'schlag *m.* –s, ⸗e handclasp
Hand'schuh *m.* –s, –e gauntlet
Hand'werk *n.* –s, –e trade

han'gen (hing, gehangen; hängt)
hang
hän'gen *tr., intr.* hang
här'men *refl.* grieve
harm'los *adj.* harmless
harmo'nisch *adj.* harmonious
Har'nisch *m.* -es, -e harness, armor
Har'ras *m.* master of horse
har'ren (*gen.* or **auf** and *acc.*) wait
for, await, expect
hart (härter, härtest) *adj.* hard;
harsh; *adv.* hard (close) by,
3093
här'ten *tr.* harden, temper
ha'schen *tr.* snatch, seize
Haß *m.* -sses hate
has'sen *tr.* hate
Hast *f.* haste
Hau'be *f.* -n cap, hood
Hauch *m.* -(e)s, (-e) breath, air
Hau'fe(n) *m.* -ns, -n troop, body
(*of men*)
häu'fen *refl.* be heaped
Haupt *n.* -es, ⸚er head; leader,
president
Haupt'ort *m.* -es, ⸚er chief town
Haus *n.* -es, ⸚er house, home; house
(= family); **zu —e** at home;
nach —e home
hau'sen live; stay, be
Haus'flur *f.* -en *primarily* entrance
hall; living room
Haus'gebrauch *m.* -s, ⸚e family
custom
Haus'genoß(e) *m.* -ssen, -ssen
(household) companion
haus'halten (hielt, gehalten; hält)
keep house, live
Häus'lein *n.* -s, — little house
häus'lich *adj.* domestic
Haus'recht *n.* -(e)s, -e household
(family) right
Haus'vater *m.* -s, ⸚ family man,
father of a family
he'ben (hob, gehoben) *tr.* lift, raise

Heer *n.* -es, -e army, host
Heer'macht *f.* ⸚e army, armed force
Heer'weg *m.* -es, -e highway, road
Heer'zug *m.* -es, ⸚e host
hef'tig *adj.* violent, vehement, sharp
Hef'tigkeit *f.* vehemence, violence
Hei'de *m.* -n, -n heathen
Heil *n.* -es health; *interj.* Hail!
hei'len *tr.* heal, cure
hei'lig *adj.* holy; **—er Gott!** merciful
Heaven!
Hei'ligtum *n.* -s, ⸚er sanctuary
Hei'mat *f.* -en home, native land,
dwelling-place
hei'matlich *adj.* native
heim'bringen (brachte, gebracht) *tr.*
bring home
hei'misch *adv.* at home
Heim'kehr *f.* return home
heim'kehren *s.* return home
heim'lich *adj.* secret
heim'sehnen *refl.* long for home
heim'treiben (trieb, getrieben) *tr.*
drive home
hei'schen *tr.* ask for
hei'ser *adj.* hoarse
hei'ßen (hieß, geheißen) be called
(named); mean, be; **es hieß**
they said
hei'ter *adj.* merry, gay, bright
Hel'denkraft *f.* ⸚e heroic strength
Hel'denkühnheit *f.* heroic courage
hel'fen (half, geholfen; hilft) (*dat.*)
help
Hel'fer *m.* -s, — helper, accomplice
hell *adj.* clear, bright; shrill
Helm *m.* -es, -e helmet
her *adv. and sep. pref.* here, hither;
lange — long since
herab' *adv. and sep. pref.* down
(from)
herab-flammen *s.* flash down
herab-kommen (kam, gekommen)
come down

herab-reiten (ritt, geritten) s. ride down

herab-senden (sandte, gesandt) tr. send down

herab-steigen (stieg, gestiegen) s. climb down

heran' adv. and sep. pref. here, this way, up, near

heran-begeben (begab, begeben; begibt) refl. come near

heran-ziehen (zog, gezogen) s. come on, approach

herauf' adv. and sep. pref. up, up here

heraus' adv. and sep. pref. out here, from, forth

heraus-finden (fand, gefunden) tr. find out, recognize one another

heraus-geben (gab, gegeben; gibt) tr. give (deliver) up

heraus-nehmen (nahm, genommen; nimmt) tr. take out

heraus-schrecken tr. frighten out (of **aus**)

heraus-stürzen s. rush out

heraus-treten (trat, getreten; tritt) s. step out

heraus-wachsen (wuchs, gewachsen; wächst) s. grow out of

herb adj. bitter

herbei' adv. and sep. pref. here, this way, up; Here with!

herbei-eilen s. hasten up

herbei-kommen (kam, gekommen) s. come up

Her'berg(e) f. –en inn; — **nehmen** seek shelter

Herd m. –es, –e hearth

Her'de f. –n herd, flock

Her'de(n)glocke f. –n herd bell

Her'denreihen m. –s, — herdsman's call (= **Kuh'reihen**)

herein' adv. and sep. pref. in, in here

herein-dringen (drang, gedrungen) s. press (force way) in, penetrate

herein-eilen s. hurry in

herein-führen tr. bring (lead) in

herein-rufen (rief, gerufen) tr. call in

herein-stürzen s. rush in; noun, 2797 *; **im** — as they rush (come) up

herein-treten (trat, getreten; tritt) s. step in, enter

herein-ziehen (zog, gezogen) tr. draw in

her-finden (fand, gefunden) refl. find one's way

her-führen tr. lead (bring) here

herfür' (old for **hervor**) adv. and sep. pref. forth, out

herfür-brechen (brach, gebrochen; bricht) (for **hervor-brechen**) s. break out

herfür-ziehen (old for **hervor-ziehen**) **(zog, gezogen)** tr. draw (take) out

her-geben (gab, gegeben; gibt) tr. give up

her-hangen (hing, gehangen; hängt) s. hang down over

He'ribann (for **Heer'bann**) m. –s call to arms

her-kommen (kam, gekommen) s. come here

He'roldsruf m. –es, –e herald's call

Herr m. –n, –en lord, Lord, master; old form **Herre** Sir, 1559; husband, 3109

her-reichen tr. reach, give

Her'renbank f. ⸚e nobles' bench

Her'renburg f. –en lordly castle

Her'renknecht m. –s, –e vassal, slave

Her'renleute pl. well-to-do citizens, men of standing

her'renlos adj. without a (feudal) lord, 1217; unclaimed, owner-less, 1251

Her'renschiff *n.* –(e)s, –e governor's
boat

herr'lich *adj.* splendid, glorious;
noun glory

Herr'schaft *f.* –en authority, rule

herr'schen rule, reign

Herr'scher *m.* –s, — ruler

her-schicken *tr.* send here

herü'ber *adv. and sep. pref.* across,
over here

herü'ber-klingen (klang, geklungen)
ring (sound) over here

**herü'ber-kommen (kam, gekom-
men) s.** come over here

herum' *adv. and sep. pref.* around,
about

herum-gehen (ging, gegangen) s.
go (be passed) round

herum-schlendern s. dawdle around

herun'ter *adv. and sep. pref.* down

herun'ter-gießen (goß, gegossen)
pour down

herun'ter-holen *tr.* bring down

**herun'ter-sinken (sank, gesunken)
s.** sink down

**herun'ter-steigen (stieg, gestiegen)
s.** descend

hervor' *adv. and sep. pref.* forth,
out

**hervor-graben (grub, gegraben;
gräbt) tr.** dig out from under
(**unter** *dat.*)

**hervor-kommen (kam, gekommen)
s.** come forth

hervor-stürzen s. rush forth

**hervor-treten (trat, getreten; tritt)
s.** step forward

herzei'nig *adj.* one at heart

herz'haft *adv.* boldly

herz'lich *adv.* heartily, warmly; very

Her'zog *m.* –s, ⁻e duke

heu'len howl, roar

heu'te *adv.* to-day

hiedan'nen (= **von dannen**) *adv.*
out of this, away from here

hieher(*for* **hierher)-kommen (kam,
gekommen) s.** get here

Hil'fe *f.* help; *interj.* Help! **zu** —
Help!

hilf'los *adj.* helpless

hilf'reich *adj.* helpful

Him'mel *m.* –s, — heaven; sky

him'melhoch *adj.* sky-high

him'melschreiend *part. adj.* atro-
cious, outrageous

Him'melsdach *n.* –s sky

Him'melsgabe *f.* –n gift of heav-
en

Him'melsglück *n.* –(e)s heavenly
bliss

Him'melslicht *n.* –s, –er light of
heaven

Him'melsraum *m.* –es, ⁻e quarter
of heaven, direction

hin *adv. and sep. pref.* hence,
thither, away (*from speaker*);
over, gone; **wo ... hin** whither,
where

hinab' *adv. and sep. pref.* down

**hinab-dringen (drang, gedrungen)
s.** penetrate

hinab-drücken *tr.* press down, re-
press

hinab-führen *tr.* lead down

hinab-senden (sandte, gesandt) tr.
send down

hinab-sinken (sank, gesunken) s.
sink down

hinab-steigen (stieg, gestiegen) s.
descend

hinan' *adv.* up

**hinan-klimmen (klomm, geklom-
men) s.** climb up

hinauf' *adv. and sep. pref.* up

hinauf-greifen (griff, gegriffen) reach
up

hinauf-heben (hob, gehoben) tr.
lift up

**hinauf-schwingen (schwang, ge-
schwungen) tr.** swing up on

hinauf-sehen (sah, gesehen; sieht) look up

hinauf-steigen (stieg, gestiegen) s. ascend

hinaus-eilen s. hasten out

hinaus-schicken *tr.* send out

Hin'dernis *n.* –sses, –sse hindrance

hin-deuten point towards

hin-drücken *tr.* press towards

hindurch' *adv.* through

hin-eilen s. run up

hinein-gehen (ging, gegangen) s. go inside

hinein-werfen (warf, geworfen; wirft) *tr.* throw in

hin-fahren (fuhr, gefahren; fährt) s. go away; *imper.* Away! 617, 1693; row along, 2249

hin-fallen (fiel, gefallen; fällt) s. fall (kneel) down

hin-finden (fand, gefunden) *refl.* find one's way

hin-flüchten *refl.* take refuge

hinfort' *adv.* henceforth

hin-führen lead (run) along

hin-gehen (ging, gegangen) s. go there; **wo gehst du hin?** where are you going?

hin-kommen (kam, gekommen) s. get to (there); **wo kam . . . hin?** what became of?

hin-leben live along

hin'nen *adv.* **von —** away

hin-pflanzen *tr.* set up

hin-reichen *tr.* reach out

hin-reiten (ritt, geritten) s. ride along

Hin'scheid *m.* –s death

hin-schiffen s. sail along

hin-sehen (sah, gesehen) look there (that way)

hin-senden (sandte, gesandt) *tr.* send thither

hin-stehen (stand, gestanden) stand, go stand

hin-stellen *tr.* put; *refl.* take a stand

hin'ten *adv.* behind, back

hin'ter (*superl.* **hinterst**) *adj.* rear; **—n Gransen** stern

hin'ter *prep.* (*dat.*, *acc.*) behind, after; *adv.*, *sep.*, *insep. pref.* behind, back

hinterge'hen (hinterging', hintergan'gen) *tr.* deceive, elude

Hin'tergrund *m.* –s, ⸗e background

Hin'terhalt *m.* –s ambush

hinterhal'ten (hinterhielt', hinterhal'ten; hinterhält') *tr.* withhold (from *dat.*)

hin'terst *adj. superl. of* hinter

hinü'ber *adv. and sep. pref.* over, across; gone

hinü'ber-dringen (drang, gedrungen) s. reach across

hinü'ber-gehen (ging, gegangen) s. go over, cross

hinü'ber-schaffen *tr.* take (set) over (across)

hinü'ber-tragen (trug, getragen; trägt) *tr.* take (carry) over

hinü'ber-ziehen (zog, gezogen) s. go (move) over (across)

hinun'ter *adv. and sep. pref.* down-(wards)

hinun'ter-schiffen s. go (sail) down

hinun'ter-steigen (stieg, gestiegen) s. descend

hinweg' *adv. and sep. pref.* away, off; **über . . . —** over, across

hinweg-gehen (ging, gegangen) s. go (pass) over (away)

hinweg-legen *tr.* lay aside

hinweg-treten (trat, getreten; tritt) s. step aside

hinweg-werfen (warf, geworfen; wirft) *tr.* throw away, cast off

hin-werfen (warf, geworfen; wirft) *tr.* throw away, throw down

hin-ziehen (zog, gezogen) *tr.* attract

hinzu' *adv. and sep. pref.* towards, up (to)
hinzu-laufen (lief, gelaufen; läuft) s. run up
Hirsch *m.* -es, -e stag
Hirt(e) *m.* -en, -en herdsman
Hir'tenknabe *m.* -n, -n herdsman's boy
hoch (höher, höchst) *adj.* *(declined* **hoher,** *etc.)* high, great, noble; *adv.* greatly, very, highly
Hoch'flug *m.* -s *(collect.)* large game birds
hoch'geboren *part. adj.* highborn, noble
Hoch'gewilde *(for* **Hoch'wild)** *n.* -s *(collect.)* large game *(animals)*; **Hochflug und** — large game *(bird and beast)*, 901
hoch'springend *part. adj.* leaping high
hoch'verstän'dig *adj.* highly intelligent, most sensible
Hoch'wacht *f.* -en beacon fire; signal height, watchtower
hoch'würdig *adj.* most venerable; *as noun* the sacrament
Hoch'zeit *f.* -en wedding (procession)
Hoch'zeitgesellschaft *f.* -en wedding party
Hoch'zeitshaus *n.* -es, ⁺er wedding (house) feast
Hof *m.* -es, ⁺e farm(yard), court-(yard)
hof'fen *tr.* hope (for **auf** *with acc.)*
Hoff'nung *f.* -en hope
Hof'statt *f.* court
Hof'tor *n.* -s, -e yard gate
Hö'he *f.* -n height, top; **in die** — up
Ho'heit *f.* -en greatness; authority, sovereignty
hohl *adj.* hollow, empty; deep, sunken, 2561

Höh'le *f.* -n cave, hole, den; socket, 643
Hohl'weg *m.* -s, -e (sunken) road, narrow pass
hohn-sprechen (sprach, gesprochen; spricht) mock (at *dat.)*
hold *adj.* gracious, kind, sweet, propitious; — **sein** like, love, 1415
ho'len *tr.* fetch, get, bring
Höl'lenqual *f.* -en (hellish) awful agony
Höl'lenrachen *m.* -s, — mouth of hell
Holun'derstrauch *m.* -s, ⁺er elderbush
hor'chen hearken, listen
Hor'de *f.* -n horde
Hor'nisse *f.* -n hornet
hübsch *adj.* pretty, nice
Huf *m.* -es, -e hoof
hul'digen *tr.* give homage (allegiance)
Hul'digung *f.* -en homage
hur'tig *adj.* quick; **mach'** — make haste
Hütte *f.* -n hut, cottage

I

im'mer *adv.* always; **auf** — forever
im'merdar *adv.* always; **auf** — forever
In'brunst *f.* fervor
indem' *conj.* while, as, when; *adv.* meanwhile
indes', indes'sen *conj.* while; *adv.* meanwhile
In'halt *m.* -s substance, contents
in'ne *adv.* within
in'ne-halten (hielt, gehalten; hält) pause, stop
in'ner *adj.* inner; *as noun* interior; heart
in'nerst *adj. as noun* inmost heart

(thoughts), 297; inmost recesses, 505
In'sel *f.* –n isle
ir'disch *adj.* earthly; *as noun* earthly things
ir'r(e) *adj.* astray
ir'ren wander; *refl.* be mistaken
Irr'tum *m.* –s, ⁻er error
Ita'lien *n.* –s Italy

J

ja *adv.* yes, surely, you know
Jagd *f.* –en hunt, chase
Jagd'horn *n.* –s, ⁻er hunting horn
Jagd'kleid *n.* –s, –er hunting costume
ja'gen *tr., intr.* hunt, pursue
Jä'ger *m.* –s, — hunter
Jahr *n.* –es, –e year
Jah'reszeit *f.* –en season
Jahr'markt *m.* –s, ⁻e fair(time)
Jam'mer *m.* –s grief, wretchedness
jam'mern *tr., intr.* pity, grieve, move to pity *impers.* (*gen.*); **mich jammert sein** I pity him
Jam'merruf *m.* –s, –e cry of distress
je *adv.* ever, each time; — **der zehnte** every tenth
jed'we'der (–e, –es) *adj., pron.* old *for* **jeder**
je'mand *pron.* someone, somebody
jen'seits *adv. and prep.* (*gen.*) beyond, on the other side of
jet'zo *adv., old for* **jetzt**
jetzt *adv.* now; **bis** — until now
Joch *n.* –es, –e yoke; (mountain) ridge
Ju'gend *f.* youth
ju'gendlich *adj.* youthful
Jüng'ling *m.* –s, –e young man
jüngst *adv.* recently, lately
Jun'ker *m.* –s, — young nobleman
just *adv.* just (then)

K

Kahn *m.* –s, ⁻e boat
Kai'serhof *m.* –s, ⁻e imperial court
Kai'serkrone *f.* –n imperial crown
Kai'sermord *m.* –s, –e murder of an emperor
Kalk *m.* –es, –e lime
Kam'mer *f.* –n chamber, room
Kampf *m.* –es, ⁻e conflict, battle, struggle
kämp'fen fight, struggle
karg *adv.* sparingly
Kauf'mann *m.* –s, **Kauf'leute** merchant
Kauf'mannsschiff *n.* –(e)s, –e merchant ship, trading boat
Kauf'mannsstraße *f.* –n commercial highway
kaum *adv.* scarcely, hardly
keck *adj.* bold, daring
keck'lich *adv.* boldly
Keh'le *f.* –n throat
keh'ren *refl. tr.* turn
Keim *m.* –es, –e germ
Kel'ler *m.* –s, — cellar (= dungeon)
ken'nen (**kannte, gekannt**) *tr.* know; — **lernen** become acquainted with
Ker'ker *m.* –s, — prison, dungeon
Kerl *m.* –s, –e fellow
Ket'te *f.* –n chain
Kin'deskind *n.* –es, –er *pl.* children's children
Kis'sen *n.* –s, — cushion
Kla'ge *f.* –n grievance, complaint
kla'gen complain of (**wider, über** *with acc.*)
Klang *m.* –es, ⁻e sound, ring
Kleid *n.* –s, –er dress; garb
klei'den *tr.* clothe, dress
Klein'od *n.* –s, –e *or* –ien jewel, treasure
klim'men (**klomm, geklommen**) (*also weak*) **s.** climb

klin'gen (klang, geklungen) sound;
as noun, 3
Klip'pe *f.* **-n** cliff
klop'fen knock
Klo'ster *n.* **-s,** ⁻ convent, monastery
Klo'sterleute *pl.* people (serfs) of a
monastery
Klo'stermei(e)r *m.* **-s,** — monastery
overseer
Kluft *f.* ⁻**e** cleft, gorge
klug (klüger, klügst) *adj.* shrewd,
wise, prudent
Knecht *m.* **-s,** **-e** servant, vassal,
slave
Knecht'schaft *f.* bondage, servitude
kni'en kneel
knüp'fen *tr.* join, connect
Kö'cher *m.* **-s,** — quiver
kom'men (kam, gekommen) s. come,
arrive; *with* **an** *acc.* get at,
1547; *with* **auf** think of, 1518;
zu sich — come to (compose)
oneself; **dahin** — come to that
komm'lich *adj.* (*Swiss*) comfortable,
good
Kö'nigsburg *f.* **-en** king's castle
kön'nen (konnte, gekonnt; kann)
tr. and modal aux. can, may, be
able; *with* **bei** get at = hurt,
2708
Korn *n.* **-(e)s,** ⁻**er** corn (= wheat)
grain
köst'lich *adj.* choice, precious
kra'chen crash, crack
kräch'zen croak
Kraft *f.* ⁻**e** force, strength
kräf'tiglich *adv.* strongly, vigorously; *old for* **kräftig**
kraft'los *adj.* powerless, weak; in
vain, 2608
krä'hen crow
krampf'haft *adj.* convulsive
krän'ken *tr.* hurt (*feelings*), grieve,
wrong
Kranz *m.* **-es,** ⁻**e** wreath, crown

Kränz'lein *n.* **-s,** — little wreath
(garland)
Kraut *n.* **-s,** ⁻**er** herb, plant
Kreis *m.* **-es,** **-e** circle; sphere, 762;
socket, 678; round, 2402
Kreuz *n.* **-es,** **-e** cross
Kreuz'lein *n.* **-s,** — little cross
krie'chen (kroch, gekrochen) s. *or* h.
creep, crawl
krie'gerisch *adj.* warlike
Krie'gesmacht *f.* ⁻**e** military force
Krie'gesnot *f.* ⁻**e** distress of war
Kriegs'dromme'te (*for* **-trompe'te**)
war trumpet
Kro'ne *f.* **-n** crown
krö'nen *tr.* crown
Krüm'me *f.* **-n** winding, bend
Ku'ckuck *m.* **-s,** **-e** cuckoo
küh'len *tr.* cool
kühn *adj.* bold
Kühn'heit *f.* **-en** boldness
Kulm *m.* **-es,** **-e** peak, crest
Kum'mer *m.* **-s** anxiety, grief
küm'mern *tr.* concern
kum'mervoll *adj.* sorrowful, anxious
Kun'de *f.* **-n** knowledge, news
kun'dig *adj.* having knowledge;
— **sein** (*with gen.*) know, be
familiar with
Kund'schaft *f.* spies, espionage
Kunst *f.* ⁻**e** art, skill
kunst'geübt *part. adj.* practiced,
skillful
kür'zen *tr.* (*lit.* shorten) cut off,
deprive of (**um** *with acc.*)
Kurz'weil *f.* (*also m. and n.* **-s**)
pleasantry, jest

L

la'ben *tr.* refresh
La'bung *f.* **-en** refreshment
lä'cheln smile
la'den (lud, geladen; lädt *or* **ladet)**
tr. load; invite, summon

La'ger *n.* -s, — court

Läm'mergeier *m.* -s, — lamb's vulture, lammergeier

Land'ammann *m.* -s, ⸗er chief magistrate, landammann

Land'bedrücker *m.* -s, — oppressor of the country

Län'dergier *f.* greed for land

Län'derkauf *m.* -s, ⸗e purchase of land

Län'derkette *f.* -n chain of lands

Lan'desammann cf. **Landammann**

Lan'desfeind *m.* -(e)s, -e enemy of the country

Lan'desmark *f.* -en boundary, border

Lan'desunglück *n.* -s, -e national calamity

Land'leute *pl.* peasants, men

Land'mann *m.* -s, **Landleute** countryman, peasant

Land'mark *f.* -en border, boundary

Land'schaft *f.* -en landscape, scene

Lands'gemeinde *f.* -n general assembly

Lands'gesetz *n.* -es, -e law of the land

Lands'mann *m.* -s, **Landsleute** fellow countryman

Land'straße *f.* -n highroad

Land'sturm *m.* -s militia, home guards

Land'vogt *m.* -s, ⸗e governor

Land'wehr *f.* -en bulwark

lan'gen *tr.* reach, take (down)

lang'sam *adj.* slow

längst *adv.* long, long ago

Lan'ze *f.* -n lance

las'sen (ließ, gelassen; läßt) *tr. and intr.* leave, let alone, give up, lose; let, allow; make, cause, have done; **sich — *with inf.*** enable, can (may) be; **laßt's gut sein** never mind

Last *f.* -en load, burden

la'sten weigh upon, oppress

La'ster *n.* -s, — crime

lau'ern lurk, lie in wait (for **auf**)

Lauf *m.* -(e)s, ⸗e course; **im —** under way, started, 2865

lau'fen (lief, gelaufen; läuft) *s. or h.* run, move, pass; **ge— kommen** come running

lau'schen listen, lurk

Laut *m.* -es, -e sound

lau'ten sound, run; stand written

läu'ten *tr. and intr.* ring; toll

lau'ter *adj.* pure, clear

Lawi'ne *f.* -n avalanche

le'ben live; **lebt wohl** Farewell! **von etwas —** live on; **es lebe** long live!

Le'ben *n.* -s, — life; **geht ums —, gilt das —** life is at stake

leben'dig *adj.* living, alive; *as noun,* 2150

Le'bensblut *n.* -s life blood

Le'bensglück *n.* -s life happiness

leb'haft *adv.* eagerly

Leb'tag *m.* -s, -e all the days of one's life, 2703

lech'zen long (languish, thirst) for (**nach**)

le'dig *adj.* free, loose

leer *adj.* empty; vain

lee'ren *tr.* clear, empty

le'gen *tr.* lay, put

Le'h(e)n *n.* -s, — fief; **zu — tragen** hold in fief

Le'henhof *m.* -s, ⸗e feudal court

Le'henherr *m.* -n, -en feudal (liege) lord

leh'nen lean (on **auf**)

leh'ren *tr.* teach

Leib *m.* -es, -er body, person (1839); life; **— und Leben** life and limb, 1925; **— und Blut** life, 661

Lei'beskraft *f.* ⸗e bodily strength; *pl.* all my might

leib'lich *adj.* one's own
Leich'nam *m.* –s, –e (dead) body, corpse
leicht *adj.* light, easy; slight, 1926; frivolous, 794; ready, 300; *adv.* quickly, easily, promptly
leicht'fertig *adj.* wanton, impudent
lei'den (**litt, gelitten**) *tr.* endure, suffer; *intr.* allow, 2341
Lei'den *n.* –s, — suffering
lei'der *interj.* Alas!
lei'hen (**lieh, geliehen**) *tr.* lend
lei'sten *tr.* do, accomplish; **Pflicht** — fulfill duty; **Bürgschaft** — give bail
lei'ten *tr.* lead; bring, 1353; **Steg** — lay bridge
Lei'ter *f.* –n ladder
len'ken *tr.* direct, guide
Lenz *m.* –es, –e springtime
letzt *adj.* last; *as noun* last, 862; last resort, 1319; worst, 3180
leuch'ten light, shine on, give light; *as noun*, 1443
lich'ten *tr.* light = clear (*forest*)
lieb *adj.* dear, beloved; —**er** rather; — **haben** love
Lie'be *f.* love; kindness, favor, 2291
lie'ber *comp. of* **lieb**, *adv.* rather
lieb'lich *adj.* lovely
lie'gen (**lag, gelegen**) *intr. h. and s.* lie, be (situated); *with* **an** *and dat.* concern, be important, 709; **nichts liegt mir am Leben** life is worth nothing to me; **an mir** — be my fault
Lin'de *f.* –n linden tree
link *adj.* left; **zur Linken** to the left (hand)
links *adv.* on the left
Lip'pe *f.* –n lip
Lo'cke *f.* –n lock
lo'cken *tr.* entice, attract

lo'dern blaze
loh *adv.* brightly, with a blaze
Lohn *m.* –es reward
loh'nen *tr.* reward, repay
los *adj.* loose; up, 109; free from, rid of (*gen.*); — **werden** get rid of (*gen.*); *sep. pref.* loose, off, free
Los *n.* –es, –e lot, fate
los-binden (**band, gebunden**) *tr.* unloose, unfasten
lö'sen *tr.* loosen, throw off; acquit, 2048; redeem, 3236
los-geben (**gab, gegeben;** **gibt**) *tr.* set free
los-lassen (**ließ, gelassen;** **läßt**) *tr.* let loose
los-reißen (**riß, gerissen**) *refl.* tear oneself away
Luft *f.* ⁓e air, breeze
lu'gen (*Swiss*) look (and see)
lü'gen (**log, gelogen**) lie; be wrong, 258; **das lügst du** that's a lie
Lust *f.* ⁓e lust, desire; pleasure; **böse** — malice, 272
lü'stern *adj.* hot, impetuous

M

ma'chen *tr.* make, do; fix, 1479; play (part of), 759; *intr.* **mach' hurtig** be quick
Macht *f.* ⁓e might, authority
mäch'tig *adj.* mighty, strong; *with gen.* master of
mah'nen *tr.* remind; *part. as noun* claimant, 2956
Mai'entau *m.* –s May dew
ma'lerisch *adj.* picturesque
Mandat' *n.* –s, –e order
Män'nerwert *m.* –s manly worth
Man'neswort *n.* –s, –e word of a (true) man
männ'lich (*old form* **mannlich,** 2875), manly, brave

Man'tel *m.* −s, ⁔ mantle

Markt *m.* −es, ⁔e market (place)

Mar'ter *f.* −n pain, torture

Maß *n.* −es, −e measure

mä'ßigen *refl.* restrain oneself, be moderate

matt *adj.* faint, weak

Mat'te *f.* −n mead(ow); *Swiss for* Wiese

Mau'er *f.* −n wall

Mau'erstein *m.* −s, −e stone (*for building*)

Maul'wurfshaufe(n) *m.* −ns, −n molehill

Mehr *n.* −es majority

meh'ren *tr.* increase, favor

meh'rere *pl. adj.* several

Mehr'heit *f.* majority

mehrst *superl. adj., old for* meist most

mei'den (mied, gemieden) *tr.* avoid, shun

Mei'er *m.* −s — overseer, steward; *often proper name*

mei'nen *intr. and tr.* think, mean, intend; expect

mei'nig (der −e, die −e, das −e) *poss. adj., pron.* mine; *as noun* my own, 3136

Mei'nung *f.* −en opinion, wish, 396; intentions, 2021

Mei'sterschuß *m.* −sses, ⁔sse master-shot

mel'ken *tr.* milk

Melk'napf *m.* −s, ⁔e milkpail

Men'ge *f.* −n crowd

Mensch *m.* −en, −en man, human being; kein — nobody

Men'schendenken *n.* −s memory of man; seit — within man's memory

men'schenleer *adj.* deserted, lonely

Men'schenspur *f.* −en human trace

Mensch'heit *f.* humanity

mensch'lich *adj.* human; *as noun* anything (human, i.e. accident), 159

Mensch'lichkeit *f.* humanity, humaneness

mer'ken *tr.* notice, mark

Merk'mal *n.* −s, −e mark, sign

mes'sen (maß, gemessen; mißt) *tr.* measure; mit Augen — look at closely; *refl.* be equal to (2024), vie with

Met'tenglöcklein *n.* −s, — matin bell

Meu'te *f.* −n pack (*hounds*)

Meuterei' *f.* −en riot

Mil'de *f.* mildness, gentleness

mild'tätig *adj.* benevolent, charitable

mißbrau'chen *tr.* misuse, abuse

Miß'gunst *f.* ill-will, malice

mit *prep.* (*dat.*), *adv. sep. pref.* with, together; along (too, 2183); by, on, in; — dabei there too

mit-bringen (brachte, gebracht) *tr.* bring along with = require, 1402

mit-führen *tr.* take (carry) along with

mit-geben (gab, gegeben; gibt) *tr.* give to one departing; *with* in (*acc.*) put in with

mit-kommen (kam, gekommen) *s.* come along with

Mit'leid *n.* −s pity, sympathy

mit-nehmen (nahm, genommen; nimmt) *tr.* take, accept, enjoy

mit-nennen (nannte, genannt) *tr.* mention (name) too

mitsamt' *prep.* (*dat.*) together with

Mit'schuld *f.* (joint) guilt

mit-schwören (schwor, geschworen) swear too (= with others)

Mit'tagsonne *f.* −n midday-sun = south

Mit'tagsstunde *f.* −n midday-hour. noon

Mit′te *f.* middle, midst

mit-teilen *tr.* tell

Mit′tel *n.* -s, — means, way, resort

mit′ten *adv.* in the middle (midst) of, right in

Mit′ternacht *f.* ‑e midnight; north, 1169

mit-ziehen (zog, gezogen) *s.* march along with

mö′gen (mochte, gemocht; mag) *tr. and modal aux.* may, can; like (*with acc.*)

mög′lich *adj.* possible

Mönch *m.* -s, -e monk

Mond′regenbogen *m.* -s, — or ‑ moon rainbow

Monstranz′ *f.* -en monstrance, sacrament box

Mord *m.* -s, -e murder

Mör′der *m.* -s, — murderer

mör′derisch *adj.* murderous

Mord′gedanke *m.* -ns, -n murderous thought

Mord′gewehr *n.* -s, -e murderous (deadly) weapon

mor′gen *adv.* to-morrow

Mor′genröte *f.* -n morning red, dawn

Mor′genstrahl *m.* -s, -en morning light

Mör′tel *m.* -s, — mortar

mü′de *adj.* tired, weary

Mü′he *f.* -n trouble, hardship

mun′ter *adj.* lively, brisk; rapid

mur′ren murmur, grumble

mü′ßig *adj.* idle

mu′stern *tr.* look at intently

Mut *m.* -(e)s courage, heart; mood, desire, 1771; **gutes —es** of good cheer; **getrosten —es** confidently

mu′tig *adj.* brave, courageous; martial, 835; *as noun*, 313

müt′terlich *adj.* maternal; *as noun* mother's estate, 1345

Mut′terschmerz *m.* -e(n)s, -en birth pains

Müt′ze *f.* -n cap

N

nach *prep.* (*dat.*), *adv.*, *sep. pref.* after, to, towards, according to, along, about; **will** — starts to follow, 3126

Nach′bar *m.* -s (*or* -n), -n neighbor

nachdem′ *conj.* after

nach-drängen press (crowd) after

nach-dringen (drang, gedrungen) *s.* (press) follow after

nach-eilen *s.* hurry after

Na′chen *m.* -s, — boat

nach-folgen *s.* follow (after)

nach-gehen (ging, gegangen) (*dat.*) *s.* pursue, follow (= be engaged in)

nachher′ *adv.* afterwards

nach-jagen *s.* pursue, rush after (*dat.*)

nach-kommen (kam, gekommen) *s.* follow; come up (*dat.*)

Nach′richt *f.* -en news, report

nach-setzen set after, pursue (*dat.*)

nach-sprechen (sprach, gesprochen; spricht) *tr.* repeat

nächst *prep.* (*dat.*) next to, close by; *adj.* (*superl. of* **nah**) next, first; *as noun* neighbor, 107

nach-stürzen *s.* hurry after

nächt′lich *adj.* nightly, nocturnal; *adv.* by night

nachts, des Nachts *as adv.* the (at) night, 1781, 2876

nach-tun (tat, getan) *tr.* (*dat. pers.*) imitate (in), do after

nach-ziehen (zog, gezogen) *tr.* draw (up) after

Na′cken *m.* -s, — neck

nackt *adj.* naked

na'h(e) (näher, nächst) *adj.* near
(by), close
Nä'he *f.* (*lit.* nearness), presence
na'hen come (near), approach
nä'hern *refl.* draw near, approach
näh'ren *tr.* nourish, feed, support
Nah'rung *f.* food, nourishment
Na'me *m.* -ns, -n name; mit —n
by its name, 531
när'risch *adj.* foolish, queer
Natur' *f.* nature
natur'vergessen *part. adj.* unnatural
Nau'e *f.* -n (*Swiss*) boat
Ne'beldecke *f.* -n veil of fog
ne'ben *prep.* (*dat. or acc.*) by, near,
beside
neb'licht (*old for* nebelig) *adj.* misty,
foggy
nebst *prep.* (*dat.*) together with
Nef'fe *m.* -n, -n nephew
neh'men (nahm, genommen; nimmt)
tr. take (from *dat. pers.*);
accept; überhand — get the
upper hand
Neid *m.* -es envy
nei'disch *adj.* envious (*dat.*)
nen'nen (nannte, genannt) *tr.* name,
call; tell, 2283; *refl.* be named
(called), 369
Netz *n.* -es, -e net
neu *adj.* new, fresh, recent; *adv.*
anew, afresh; von —em, aufs
—e anew, again
Neu'erung *f.* -en innovation
Neu'gier *f.* curiosity
Neujahrs'geschenk *n.* -s, -e New
Year's present
nicht *adv.* not; gar — not at all;
noch — not yet
nid (*Swiss*) *prep.* (*dat.*) below
nie *adv.* never; noch — never before
nie'der-brennen (brannte, gebrannt)
tr. burn down

nie'der-fallen (fiel, gefallen; fällt)
s. fall down
nie'der-knien kneel (down)
nie'der-lassen (ließ, gelassen; läßt)
tr. let down
nie'der-quellen (quoll, gequollen;
quillt) s. trickle down
nie'der-reißen (riß, gerissen) *tr.* tear
(pull) down
nie'der-schlagen (schlug, geschlagen; schlägt) *tr.* strike down
nie'der-schmelzen (schmolz, geschmolzen; schmilzt) s. melt
down
nie'der-senden (sandte, gesandt) *tr.*
send down
nie'der-sinken (sank, gesunken) s.
sink down
nie'der-steigen (stieg, gestiegen) s.
descend
nie'der-stoßen (stieß, gestoßen;
stößt) *tr.* strike down
Nie'derung *f.* -en lowland
nie'der-werfen (warf, geworfen;
wirft) *refl.* prostrate oneself
nie'mals *adv.* never
nie'mand *pron.* no one, nobody
nim'mer *adv.* never
nim'mermehr *adv.* Never!
nir'gend(s) *adv.* nowhere
nit *adv.* not; *colloq. for* nicht
noch *adv.* yet, still, as yet, even,
besides, more, other; *conj.* nor,
1917, 1943
Not *f.* ⸚e need, distress; not tun
(*or* sein) be necessary
not'gedrungen *part. adj. as adv.*
by necessity, under constraint
Not'gewehr *n.* -s, -e means of defense
Not'wehr *f.* self-defense
nun *adv.* now; *interj.* Well!
nur *adv.* only; just, do, pray, *with
imperative*

O

ob *conj.* whether, if; though, 1159; *with* **schon, gleich, wohl** = although; *prep. dat. (gen.)* on account of; **ob** *in compounds implies* above, over

Ob'dach *n.* –s lodging, shelter

o'ben *adv.* above, up there, high up; before

O'berhaupt *n.* –s, ⸚er chief (ruler), head

o'berherrlich *adj.* sovereign

obgleich' *conj.* although

Ob'mann *m.* –s, ⸚er judge, arbitrator

Ob'rigkeit *f.* –en magistrates, superiors

ö'de *adj.* desolate, lonely

offenba'ren *tr.* open, disclose

of'fenstehend *part. adj.* (standing) open

öf'fentlich *adj.* public

öff'nen *tr.* open; *refl.* open (up), widen

O'heim *m.* –s, –e uncle

Ohm *m.* –s, –e uncle *(old)*

ohn'mächtig *adj.* impotent, vain, powerless

Op'fer *n.* –s, — sacrifice; victim; offering

or'dentlich *adv.* properly

Ord'nung *f.* –en order

Ort *m.* –es, –e *(or* ⸚er*)* place; *pl.* —e canton

Öst'(er)reich *n.* –s Austria

öst'lich *adj.* eastern

P

Pair *(pronounce* **Pär)** *m.* –s, –s peer

Papst *m.* –es, ⸚e pope

Partei'ung *f.* –en discord

Paß *m.* –sses, ⸚sse *(mountain)* pass

Pau'se *f.* –n pause; moment

Pelz'wams *n.* –es, ⸚er fur coat

Pergament' *n.* –s, –e parchment, charter

Person' *f.* –en person; rôle, part, 812; *pl.* characters

Pfad *m.* –es, –e path

Pfaff(e) *m.* –n, –n priest

Pfalz *f.* –en palace, court

Pfand *n.* –es, ⸚er pledge, security; trust, 2508

Pfar'rer *m.* –s, — pastor

Pfau'enfeder *f.* –n peacock-feather

Pfei'fe *f.* –n shrill call

Pfeil *m.* –es, –e arrow

Pferd *n.* –es, –e horse; **zu** — on horseback

Pflan'ze *f.* –n plant

pflan'zen *tr.* plant

Pfle'ge *f.* care, nursing

pfle'gen be accustomed, used to; **Rats** — take counsel

Pflicht *f.* –en duty, obligation

pflicht'gemäß *adv.* dutifully, duly

pflich'tig *adj.* subject (bound) to

Pflug *m.* –es, ⸚e plow

Pflug'stier *m.* –s, –e plow-ox

Pfor'te *f.* –n gate, door

Pfo'sten *m.* –s, — post

Pi'ke *f.* –n pike

Pil'ger *m.* –s, — pilgrim

Pil'gerstracht *f.* –en pilgrim dress

pla'gen *refl.* worry, be troubled

Plat'te *f.* –n ledge *(of rock)*

Platz *m.* –es, ⸚e place; square, common; ground, 964; *interj.* Make way!

plötz'lich *adj.* sudden

Po'panz *m.* –es, –e scarecrow

pracht'voll *adj.* splendid, spirited

pran'gen shine, be gorgeous; parade

Pran'ger *m.* –s, — pillory

pras'seln crackle

Preis *m.* –es, –e prize

prei'sen (pries, gepriesen) *tr.* praise;

refl. be glad, call . . . fortunate, 1084

pres'sen *tr.* trouble, worry

Prospekt' *m.* –s, –e prospect, view

prü'fen *tr.* prove, weigh, test

Prü'fung *f.* –en test, trial

Puls *m.* –es, –e pulse = moment

Pur'purmantel *m.* –s, ⸗ red mantle

Q

Qual *f.* –en torment, pang

quä'len *refl.* distress oneself, worry

Qualm *m.* –s smoke

Quell *m.* –es, –e fountain

Quel'le *f.* –n spring, fountain

R

Ra'be *m.* –n, –n raven

Ra'che *f.* vengeance, revenge

Ra'chegeist *m.* –es, –er spirit of vengeance, Fury

rä'chen *tr.*, *refl.* avenge (on **an** *dat.*)

Rä'cher *m.* –s, — avenger

Rach'gefühl *n.* –s, –e thirst for vengeance

ra'gen stand out, loom up

Rand *m.* –es, ⸗er edge, brink

Rän'ke *pl.* tricks, intrigues

rasch *adj.* quick, prompt; rash, impetuous

ra'sen rave, rage, be mad; *part.* mad; *as noun* madman

rast'los *adv.* restlessly, unceasingly

Rat *m.* –es, **Ratschläge** advice, counsel; *pl.* **Räte** councilor; **zu —e gehen, —s pflegen** take counsel; — **wissen** know what to do

ra'ten (**riet, geraten; rät**) *tr.* (*dat. pers.*) advise, counsel; *intr.* (**zu** *dat.*), 1972

Rat'haus *n.* –es, ⸗er town hall

Raub *m.* –es robbery, prey

rau'ben *tr.* rob, plunder; take from (*dat.*), 606; carry away, 2532

Räu'ber *m.* –s, — robber

Raub'tier *n.* –s, –e wild animal, beast of prey

Rauch *m.* –(e)s smoke

Raum *m.* –(e)s, ⸗e room; distance

räu'men *tr.* quit, leave

rau'schen rush, roar; creak, 503; *as noun*, 2098 *

Re'chen *m.* –s, — rake

rech'nen count, rely (on **auf**)

Rech'nung *f.* –en reckoning

recht *adj.* right, just; true, real, genuine; decent, respectable, 1480; **Rechte** right hand; **zur Rechten** to the right; *adv.* well, thoroughly, truly, very

Recht *n.* –es, –e right, privilege; justice; — **sprechen** dispense justice

rech'ten be at law about (**um**)

recht'fertigen *tr.* justify

recht'los *adj.* without rights, outlawed

rechts *adv.* on (to) the right

Re'de *f.* –n, talk, words; — **stehen** answer, render account; **zur — kommen** be spoken of

red'lich *adj.* honest, candid; *as noun* good people, 276; *adv.* frankly, 292, well, 287; stoutly, 489; steadily, 2249

Red'lichkeit *f.* integrity

re'ge *adj.* busy, lively

re'gen *refl.* stir, move

Re'genbogen *m.* –s, — *or* ⸗ rainbow

Regent' *m.* –en, –en regent, governor

regie'ren *tr. and intr.* rule, reign; control, 757

Regiment' *n.* –s rule, government; management, 342

reich *adj.* rich; *adv.* well, abundantly, richly

Reich *n.* –(e)s, –e empire; throne

rei'chen *tr.* reach, give, extend

reich'lich *adv.* abundantly
Reichs'bote *m.* –n, –n imperial messenger
Reichs'fürst *m.* –en, –en imperial prince
Reichs'panier' *n.* –s, –e imperial banner
Reichs'vogt *m.* –s, ⁺e imperial bailiff, governor
Rei'he *f.* –n row, line
Rei'hen *m.* –s, — row, procession
rein *adj.* clean, pure, clear of, innocent, free from; *adv.* clearly, perfectly
Reis *n.* –es, –er twig
Reis'holz *n.* –es, ⁺er brushwood
Rei'sigen (*pl.* of **reisig** *mounted*) trooper
rei'ßen (**riß, gerissen**) *tr.* tear, drag, dash; pull down, 2766 *
rei'ten (**ritt, geritten**) s. ride; **geritten** *with verb* = riding
Rei'ter *m.* –s, — trooper
Rei'tersmann *m.* –s, ⁺er (–leute) horseman, trooper
rei'zen *tr.* anger, rouse, irritate; —d charming, 1712
ren'nen (**rannte, gerannt**) s. run
Respekt' *m.* –es respect
Rest *m.* –es, –e (*pl.*) remains
ret'ten *tr.* save, rescue, deliver
Ret'ter *m.* –s, — rescuer, deliverer
Ret'tung *f.* –en deliverance
ret'tungslos *adv.* past help
Ret'tungsufer *n.* –s, — shore of safety
Reu'e *f.* repentance
reu'en *impers.* (*acc.*) regret, repent of
Reu'eträne *f.* –n penitent tear
Reverenz' *f.* –en homage, obeisance
rich'ten *tr.* turn to, direct against; address to; *refl.* rise (up **in die Höhe**), 2416 *; judge, 3056
Rich'ter *m.* –s, — judge

rich'terlich *adj.* judicial
Rich'terspruch *m.* –s, ⁺e sentence, verdict
Richt'maß *n.* –es, –e rule, measure
Rie'gel *m.* –s, — bolt
Rind *n.* –es, –er ox; *pl.* cattle
rin'gen, rang, gerungen writhe, struggle; wring, 180 *; *refl.* get out of (**aus**), 1512
rings *adv.* around
ringsum' *adv.* all around
ringsumher' *adv.* all around
rin'nen (**rann, geron'nen**) s. run, flow
Riß *m.* –sses, –sse rift, crack
Rit'ter *m.* –s, — knight
Rit'terfräulein *n.* –s, — maid of noble birth
Rit'terkleidung *f.* knight's dress
rit'terlich *adj.* knightly
Rit'termantel *m.* –s, ⁺ knight's mantle
Rit'terpflicht *f.* –en knightly duty
Rit'terwort *n.* –s, –e knightly word
roh *adj.* rough, rude, cruel
Rohr *n.* –(e)s, –e reed
rol'len *intr. and tr.* roll
Rö'merkrone *f.* –n Roman crown
Rö'merzug *m.* –es, ⁺e journey to Rome
Roß *n.* –sses, –sse horse
ro'sten s. rust
ro'stig *adj.* rusty
rot (**röter, rötest**) *adj.* red
rucht'bar (*for* **ruch'bar**) known, public
Rü'cken *m.* –s, — back, rear; backing, support, 662, 1844
rück'springend *part. adj.* leaping backwards
Ru'der *n.* –s, — oar
Ru'derer *m.* –s, — oarsman
Ruf *m.* –es, –e report
ru'fen (**rief, gerufen**) *tr. and intr.* call, summon; cry (call) to

Ruf′fi (*Swiss*) *n. or f.* −s *or* −nen landslide

Ru′he *f.* rest, peace, quiet; *exclam.*, 1396

ru′hen rest

ru′hig *adj.* quiet, calm, peaceful; *exclam.*, 1299

Ruhm *m.* −(e)s fame, glory

rüh′men *tr.* praise; *refl.* boast (of *gen.*), glory in, be proud to be

rühm′lich *adj.* laudable

rüh′ren *tr.* stir, move; beat (*drum*), 402 *; touch, 1952

Rui′ne *f.* −n ruin

Run′se *f.* −n gully

rü′sten *tr. and refl.* prepare, 93; arm, equip

S

Saal *m.* −es, Säle hall

Saat *f.* −en seed

Sa′che *f.* −n thing, matter, affair; cause

sä′en *tr.* sow

Salz *n.* −es, (−e) salt

sam′meln *tr.* gather (alms)

Samm′lung *f.* (−en) meditation, thought, devotion

sanft (sanfter, sanftest) *adj.* soft, gentle, kind; — tun cajole, deal gently with

Sar′ner *adj.* of Sarnen

Sas′se *m.* −n, −n tenant, settler; bondman, 1209

Sät′igtung *f.* satisfaction

sau′er *adj.* sour; hard, toilsome

sau′gen (sog, gesogen) *tr.* suck, drink in

Säu′le *f.* −n (pillar) pole

säu′men delay, hesitate, linger; *as noun*, 2281, 2513

Säu′mer *m.* −s, — pack-horse driver

Saum′roß *n.* −sses, −sse pack-horse

Schä′del *m.* −s, — skull

Scha′de(n) *m.* −ns, −n *or* ⁼n harm, damage

scha′den do harm (damage)

schä′digen *tr.* injure, hurt, damage (an *with dat.* in)

Schaf *n.* −es, −e sheep

schaf′fen *tr.* do, accomplish, 148; get, find, procure, secure, 1012, 2799; get (= take) away, across, 1527, 2757; es — act, 281; produce, 572

Schaff′ner *m.* −s — manager, overseer; — machen be (play) the overseer

Schall *m.* −(e)s, −e sound

schal′len (scholl, geschollen *also weak*) h. *and* s. resound

schal′ten rule, hold sway

Scham *f.* shame

schä′men *refl.* (*gen.*) be ashamed of

scham′los *adj.* shameless

Schan′de *f.* −n shame, disgrace

schän′den *tr.* dishonor, disgrace

Schän′der *m.* −s, — despoiler

Schänd′lichkeit *f.* −en shame, disgrace, ignominy

Schan′ze *f.* −n chance; in die — schlagen risk, venture

Schar *f.* −en troop, herd; (multitude) forest (*of lances*)

scharf (schärfer, schärfest) *adj.* sharp, keen

schar′ren *tr.* scratch, paw

Schat′te(n) *m.* −ns, −n shadow

Schatz *m.* −es, ⁼e treasure

Schau *f.* show; zur — tragen display, make show of

schau′dern shudder

schau′en *tr.* see, look at, behold

schau′erlich *adj.* awful, dreadful

schäu′men foam

Schau′platz *m.* −es, ⁼e scene

Schau′spiel *n.* −s, −e sight, spectacle; drama

scheel *adj.* (*lit.* squint-eyed), envious, jealous

Schei'be *f.* -n target

schei'den (**schied, geschieden**) *tr.*
separate; *intr.*, **s.** go, depart,
leave; pass away, 954; go,
die, 2393; **dahin** — die, 2463

Schein *m.* -s (shine) light; excuse,
pretext, 306, 310; semblance,
appearances, 1636

schei'nen (**schien, geschienen**) seem

schel'len *intr.* (*tr.*) ring (*bell*)

schel'ten (**schalt, gescholten; schilt**)
tr. scold, blame; nickname,
call, 826

schen'ken *tr.* give, grant, bestow on
(*dat.*)

Scherz *m.* -es, -e jest, fun

scher'zen jest

scheu *adv.* timidly, in fear

scheu'en *tr.* shun, fear

Scheu'ne *f.* -n barn

scheuß'lich *adj.* hideous, horrible

schi'cken *tr. and intr.* (*with* **nach**)
send (for)

Schick'sal *n.* -s, -e fate, lot

Schick'salsprobe *f.* -n trial (*of fate*)

Schi'ckung *f.* -en decree, Providence

Schie'ferdecker *m.* -s, — slater

schie'len steal a glance

schie'ßen (**schoß, geschossen**) *intr.*
and tr. shoot

Schieß'zeug *n.* -s shooting-things
(= bow and arrows)

Schiff *n.* -(e)s, -e (ship) boat

Schiff'bruch *m.* -s, ⸚e shipwreck

schif'fen take ship, sail

Schif'fer *m.* -s, — boatman

Schiff'lein *n.* -s, — little boat

Schild *n.* -es, -e shield

Schild'wache *f.* -n sentinel, guard

Schim'mer *m.* -s, — shimmer, ray

schim'mern gleam, shimmer

Schimpf *m.* -es disgrace, insult

Schirm *m.* -es protection, support;
Schutz und — shield and shelter

schir'men *tr.* protect, defend; *refl.*
shield oneself, 1058

Schir'mer *m.* -s, — protector

Schlacht *f.* -en battle

Schlacht'schwert *n.* -s, -er (battle-)
sword

Schlaf *m.* -(e)s sleep

Schlä'fer *m.* -s, — sleeper

Schlag'baum *m.* -s, ⸚e tollgate,
barrier

schla'gen (**schlug, geschlagen;
schlägt**) *tr.* strike, smite; fight,
1230; *with* **um** throw around,
782; 1436, *cf.* **Schanze;** *with*
in cast, put, 2339; *refl.* fight
(force, make) one's way, 1175,
1485; *intr.* beat, strike (**an,**
1289 *, 1684, 2167); rise, 2879

Schlag'lawi'ne *f.* -n avalanche

Schlan'ge *f.* -n serpent

schlecht *adj.* bad, worthless

schlei'chen (**schlich, geschlichen**)
refl. (*also intr.*, **s.**) slink, steal
(*one's way*)

schlen'dern be slow, dawdle

schlep'pen *refl.* drag (oneself) along

schleu'dern *tr.* fling, hurl

schleu'nig *adv.* quickly

Schlich *m.* -es, -e secret path

schlicht *adv.* plainly, simply

schlich'ten *tr.* arrange, settle

schlie'ßen (**schloß, geschlossen**) *tr.*
shut in, enclose; end, conclude,
form, establish, 1855 *, 2400,
2833 *

schlimm *adj.* bad

Schlin'ge *f.* -n noose, snare

Schloß *n.* -sses, ⸚sser lock; castle,
stronghold

schlum'mern slumber

Schlund *m.* -(e)s, ⸚e gorge; abyss
(*of waters*), 2139

Schluß *m.* –sses, ⁻sse conclusion; decision, 3208

Schmach *f.* dishonor, shame; outrage, insult

schmach′ten long (yearn) for

schmei′cheln (*dat.*) flatter, cajole

Schmelz *m.* –es luster

Schmerz *m.* –e(n)s, –en pain, grief

schmer′zen *tr.* hurt, pain

Schmer′zenspfeil *m.* –s, –e painful arrow

Schmer′zenssehn′sucht *f.* painful (*say* pain and) longing

schmerz′lich *adj.* painful

schmerz′zerrissen *part. adj.* griefstricken, torn with grief

Schmied *m.* –(e)s, –e smith

schmie′den *tr.* forge

schmie′gen *refl.* cling (to **an** *acc.*)

schmuck *adj.* nice, pretty, fine

schmü′cken *tr.* adorn

Schne′cke *f.* –n snail

Schnee′gebirg(e) *n.* –(e)s, –e snowcovered mountains

schnei′den (schnitt, geschnitten) *tr., intr.* (*with* **in** *and* *acc.*) cut

schnell *adj.* quick; rash, violent

schon *adv.* already; surely; even; all right; *often adds mere tone of emphasis*

schön *adj.* fair, fine, handsome, noble

scho′nen *tr. and intr.* (*gen. or acc.*) spare

schöp′fen *tr.* get, find, draw

Schöp′fung *f.* –en creation

Schöp′fungstag *m.* –(e)s, –e day of creation

Schoß *m.* –es, ⁻e lap, bosom

Schran′ke *f.* –n bound, limit

schre′cken *tr.* frighten, terrify

Schre′cken *m.* –s, — fright, terror, alarm

Schre′ckensstraße *f.* –n road of terror

schreck′lich *adj.* fearful, terrible; *superl. as noun,* 3179

Schreck′nis *n.* –sses, –sse horror

Schrei′ben *n.* –s, — letter, document

schrei′en (schrie, geschrieen) cry (call) to, scream; *part. adj.* shameful, outrageous, 1841

schrei′ten (schritt, geschritten) **s.** stride, walk; **geschritten** striding, 1563

Schritt *m.* –(e)s, –e step, pace

schroff *adj.* steep

Schuld *f.* –en debt; fault, guilt

schul′dig *adj.* owing; — **blieb** owed; *as noun* guilty one

Schul′ter *f.* –n shoulder

schü′ren *tr.* fan (*flame*)

Schur′ke *m.* –n, –n rascal, scoundrel

schür′zen *tr.* gird

Schuß *m.* –sses, ⁻sse shot

schüt′teln *tr.* shake

Schutz *m.* –es protection, defense; — **und Trutz** defense and defiance, offense and defense, 743, 1485; — **und Schirm** shield and shelter

Schütz(e) *m.* –en, –en hunter, archer

schüt′zen *tr.* protect, defend (from **vor** *dat.*)

Schüt′zenregel *f.* –n archer's rule (custom)

Schwa′ben *n.* –s Swabia

schwä′bisch *adj.* Swabian

schwach (schwächer, schwächst) *adj.* weak; poor, little

Schwä′her *m.* –s, — father-in-law

schwa′nen *impers.* (*dat.*) have forebodings

schwank *adj.* pliant, 927; swaying, 1417

schwan′ken stagger, totter; toss

Schwarm *m.* –es, ⁻e swarm

schwarz (schwärzer, schwärzest) *adj.* black; *as noun* black = bull's eye

schwe′ben hover

schwei'gen (schwieg, geschwiegen) be (keep) silent; —**d** silently; *as noun* silence, 421

Schwei'zerin *f.* –**nen** Swiss woman

schwel'gen feast, revel

Schwel'le *f.* –**n** threshold

schwer *adj.* heavy, severe, grievous, hard, grave; *as noun* hardship, trial, 190; serious things, 546; crime, 2745

Schwert *n.* –**es,** –**er** sword

Schwe'ster *f.* –**n** sister

Schwe'stersohn *m.* –(e)s, ⸚e sister's son, nephew

schwim'men (schwamm, geschwommen) h. *and* s. swim; 1984 *translate* I am dizzy, *or* my head swims.

Schwim'mer *m.* –s, — swimmer

schwind'licht *adj.* dizzy

schwin'gen (schwang, geschwungen) *tr.* swing, wield

schwö'ren (schwor *or* **schwur, geschworen)** *tr. and intr.* swear (allegiance) to (**zu**); vow

Schwung *m.* –(e)s, ⸚e swing, strain, flourish

Schwur *m.* –(e)s, ⸚e oath, vow

Schwy'zer *adj.* of Schwyz; *as noun* Schwyzer, 254, 659

Schwy'zerland *n.* –**es,** –**e** canton Schwyz; *pl.* Swiss cantons, 3039

See *m.* –**s,** –**n** lake

See'le *f.* –**n** soul

Se'gen *m.* –**s,** — blessing; rich crop, 1801

se'genvoll *adj.* rich in blessing

seg'nen *tr.* bless

se'hen (sah, gesehen; sieht) *tr. and intr.* see (with **an** *dat.* by, from) look, behold; *as noun* sight, 587

Se'her *m.* –**s,** — seer, prophet

seh'nen *refl.* long (yearn) for;

heim— be homesick for (**nach**), 844; *as noun* longing, 1676

Sei'de *f.* –**n** silk

Seil *m.* –**es,** –**e** cord, tie

sein (war, gewesen; ist) s. be; *with gen.* belong to; **wie dem** ... **sei** however that may be, 2959; **sei dem wie ihm wolle** be that as it may

sein *poss. adj.* his, its; **die Seinen** his own people; **das Seine** his own land

seit *prep.* (*dat.*) since, for; *conj.* since

seitdem' *adv.* since, since then

Sei'te *f.* –**n** side

seit'wärts *adv.* sideways

selban'der *pron.* together (with another)

sel'ber *pron. indec.* –self, –selves

selbst *pron. indec.* –self; **von** — of their own accord, 431; *adv.* even, 1208

Selbst'herr *m.* –**n,** –**en** one's own master

se'lig *adj.* blessed, happy

sel'ten *adj.* rare; *adv.* rarely, seldom

selt'sam *adj.* strange, odd, singular; *as noun*, 1907

sen'den (sandte, gesandt *also weak*) *tr.* send (**nach** for)

Senn'n(e) *m.* –**en,** –**en** herdsman

Senn'hütte *f.* –**n** herdsman's hut

Sen'se *f.* –**n** scythe

Sen'te *f.* –**n** herd

set'zen *tr.* set, put; **dran** — stake (on); *refl.* take a seat

si'cher *adj.* safe, secure; certain

Si'cherheit *f.* safety, security

si'chern *tr.* guarantee, assure (of), promise

sicht'bar *adj.* evident, visible

Sieg *m.* –(e)s, –**e** victory

sieg'berühmt *part. adj.* crowned with victory

sie'gen conquer; *part. adj.* triumphant, 2447

Sie'ger *m.* **-s,** — victor

sieg'reich *adj.* victorious

Signal'feuer *n.* **-s,** — signal-fire

Sigrist' *m.* **-en, -en** sacristan

Sinn *m.* **-es, -e** sense; mind; mood; meaning; **bei** —**en** in his senses, 138; **zu** — **kommen** intend, mean, 1894

sin'nen (**sann, gesonnen**) *tr.* think (of), intend

Sit'te *f.* **-n** custom, manners, morals

Sitz *m.* **-es, -e** seat, residence

sit'zen (**saß, gesessen**) sit; live, have one's seat

Skla've *m.* **-n, -n** slave

skla'visch *adj.* slavish

so *adv. and conj.* so thus, as; then, 48, 438; well then, 3288; **so** ... **so** as ... so, 2756; — **wie** just as; — **oder** — one way or another, 2732

soe'ben *adv.* just (now)

sogleich' *adv.* at once

solang' *conj.* so long as

Söld'ner *m.* **-s,** — hired soldier

sol'len *weak; pres. indic.* **soll,** *modal aux.* shall, ought, must; be to, be intended, be said to (2976, 1311); mean, 391; let them, 913; **soll** *with inf.* am to, is to; *without inf.* am (is) to go, to do, *etc.*, 2806, 2848

son'dern *conj.* (*with neg.*) but

son'nenscheu *adj.* sun-shy, light-dreading

sonst *adv.* otherwise, else, besides, once = formerly; — **einmal** some other time

Sor'ge *f.* **-n** care, anxiety

sor'gen worry, fear, care (for); look out for (368), provide for, 3067

sor'genvoll *adj.* anxious

Sorg'falt *f.* care, solicitude

Spä'her *m.* **-s,** — spy

span'nen *tr.* draw, bend (*bow*) *with* **von** *or* **aus** unyoke

Span'nung *f.* expectation; excitement, 569 *

spa'ren *tr.* spare, save; put off, 2549

spät *adj.* late; distant (*in time*)

Speer *m.* **-(e)s, -e** spear

sper'ren *tr.* block up, bar

Spie'gel *m.* **-s,** — mirror

Spiel *n.* **-(e)s, -e** game, sport; — **treiben** make sport of (**mit**)

spie'len *tr.* play, personate; *intr.* play; trifle with, 1924

Spiel'mann *m.* **-s, -männer** *or* **-leute** minstrel

Spieß *m.* **-es, -e** spear, pike

spin'nen (**spann, gesponnen**) *tr.* spin; plan, plot, 1107; **es spinnt sich etwas** something is on foot (plotting)

Spit'ze *f.* **-n** point, peak

spit'zen *tr.* point (*ears*), prick up

spit'zig *adj.* pointed, sharp

Spott *m.* **-es** scorn, ridicule

spot'ten (*gen.*) mock, laugh at

spre'chen (**sprach, gesprochen, spricht**) *tr. and intr.* say, talk, speak; see (= speak with), 2309, 2670

spren'gen *tr.* burst, break, shatter

sprin'gen (**sprang, gesprungen**) *s.* spring, jump, run; **gesprungen** *with inf.* running

Spruch *m.* **-es, -̈e** saying; sentence, 1935; judgment, 3056

spü'len wash, play (*of water*)

Spur *f.* **-en** trace, sign (= evidence); trail, path

spur'los *adj.* leaving no trace

Staat *m.* **-(e)s, -en** state

staats'klug *adv.* wisely, shrewdly

Stab *m.* **-(e)s, -̈e** staff, stick

Sta'chel *m.* **-s,** — sting; goad

Stahl *m.* –(e)s steel

Stall *m.* –(e)s, ⸗e stall, stable

Stall′meister *m.* –s, — master of horse

Stamm *m.* –(e)s, ⸗e race, lineage; house (= family), 890

Stamm′holz *n.* –es, ⸗er solid (trunk-) wood

Stand *m.* –es, ⸗e rank, class; struggle, resistance, 1429; estate, district, 2993

Stan′ge *f.* –n pole

stark (stärker, stärkst) *adj.* strong; *as noun,* 438, 1843

stär′ken *tr.* strengthen; *refl.* gain strength

starr *adj.* stiff; frozen, 1050; obstinate, 2783

Statt *f.* stead, place

statt *prep.* (*gen. or inf. and* **zu***; with* **daß** *clause*) instead of

Stät′te *f.* –n place

statt′lich *adj.* splendid, fine

Statur′ *f.* (–en) stature

Staub *m.* –es dust

Staub′bach *m.* –s, ⸗e spray brook, cascade

stäu′ben scatter, spray

ste′chen (stach, gestochen; sticht) *tr. and intr.* sting, strike; prompt, impel, 1771

ste′cken *tr.* stick; put; **stecktest zu dir** concealed about you, 2050

Steg *m.* –es, –e footbridge; path

ste′hen (**stand,** *old form* **stund, gestanden**) stand; *with* **um** be, 570, 1719, 1768; *with dat. and adv.* fit, become, 53; **Rede —** answer, give account, 75, 1954; *with* **zu** stand by; **—den Fußes** at once, 333

stei′fen *refl.* be stubborn

Steig *m.* –es, –e path

stei′gen (**stieg, gestiegen**) **s.** climb (up *or* down), rise, ascend, descend, go

steil *adj.* steep

stei′nern *adj.* stony

Stein′metz *m.* –en, –en stonecutter

Stel′le *f.* –n place; passage; **zur — schaffen** produce

stel′len *tr.* put, station; *refl.* take one's stand; stand at bay, 648

Stel′lung *f.* –en position

ster′ben (**starb, gestorben; stirbt**) **s.** die; *part. as noun,* 2809 *;* **im —** at point of death

Stern *m.* –es, –e star; pupil (*of eye*)

Ster′nenhimmel *m.* –s, — starry heaven

stets *adv.* always

Steu′er *n.* –s, — helm, rudder

Steu′erleute *pl.* steersmen

Steu′ermann *m.* –s, –männer *or* –leute steersman

steu′ern *tr. and intr.* steer

steu′ern pay taxes (to **an**)

Steu′erruder *n.* –s, — helm, rudder

Steu′(e)rer *m.* –s, — helmsman

Stier *m.* –(e)s, –e bull, ox

stif′ten *tr.* found, establish

Stif′ter *m.* –s, — founder

still *adj.* still, quiet, silent, secret; **im –en** quietly, secretly; *interj.* Be still! Silence! 392

Stil′le *f.* silence

stil′len *tr.* still, quench (*thirst*)

Stim′me *f.* –n voice; vote

stim′men vote, 1147; accord, suit, 2658

Stir′ne *f.* –n brow; face, front, 2124

Stoff *m.* –es, –e subject

stolz *adj.* proud, haughty

Stolz *m.* –es pride

stö′ren *tr.* disturb

sto′ßen (**stieß, gestoßen; stößt**) *tr. and intr.* thrust, exclude (**aus**), 1304; strike (on it **auf**), see, 2724

Stra′fe *f.* –n punishment; **in —**

fallen become liable to punishment, 473

stra'fen *tr.* punish

sträf'lich *adj.* (*as noun*) punishable, criminal, 465

straf'los *adj.* unpunished

Strahl *m.* –(e)s, –en beam, ray, gleam; bolt, 2559

Strang *m.* –es, ⸗e string, cord

Stra'ße *f.* –n way; road, highway

Strauß *m.* –es, ⸗e struggle

stre'ben strive; *as noun*, 1677, 1682

Stre'bepfeiler *m.* –s, — buttress (*for side wall*)

stre'cken *tr.* stretch (reach) out

Streich *m.* –es, –e stroke, blow

Streit *m.* –(e)s, –e fight, struggle; question, dispute

Streit'axt *f.* ⸗e battle-ax

strei'ten (**stritt, gestritten**) contend, strive (fight) for

streng *adj.* strict, stern, severe

Stren'ge *f.* severity, sternness; rigor, 2638

streu'en *tr.* strew, scatter

Strich *m.* –es, –e track, direction

Strick *m.* –es, –e cord; snare

Stroh *n.* –(e)s straw

Strom *m.* –(e)s, ⸗e stream, current, flood, river

stumm *adj.* dumb, silent

Stun'de *f.* –n hour, time

Sturm *m.* –es, ⸗e storm

stür'zen *intr.* **s.** fall, rush (at **auf;** into **in**); *tr.* tear down; plunge, cast; *refl.* throw (cast) oneself

stüt'zen *tr.* support; *past part.* leaning (on **auf**), 1150 *

su'chen *tr.* seek, look for; want (from **an**), 2692

Sumpf *m.* –es, ⸗e swamp

Sump'fesluft *f.* ⸗e swamp air

Sün'de *f.* –n sin

Sünd'flut *f.* flood

Sze'ne *f.* –n scene, stage; **in die —**

into the wings; **vordere —** foreground; **bei eröffneter —** after curtain is up

T

Ta'del *m.* –s blame, reproach

Ta'fel *f.* –n table

Tag *m.* –es, –e day; assembly, meeting, 1146

Tag'dieb *m.* –(e)s, –e idler, loiterer

ta'gelang *adv.* days at a time

ta'gen dawn, 752; hold a meeting, meet

Ta'gesanbruch *m.* –s, ⸗e daybreak

Ta'gesordnung *f.* –en order of the day, regular business

Ta'gewerk *n.* –(e)s, –e (day) labor

Tal *n.* –es, ⸗er valley

Tal'grund *m.* –(e)s, ⸗e (bottom of a) valley

Tal'vogt *m.* –(e)s, ⸗e dale-governor, lord of the valley

tap'fer *adj.* brave

Tat *f.* –en deed, action, act; **über frischer —** in the very act, 1862; **mit frischer —** at once, 1971

Tä'ter *m.* –s, — doer, perpetrator

tau'meln reel

täu'schen *tr.* deceive, escape

tau'sendjährig *adj.* of a thousand years

tau'sendmal *adv.* a thousand times

Teil *m.* (*or n.*) –es, –e part, share

tei'len *tr.* divide, share; have in common, 3184

teil'haft, teilhaf'tig *adj.* having part (share) in; *with* **sein** to share, be involved in

teu'er *adj.* dear, beloved; precious, 1041

Teu'fel *m.* –s, — devil

teu'felisch *adj.* devilish

Teu'(e)rung *f.* –en famine

Tie'fe *f.* –n depth(s), deep; background (*of stage*)
Tier *n.* –es, –e animal, beast
to'ben rage, struggle
Tod *m.* –es, **Todesfälle** death; **am** — at point of death; **auf** — **und Leben** for life and death; **des** —**es** doomed
Tod'feind *m.* –es, –e mortal enemy
Ton *m.* –(e)s, ⁼e tone; voice
Tor *n.* –(e)s, –e gate(way)
tö'richt *adv.* foolishly
to'sen rage, roar; *as noun*, 2098 *
tot *adj.* dead; *as noun often*
tö'ten *tr.* kill, put to death; **tötet** is deadly, means death, 106
To'tenhand *f.* ⁼e dead hand
Trach'ten (*inf. as noun*) *n.* –s thought, purpose, intention
tra'gen (**trug, getragen; trägt**) *tr.* carry; bear, endure; hold in fief, 263, 1360; feel, have, cherish, 549, 3043
trau'en trust in, rely on
trau'ern grieve, be sad; mourn (for **um**)
trau'lich *adj.* familiar, cordial
träu'men *tr.* dream
Träu'mer *m.* –s, — dreamer
traun *interj.* Faith! Really!
trau'rig *adj.* sad, sorrowful
tref'fen (**traf, getroffen; trifft**) *tr.* strike, hit, meet
treff'lich *adj.* fine, good; *as noun*, 2338
trei'ben (**trieb, getrieben**) *tr.* drive, impel; do (conduct things), carry (on), 407, 542, 724, 1993, 1995; *real intr.* toss, drift, 2209, 2269; *apparent intr.*, 62, 541
tren'nen *tr. and refl.* separate, part from, leave
tre'ten (**trat, getreten; tritt**) **s.** step, go; *with prep. with acc.* ap-

proach, 2810, enter; *tr.* trample, 2770
treu *adj.* true, faithful
Treu'e *f.* faithfulness, loyalty
treu'lich *adv.* faithfully, loyally
treu'los *adj.* faithless, untrue (to **an** *dat.*)
Trieb *m.* –es, –e natural impulse; love (*of country*), 849
trie'fen (**troff, getroffen**) drip (with **von**)
Trom'mel *f.* –n drum
Trost *m.* –es consolation, comfort; hope, 2093
trö'sten *tr.* console, comfort; *refl.* find consolation
trost'los *adj.* disconsolate, wretched, despairing
Trotz *m.* –es defiance
trotz *prep.* (*dat.*) in spite of
trot'zen defy
trü'ben *tr.* disturb, trouble
Trüb'sinn *m.* –s melancholy, care
trü'gerisch *adj.* treacherous
Trüm'mer *pl.* ruins, pieces
Trupp *m.* –s, –e troop (*of horse*)
Trutz *m.* –es defiance; **Schutz und** — defense and defiance = offense and defense
trut'ziglich (*old for* **trotzig**) *adv.* defiantly
Tu'gend *f.* –en virtue; quality
tu'gendhaft *adj.* virtuous
tumultua'risch *adv.* tumultuously
tun (**tat, getan**) *tr. and intr.* do, act, make; **gut** — be well, 286; **not** — be necessary, 506; **sanft** — cajole, 2713; **wohl tut** (*dat.*) does good, 807; **zu** — **um** concern
Turm *m.* –(e)s, ⁼e tower; prison
Turnier' *n.* –s, –e tournament
Twing *m.* –(e)s, –e prison, dungeon
Twing'hof *m.* –(e)s, ⁼e prison
Tyrann' *m.* –en, –en tyrant

Tyran'nenjoch n. -(e)s tyrant's yoke
Tyran'nenmacht f. ⁺e tyrant's power, tyranny
Tyran'nenschloß n. -sses, ⁺sser tyrant's castle
Tyran'nenschwert n. -es, -er tyrant's sword
tyran'nisch adj. tyrannical

U

ü'bel adv. ill, wrong
Ü'bel n. -s, — evil, wrong
ü'ben refl. practice
ü'ber prep. (dat. and acc.) adv., sep. and insep. pref. over, above; beyond, across; of, about, concerning; by way of; **drüber** more than that; **die Zeit —** during the time
überall' adv. everywhere
überden'ken (**überdach'te, überdacht'**) tr. think over (of)
Ü'berdruß m. -sses disgust, disdain
Ü'berfahrt f. -en passage; **um die — to take him across,** 132
überhand-nehmen (**nahm, genommen; nimmt**) increase, get worse
überlas'sen (**überließ', überlas'sen; überläßt'**) tr. give up to
überlie'fern tr. give up, hand over
Ü'bermut m. -s insolence
überneh'men (**übernahm', übernom'men; übernimmt'**) tr. overcome, get best of, 482; undertake, 1414
überra'schen tr. surprise
ü'ber-schwellen (**schwoll, geschwollen; schwillt**) s. overflow
ü'ber-setzen tr. set (take) over (across)
überste'hen (**überstand', überstan'den**) tr. stand, overcome; part. over, past, 2260

ü'ber-treten (**trat, getreten; tritt**) **s.** go over (to **zu**)
ü'brig adj. over, left (over); **die —en** the others; **— bleiben** be left (over), remain
U'fer n. -s, — shore, bank
Uhr f. -en clock
um prep. (acc.), adv., sep. and insep. pref. round, about, over; for; concerning (570); at (of time); **— ... willen** for sake of, because of, for; with **zu** and inf. in order, so as (to); with **verdienen** at hands of, from; **— ... her** about, around
umar'men tr. embrace
umdrän'gen tr. crowd around
umfas'sen tr. embrace
umgar'nen tr. surround
umge'ben (**umgab', umge'ben; umgibt'**) tr. surround, enclose
um-gehen (**ging, gegangen**) **s.** go round
umher' adv. and sep. pref. around, round about; **um** (acc.) **her** around
umher-blicken look around
umher-merken look about
umher-sitzen (**saß, gesessen**) **s.** sit around
umher-spähen look about
umher-stehen (**stand, gestanden**) **s.** stand around
umher-streifen s. roam around
umhül'len tr. cover, veil
um-kehren intr. **s.** and refl. turn round; come back, return
Um'kreis m. -es, -e circuit
umrin'gen tr. surround
umschlie'ßen (**umschloß', umschlos'sen**) tr. enclose, surround
um-sehen (**sah, gesehen; sieht**) refl. look (around) about
umsonst' adv. in vain
umste'hen (**umstand', umstan'den;**

umsteht′) *tr.* surround, stand around

um-wandeln *tr.* (in *acc.* or **zu** *dat.*, 1264) change, turn into

Um′weg *m.* −(e)s, −e roundabout way, circuit

umwer′ben (**umwarb′**, **umwor′ben;** **umwirbt′**) *tr.* woo, pay court to

Un′bedacht (*adj.* as *noun*) heedlessness, thoughtlessness

un′bekannt *part. adj.* unknown, unfamiliar

un′bequem *adj.* inconvenient, disagreeable; as *noun*, 2722

un′bewaffnet *part. adj.* unarmed

un′bezahlt′ *part. adj.* unpaid

un′billig *adj.* unjust; as *noun* injustice, 317

un′durchdring′lich *adj.* impenetrable, inaccessible

unentdeckt′ *part. adj.* undiscovered

unerhört′ *part. adj.* unheard-of; as *noun* outrage, 403

unersätt′lich *adj.* insatiable

unerträg′lich *adj.* unbearable

Un′gar *m.* −n, −n Hungarian

ungebo′ren *part. adj.* unborn

Un′gebühr *f.* wrong

un′gebühr′lich *adj.* improper; as *noun* improper proposal, 94

Un′geduld *f.* impatience

un′geduldig *adj.* impatient

un′geheu′er *adj.* great, terrible; monstrous; as *noun*, 1891

un′gekränkt *part. adj.* undisturbed, 1928; in peace, 2682

un′gerecht *part. adj.* unjust

un′gereizt *part. adj.* unprovoked

un′gesetzlich *adj.* illegal, irregular

ungetrö′stet *part. adj.* uncomforted

Un′gewitter *n.* −s, — (severe) storm

un′gezügelt *part. adj.* unrestrained

Un′glimpf *m.* −s harsh treatment, cruelty

Un′glück *n.* −s, −e disaster, misfortune

un′glücklich *adj.* unhappy, wretched

un′glückse′lig *adj.* unhappy; as *noun*, 501, 2887

Un′glückstat *f.* −en unhappy deed

Un′heil *n.* −s mischief, evil

unleid′lich *adj.* unbearable, intolerable

unmensch′lich *adj.* inhuman

unmög′lich *adj.* impossible

Un′mündigkeit *f.* minority, dependence

Un′mut *m.* −s ill-will, anger

un′nütz *adj.* useless

Un′recht *n.* −s wrong; guilt, crime, 982

un′ruhig *adj.* restless, impatient

Un′schuld *f.* innocence

un′schuldig *adj.* innocent

unsterb′lich *adj.* immortal

Un′tat *f.* −en evil deed, crime

un′ten *adv.* down, below

un′ter *prep.* (*dat.* and *acc.*), *adv.*, *sep.* and *insep.* *pref.* under, below; among, in, amid = during; — . . . **hervor** out from under

unterbre′chen (**unterbrach′**, **unterbro′chen;** **unterbricht′**) *tr.* interrupt, break

unterdes′sen *adv.* meanwhile

unterdrü′cken *tr.* oppress; as *noun*, 1618

Unterdrü′cker *m.* −s, — oppressor

Un′tergang *m.* −s destruction, ruin

unterneh′men (**unternahm′**, **unternom′men;** **unternimmt′**) *tr.* undertake

unterste′hen (**unterstand′**, **unterstan′den**) *refl.* dare, venture; take upon oneself, 234

un′ter-tauchen dive under

unterwegs′ *adv.* on the way

unterwer′fen (**unterwarf′**, **unterwor′-**

fen; unterwirft') *tr.* subdue; *refl.* (*dat.*) submit, yield

unterwür'fig *adv.* respectfully

un'verändert *part. adj.* unchanged

unveräu'ßerlich *adj.* inalienable

un'verdächtig *adj.* without exciting suspicion

unverletzt' *part. adj.* uninjured, safe

Un'vernunft *f.* folly, senselessness

un'vernünftig *adj.* unreasoning

un'verschämt *part. adj.* insolent; *as noun*, 476

unversehrt' *part. adj.* unhurt

unwan'delbar *adv.* invariably

un'weit *prep.* (*gen. or dat.*) not far from

Un'wille(n) *m.* -ns anger, indignation

unwillkür'lich *adv.* involuntarily

un'wirtlich *adj.* inhospitable

un'würdig *adj.* unworthy

unzerbrech'lich *adj.* indestructible

ur'alt *adj.* very old, ancient

ur'alters *adv.* of old; von — her from time immemorial

Ur'fehde *f.* -n sacred oath (*to keep the peace*)

Ur'sache *f.* -n cause, reason

Ur'sprung *m.* -s, ⁻e origin

Ur'stand *m.* -s, ⁻e original condition

Ur'teil *n.* -s, -e judgment

ur'teilen judge

V

Va'termord *m.* -s parricide

Vä'tertugend *f.* -en ancestral (inherited) virtue

verab'scheuen *tr.* abhor, despise

verach'ten *tr.* despise; disobey, 402

Verach'tung *f.* contempt, disregard

verach'tungswert *adj.* worthy of contempt

verän'dern *refl.* change

veräu'ßern *tr.* alienate (*by sale*)

verber'gen (verbarg, verborgen; verbirgt) *tr. and refl.* hide, conceal; *as noun*, 612

verbie'ten (verbot, verboten) *tr.* forbid, deny

verbin'den (verband, verbunden) *tr.* unite; bind, blindfold, 1960

verblas'sen turn pale

verblen'den *tr.* blind; delude; *part. as noun*, 840

verblu'ten *intr. and refl.* bleed to death

Verbre'chen *n.* -s, — crime

verbrei'ten *tr.* spread

verbren'nen (verbrannte, verbrannt) burn up (to death)

Verdamm'nis *f.* condemnation; damnation (*exclam.*), 2818

verdan'ken *tr.* owe, thank one for

verder'ben (verdarb, verdorben; verdirbt) *tr.* ruin, destroy

verdie'nen *tr.* deserve (at the hands of um *acc.*)

Verdrieß' (*old for* Verdruß) *m.* -es vexation; zum —e to worry, annoy

verdrie'ßen (verdroß, verdrossen) *tr.* worry; sich — lassen hesitate to, get tired of

Verdruß' *m.* -sses vexation; zum —sse to vex, spite

vere'hren *tr.* honor, respect

verei'den *tr.* bind by oath

verei'nen *tr.* unite; combine

verei'nigen *tr.* unite, join

verfal'len (verfiel, verfallen; verfällt) s. be forfeited to

verfan'gen (verfing, verfangen; verfängt) avail, 1286; *refl.* be caught, 2165

verfeh'len fail (in, of *gen.*)

verflu'chen *tr.* curse

verfol'gen *tr.* pursue; hunt down, 3073; *as noun*, afflicted, 2369

Verfol′ger *m.* –s, — pursuer
verfüh′ren *tr.* mislead, deceive
Verfüh′rung *f.* –en temptation
verge′ben (vergab, vergeben; vergibt) *tr.* forgive
verge′bens *adv.* in vain, for nothing
vergeb′lich *adj.* useless
Vergel′tung *f.* retribution, vengeance
verges′sen (vergaß, vergessen; vergißt) *tr.* forget
vergif′ten *tr.* poison
verglei′chen (verglich, verglichen) *tr.* arrange, settle; compare
vergra′ben (vergrub, vergraben; vergräbt) *tr.* bury
vergrö′ßern *tr.* increase, add to
vergü′ten *tr.* make good, atone
verhaf′ten *tr.* arrest
verhal′ten (verhielt, verhalten; verhält) *tr.* (*for* **vorenthalten**) conceal, keep back from (*dat.*); *refl.* be (stand) thus (as), 1243
verhan′deln *tr.* transact, do
verhän′gen *tr.* ordain, decree
verhaßt′ *part. adj.* hated, hateful
verheh′len *tr.* hide, conceal from
verhin′dern *tr.* hinder, prevent
verhül′len *tr. and refl.* cover; hide the face
verhü′ten *tr.* prevent; **verhüt′ es Gott** God forbid!
verir′ren *intr. and refl.* get lost
verja′gen *tr.* drive out
verkau′fen *tr.* sell
verklei′den *tr.* disguise
verküm′mern *s.* wither, languish
verkün′den *tr.* tell, announce
verkün′digen *tr. and refl.* manifest itself; proclaim, 2786
verlan′gen *tr.* demand
Verlan′gen *n.* –s, — longing, wish
verlas′sen (verließ, verlassen; verläßt) *tr.* leave, forsake; *refl.* (**auf** *with acc.*) rely on

verlau′fen (verlief, verlaufen; verläuft) *refl.* stray away
verlau′ten *impers.* be said (reported)
verle′gen *adj.* embarrassed
verlei′hen (verlieh, verliehen) *tr.* give, grant
verlet′zen *tr.* hurt; disobey, 1820
verlie′ren (verlor, verloren) *tr.* lose; *refl.* disappear, 1780
verlo′ren *part. adj.* doomed
vermau′ern *tr.* wall up
vermeh′ren *tr.* increase
vermei′den (vermied, vermieden) *tr.* avoid
vermen′gen *tr.* confound, confuse
vermö′gen *tr.* be able (to do)
Vermö′gen *n.* –s ability, means
verneh′men (vernahm, vernommen; vernimmt) *tr.* hear; learn
Vernunft′ *f.* reason
vernünf′tig *adj.* sensible
verö′det *part. adj.* deserted
verpfän′den *tr.* mortgage
Verrat′ *m.* –s treachery (towards **an** *dat.*)
verra′ten (verriet, verraten; verrät) *tr.* betray
Verrä′ter *m.* –s, — traitor
verrin′nen (verrann, verronnen) *s.* pass (away)
versa′gen *tr.* deny, refuse; *intr.* fail, 1564
versam′meln *refl.* meet, gather (come) together
Versamm′lung *f.* –en meeting, assembly
verschaf′fen *tr.* secure, get
verschei′den (verschied, verschieden) *s.* die
verschen′ken *tr.* give away
verscheu′chen *tr.* scare away
verschie′ben (verschob, verschoben) *tr.* postpone, put off
verschie′den *adj.* different
verschlei′ern *tr.* veil

verschlie′ßen (**verschloß, verschlossen**) *tr.* shut (lock) up; *part.* retired, hidden, 1689

verschlin′gen (**verschlang, verschlungen**) *tr.* swallow up

verschmä′hen *tr.* despise

verschul′den *tr.* do, be guilty of

verschüt′ten *tr.* bury, overwhelm

verschwin′den (**verschwand, verschwunden**) **s.** disappear

Verschwö′rung *f.* –en conspiracy

verse′hen (**versah, versehen***;* **versieht**) *refl.* (*with* **zu** *and dat. pers., gen. of thing*), expect of, look to for

versen′den (**versandte, versandt***; also weak*) *tr.* send (= shoot)

verset′zen *tr.* put, throw, 3038; reply, 229

versöh′nen *refl.* be reconciled, make one's peace (with)

verspre′chen (**versprach, versprochen***;* **verspricht**) *tr.* promise

verstän′dig *adj.* wise, prudent; *as noun,* 248

versteckt′ *part. adj.* hidden, remote

verste′hen (**verstand, verstanden**) *tr.* understand, mean, 216; *refl.* (**auf** *acc.*) be judge of, know, 1635; (**mit** *dat.*) have understanding with, 1397

versto′cken *refl.* be stubborn

verstoh′len (*part. adj.*) *adv.* by stealth

versu′chen *tr.* try, attempt; tempt, 1532, 2046

vertei′digen *tr., refl.* defend

Vertei′diger *m.* –s, — defender

vertil′gen *tr.* destroy, annul

vertrau′en (*dat. or* **auf** *acc.*) trust (confide) in, rely on; *tr.* confide, entrust; *as noun,* 2483

vertraut′ *part. adj.* trusted, intimate

vertrei′ben (**vertrieb, vertrieben**) *tr.* drive out, expel; *part. as noun,* 2931

verü′ben *tr.* do, commit

verwah′ren *tr.* guard; lock up

verwal′ten *tr.* administer

verwan′deln *tr. and refl.* change

Verwand′te (*part. adj. as m. noun*) relative

verwe′gen *adj.* bold, daring; *as noun,* 2022

verwei′gern *tr.* deny

verwei′len linger, stop

verwir′ken *tr.* forfeit

verwün′schen *tr.* curse; *part. as adj.* confounded, *interj.* Curse (Confound) it!

verza′gen despair; be dismayed (at **an**), distressed (about **um**)

verzei′hen (**verzieh, verziehen**) *tr.* (*dat. of person*) pardon, forgive

verzie′ren *tr.* decorate

verzwei′feln despair

Verzweif′lung *f.* despair

Verzweif′lungsangst *f.* ⸚e anguish of despair

verzweif′lungsvoll *adj.* desperate, in despair

Vet′ter *m.* –s, –n cousin; kinsman, 1035

Vieh *n.* –s cows, cattle; beasts

viel′erfahren *part. adj.* much-experienced, wise; *as noun,* 665

vielleicht′ *adv.* perhaps, possibly, may-be

vielmehr′ *conj.* but, rather

Vogt *m.* –(e)s, ⸚e bailiff, governor

voll (**voller, vollst**) *adj., adv., sep. and insep. pref.* full (of); complete; great, 65; **Jahre** — **haben** reach full age, be of age

vollbrin′gen (**vollbrach′te, vollbracht′**) *tr.* finish, accomplish, carry out; *part. as noun,* 218

vollen′den *tr.* end, finish, accomplish; go on, 565

völ'lig *adj.* full; *adv.* perfectly
Voll'macht *f.* -en authority
von *prep.* (*dat.*) of, from, by, about, because of, through; *in names and titles* of (from)
vonnö'ten (= **von Nöten**) *adv.*, needful; — **haben** have need of (*gen.*)
vor *prep.* (*dat. and acc.*), *adv.*, *and sep. pref.* before, in front of; from, 2354; for (= because of), 2239, 2674, 3130; *with dat.* (*time*) ago
voran' *adv. and sep. pref.* in front, in advance
voran-ziehen (**zog, gezogen**) *s.* precede, go ahead of (*dat.*)
voraus' *adv.* on ahead, in advance
vor-bauen take precautions (against)
vorbei' *adv. and sep. pref.* (by) past, over; **an** — past
vorbei-gehen (**ging, gegangen**) *s.* go (pass) by
vor-biegen (**bog, gebogen**) *tr.* bend over (forward)
vor'der *adj.* forward, front; —**e** Szene front of stage
Vor'dergrund *m.* -s foreground
vor'derst *adj.* foremost; **die** —**en** those in front
vor-gehen (**ging, gegangen**) *s.* go on, take place
vor-halten (**hielt, gehalten; hält**) *tr.* hold out against, present
Vor'hang *m.* -s, —e curtain
Vor'hut *f.* picket, sentinel
vo'rig *adj.* preceding, former; *as noun*, 2452 *
vor-kommen (**kam, gekommen**) *s.* come forward
vorn *adv.* in the foreground; **nach** — forward
Vor'schlag *m.* -s, —e proposition

vor'schlagen (**schlug, geschlagen; schlägt**) *tr.* propose
Vor'schub *m.* -s help, aid; — **tun** render aid, 3046
Vor'sicht *f.* foresight; caution
vor-springen (**sprang, gesprungen**) *s.* project
Vor'sprung *m.* -s, —e projecting ledge (*of rock*)
vor-stellen *tr.* stand for, represent
Vor'teil *m.* -s, -e profit; opportunity, 2252
vor-treten (**trat, getreten; tritt**) *s.* stand forth, step forward
vorü'ber *adv. and sep. pref.* by, past
vorü'ber-gehen (**ging, gegangen**) *s.* go (pass) by (on)
vorü'ber-lenken *tr.* steer past
vorü'ber-treiben (**trieb, getrieben**) *refl.* hasten past (**an** *dat.*)
vor'wärts *adv.* forward, to the front
Vor'wurf *m.* -s, —e reproach

W

Wa'che *f.* -n watch, guard; — **halten** stand guard
wach'sen (**wuchs, gewachsen; wächst**) *s.* grow, advance
Wäch'ter *m.* -s, — Watch (*dog's name*); guard, 1861
wa'cker *adj.* brave, good, worthy; *as noun*, 169
Waf'fe *f.* -n weapon; *pl.* arms
Waf'fendienst *m.* -(e)s, -e military service
Waf'fenfreund *m.* -s, -e comrade in arms
Waf'fenknecht *m.* -(e)s, -e man-at-arms, soldier
waff'nen *tr.* arm
Wa'gefahrt *f.* -en daring trip
wa'gen *tr.* dare, risk
Wa'gesprung *m.* -(e)s, —e daring leap

Wa'getat *f.* –en deed of daring

Wag'stück *n.* –(e)s, –e daring deed (thing)

Wahl *f.* –en choice

wäh'len *tr.* choose

Wahl'freiheit *f.* –en freedom of (choice) election

Wahn *m.* –s dream, delusion

wahn'sinnig *adj.* mad, insane

Wahn'sinnstat *f.* –en deed of madness

wahr *adj.* true, real

wäh'rend *prep.* (*gen.*) during; *conj.* while

Wahr'heit *f.* –en truth

wahr'lich *adv.* truly, really, certainly

Wäh'rung *f.* worth, value

Wai'se *f.* –n orphan

Wald'gebirg(e) *n.* –s, –e (forest) mountains

Wald'gegend *f.* –en forest region

Wald'kapelle *f.* –n forest chapel

Wald'stätte *pl.* Forest Cantons

Wal'dung *f.* –en woods, forest

Wald'wasser *n.* –s, — forest stream

wal'len s. make pilgrimage, go, come

wal'ten rule; control (**über** *acc.*); *as noun*, 2819

Wäl'ti *diminutive of* **Walter**

wäl'zen *tr.* roll

Wand *f.* ⁺e wall

wan'deln *intr.*, s. *and* h. walk, 2460; *tr.* (*cognate object*) go (*way, road*), 3188, 3281

wan'dern s. wander, go, travel; —**d** on my trips

Wan'dersmann *m.* –s, **Wandersleute** traveler

Wan'd(e)rer *m.* –s, — traveler

wan'ken s. *and* h. shake, totter

wann *adv.* when

Wap'penschild *n.* –(e)s, –e coat-of-arms

wapp'nen *tr.* arm

war'ten (*gen. or* **auf** *acc.*) wait, wait for; tend, 1182 (*gen.*)

was *interrog. pron.* what; *rel. pron.* what = that which, whatever; *for* **warum** why; *for* **etwas** something, anything; those who, whoever, 1482, 1740; **was für ein** what (sort of) a, 390, 613; **was . . . auch** whatever

Was'serhuhn *n.* –s, ⁺er waterfowl

Was'serkluft *f.* ⁺e gorge full of water

Was'serwüste *f.* –n waste of waters

wech'seln *intr.* (*and tr.*) change

we'cken *tr.* wake, rouse, stir up

we'der *conj.* neither; — **. . . noch** neither . . . nor

Weg *m.* –es, –e way, road, path; **des —es fahren** go along road, 348

weg *adv. and sep. pref.* away, off; **über . . . weg** from off

weg-bleiben (blieb, geblieben) s. stay away

we'gen *prep.* (*gen.*) for, on account of

weg-fahren (fuhr, gefahren; fährt) s. set out; go along

weg-führen *tr.* lead away

weg-gehen (ging, gegangen) s. go away; go (roll) over (**drüber**), 167

weg-rauben *tr.* carry away

weg-treiben (trieb, getrieben) *tr.* drive away

weg-wenden (wandte, gewandt; *also weak*) *tr. and refl.* turn away, avert

we'h(e) *interj.* woe; — **mir** Oh me!

Weh'geschrei *n.* –s cries of distress

weh'klagen *insep.* wail, lament

weh'ren *tr.* (*dat. of person*) (keep) prevent (*from doing*), 234; *intr.* (*dat.*) check, hinder, 2566

wehr'los *adj.* unarmed, defenseless

Wei'bel *m.* -s, — bailiff
wei'chen (**wich, gewichen**) **s.** yield, give way; *with* **aus** *or* **von** leave
Wei'de *f.* -n pasture
wei'den *tr.* pasture, graze; feast (*eyes*) on (**an** *dat.*), 2814
Weid'gesell *m.* -en, -en hunter
Weid'mann *m.* -(e)s, ⸗er hunter
Weid'werk *n.* -s game, chase
wei'gern *tr.* deny, refuse
Wei'h(e) *m.* -en, -en eagle
wei'hen *refl.* be devoted to
weil *conj.* because, since; *old sense* while, 341
wei'len stay, linger
wei'nen weep (for **um**)
wei'se *adj.* wise
Wei'se *f.* -n way, manner
wei'sen (**wies, gewiesen**) *tr.* direct, refer, 1333; show, 2162; reprove, 1398
weis'lich *adv.* prudently
weit *adj.* wide, broad; long, far, distant; **das Weite** distance, space, 1475, 1676; **ein Weiteres** something further, 2299; —**er** further on
Wei'te *f.* -n distance
weit'schichtig *adj.* far-reaching, vast
weit'schmettern resound afar
Wel'le *f.* -n wave
welsch *adj.* foreign (Italian)
Welsch'land *n.* -s Italy
Welt *f.* -en world, earth
wen'den (**wandte, gewandt;** *also weak*) *refl.* turn (to **an** *acc.*)
we'nig *adj.* little; few
wenn *conj.* if, when; — **auch** whenever, though, even if
wer'ben (**warb, geworben; wirbt**) *tr.* get, make, win; *intr.* sue for, woo; *as noun* request, 1314
wer'den (**ward** *or* **wurde, geworden; wird**) **s.** become, get (to be), grow; *aux.* shall, will; *pass.*

be; *with dat. or* **zuteil** become, 779; be given to, 149, 646, 1136; be done, 2747; **im Werden** in progress, 2728; **mir wird** I feel, 514
wer'fen (**warf, geworfen; wirft**) *tr.* throw, cast
Werk *n.* -(e)s, -e work; **im** — planned, on foot, 2728
Werk'leute *pl.* workmen
Werk'zeug *n.* -(e)s, -e tool
wert *adj.* worthy, dear
Wert *m.* -es, -e worth
We'sen *n.* -s, — creature
weshalb' *adv.* why
We'sten *m.* -s west
Wet'ter *n.* -s, — lightning (*lit.* weather); —**s Strahl** thunderbolt
Wet'terloch *n.* -s, ⸗er weatherhole
Wett'streit *m.* -s dispute
wet'zen *tr.* whet
wi'der *prep.* (*acc.*), *adv., and insep. pref.* against, contrary to
Wi'derpart *m.* -s, -e opponent
wi'der-prallen s. rebound
widerset'zen *refl.* resist (*dat.*)
widerste'hen (**widerstand, widerstanden**) (*dat.*) withstand
widerstre'ben (*dat.*) oppose, resist
widerstrei'ten (**widerstritt, widerstritten**) (*dat.*) be contrary to
wie *adv.* How! What! *conj.* as, as if, how, when, like; however, 474
wie'der *adv., sep. and insep. pref.* again; back
wiederho'len *tr.* repeat
wie'der-kehren s. return; *impers.* one returns, 64
wie'der-kommen (**kam, gekommen**) **s.** come back
wie'der-sehen (**sah, gesehen; sieht**) *tr.* see again
Wie'ge *f.* -n cradle

wie′gen *tr.* rock

Wie′se *f.* –n meadow

wieviel′(e) *interrog. adj.* how much, how many

Wild *n.* –es wild animals, game

wild′bewegt *part. adj.* stormy

Wild′heuer *m.* –s, — hayer, mountain haymaker

Wild′nis *f.* –sse wilderness

Wil′le(n) *m.* –ns will, wish, purpose; **um . . .** — for sake of, because of (*gen.*)

willkom′men *adj.* welcome

Will′kür *f.* caprice

Wim′per *f.* –n eyelash

Win′deswehe *f.* –n snowdrift

Wind′lawine *f.* –n wind-avalanche

Wind′licht *n.* –(e)s, –er torch

win′ken make a sign to

win′tern winter

Win′terung *f.* wintering

Wir′bel *m.* –s, — whirlpool; — **ziehen** whirl, eddy

wir′ken work

wirk′lich *adv.* really

Wirt *m.* –(e)s, –e host

Wir′tin *f.* –nen hostess; wife

wirt′lich *adj.* hospitable

wis′sen (**wußte, gewußt; weiß**) *tr.* know (how); **weiß Gott** Heavens!

Wit′wenleid *n.* –s widow's grief

wo *adv. and conj.* where, when, if; from whom, 1219

wofern′ *conj.* if, in case

wo′gen surge, seethe

woher′ *adv.* whence; how

wohin′ *adv.* whither, where

wohl *adv.* well; true, perhaps, no doubt, surely, indeed, to be sure; **lebe** — farewell! — **tun** gratify; — **dem** happy he; — **Euch (uns)** well for you (us); *interj.* Well! Very well!

Wohl *n.* –s weal, welfare

wohlan′ *interj.* Well then!

wohl′bestellt *part. adj.* duly appointed

wohl′bewahrt *part. adj.* well kept

wohl′feil *adv.* cheap

wohl′genährt *part. adj.* well-fed

wohl′gepflegt *part. adj.* well cared for

Wohl′tat *f.* –en good deed, kindness

woh′nen live, dwell; stay

wohn′lich *adj.* comfortable, home-like

Wohn′stätte *f.* –n dwelling, home

Woh′nung *f.* –en habitation, abode, home, haunt

Wol′ke *f.* –n cloud

Wol′le *f.* wool

wol′len (*weak; pres. indic.* **will**) *tr. and modal aux.* will, wish, intend; be about to; start to; mean, 390; **wollte gern** would like to, 118; **was will** what may, 492; **wollt's Gott** Would to God!

woran′ *adv.* by what, how

worauf′ *adv.* for (upon) which, whereupon

worein′ *adv.* into which

wozu′ *adv.* for which, for what purpose

Wucht *f.* weight

wun′derbar *adj.* wonderful

Wun′derding *n.* –s, –e strange thing

wun′dern *impers.* (*acc.*) wonder; surprise

Wun′derzeichen *n.* –s, — miraculous sign

Wunsch *m.* –es, ⸚e wish

wün′schen *tr.* wish

wür′dig *adj.* worthy; *as noun,* 954, 1145

Wur′zel *f.* –n root

Wü′ste *f.* –n waste, wilderness

Wut *f.* rage, anger

wü′ten rage, be furious

Wüterei' *f.* tyranny
Wü't(e)rich *m.* -s, -e tyrant
wü'tig *adj.* raging, stormy

Z

Za'cke *f.* -n peak
za'gen be afraid
Zahl *f.* -en number; **an der — in** number
zah'len *tr.* pay (for)
zäh'len *tr.* count; **— auf** (*acc.*) rely on
zäh'men *tr.* tame, overcome
zart *adj.* tender, gentle
Zau'ber *m.* -s, — charm
zau'dern hesitate, delay
zehn'fach *adj.* tenfold
Zei'chen *n.* -s, — sign, token; symbol, 2923
zei'gen *tr.* show; *refl.* appear; *intr.* **— auf, nach** point at (to); **— in** give view of
Zei'le *f.* -n line, verse
Zeit *f.* -en time
zei'tig *adv.* early
Zeit'lang *f.* while; **eine —** for a while
zeit'lich *adj.* worldly, temporal
Zel'l(e) *f.* -en cell, hermitage
Zep'ter *n.* -s, — scepter
zerbre'chen (**zerbrach, zerbrochen;** **zerbricht**) *tr.* break down (to pieces), storm
zerkni'cken *tr.* break (off)
zerlumpt' *part. adj.* ragged
zerna'gen *tr.* gnaw
zerrei'ßen (**zerriß, zerrissen**) *tr.* tear (away, apart), break
zerschmet'tern *tr.* kill, dash to pieces
zerspal'ten *tr.* split open
zersprin'gen (**zersprang, zersprungen**) *s.* break, snap
zerstö'ren *tr.* destroy, ruin; *part. as* *adj.* distorted, 3104 *
zertre'ten (**zertrat, zertreten;** **zer-** **tritt**) *tr.* tread under foot

Zeu'ge *m.* -n, -n witness
zeu'gen tell, be witness
Zeu'gung *f.* -en generation
zie'hen (**zog, gezogen**) *tr.* pull, draw, attract; **Wirbel —** eddy, whirl, 116; *intr.* **— an** (*dat.*) pull, 447; come from, 1162; flow, 1792; move, 877; go, 2967; pass, 2651; *refl.* go, pass, 2284; **gezogen kommen** come (walking) along
Ziel *n.* -s, -e end, goal; mark, aim
zie'len aim, aim at (**auf** *acc.*)
zie'men (*dat.*) behoove, be becoming
Zier *f.* ornament
Zim'meraxt *f.* ⁼e carpenter's ax
Zim'mermann *m.* -s, ⁼er *or* **Zimmer-** **leute** carpenter
zim'mern *tr.* build
zin'sen pay tribute
zit'tern tremble
zol'len pay toll
Zorn *m.* -(e)s anger, wrath
zu *prep.* (*dat.*), *adv.*, *sep. pref.* to, at, in, with, for, towards (*after the noun*), beside, on, too, as; **Reit** **zu!** Ride on! **Schieß zu!** Shoot ahead!
zu-bringen (**brachte, gebracht**) *tr.* bring to
Zucht *f.* -en breed, herd
Züch'tigung *f.* -en punishment
zu'cken quiver, twitch
zu-drücken *tr.* shut (*eyes*)
zuerst' *adv.* first
zu-fahren (**fuhr, gefahren;** **fährt**) *tr.* bring (wheel) up
zu-fallen (**fiel, gefallen;** **fällt**) *s.* fall to, devolve on
Zug *m.* -es, ⁼e procession, march; *pl.* features
zu-geben (**gab, gegeben;** **gibt**) *tr.* grant, allow
zuge'gen *adv.* present
zu-gehen (**ging, gegangen**) *s.* go

towards (**auf** *acc.*); go on, 2258, *cf. note*

Zü'gel *m.* **-s,** — bridle, rein

zugleich' *adv.* likewise, also, at the same time

zu-kehren *tr.* turn towards (*dat.*)

Zu'kunft *f.* future

zuletzt' *adv.* last, at last

zunächst' *adv.* next; close by

Zunft *f.* ⸚**e** guild

Zun'ge *f.* **-n** tongue; language

zu-reiten (ritt, geritten) s. ride on

zür'nen be angry

zurück' *adv. and sep. pref.* back, backwards; *interj.* Back!

zurück-bleiben (blieb, geblieben) s. stay behind

zurück-fahren (fuhr, gefahren; fährt) s. start back (*in surprise*)

zurück-fallen (fiel, gefallen; fällt) s. fall back

zurück-führen *tr.* bring back

zurück-geben (gab, gegeben; gibt) *tr.* give back

zurück-halten (hielt, gehalten; hält) *tr.* hold back

zurück-kehren s. return

zurück-kommen (kam, gekommen) s. come back

zurück-lassen (ließ, gelassen; läßt) *tr.* leave behind

zurück-springen (sprang, gesprungen) s. fly back

zurück-stehen (stand, gestanden) s. stand back

zurück-treten (trat, getreten; tritt) s. step (draw) back

zurück-werfen (warf, geworfen; wirft) *tr.* throw back

zu-sagen *tr.* promise

zusam'men *adv. and sep. pref.* together

zusam'men-brechen (brach, gebrochen; bricht) *tr.* break (down) to pieces

zusam'men-flechten (flocht, geflochten; flicht) *tr.* clasp, entwine

zusam'men-führen *tr.* bring together

zusam'men-grenzen meet, come together

zusam'men-halten (hielt, gehalten; hält) hold together

zusam'men-laufen (lief, gelaufen; läuft) s. run together

zusam'men-raffen *refl.* collect (control) oneself

zusam'men-rufen (rief, gerufen) *tr.* call together

zusam'men-schleichen (schlich, geschlichen) s. slink (sneak) together

zusam'men-sinken (sank, gesunken) s. fall, sink down, collapse

zusam'men-steh(e)n (stand, gestanden) s. stand together

Zu'schauer *m.* **-s,** — spectator

zu-schießen (schoß, geschossen) shoot ahead

zu-schleudern *tr.* hurl towards

zu-schließen (schloß, geschlossen) *tr.* shut, lock

zu-schnüren *tr.* stifle, choke

zu-sehen (sah, gesehen; sieht) look on

Zu'stand *m.* **-s,** ⸚**e** state, condition

zu-tragen (trug, getragen; trägt) *refl.* happen

zu'traulich *adv.* trustingly

zuvor' *adv.* before

zu-zählen *tr.* count out to

Zwang *m.* **-es** oppression

Zweck *m.* **-s, -e** object, purpose

Zwei'fel *m.* **-s,** — doubt

zwei'feln doubt

zwei'mal *adv.* twice

Zwie'tracht *f.* discord

zwin'gen (zwang, gezwungen) *tr.* force, compel; keep down; *part.* under compulsion, 2320